THE BRIDGESTONE IRISH FOOD GUIDE

The Bridgestone Irish Food Guide

JOHN MCKENNA - SALLY MCKENNA

Estragon Press

FIRST PUBLISHED IN 2007

BY ESTRAGON PRESS

DURRUS

COUNTY CORK

ISBN 978-1-874076-84-1

PRINTED IN SPAIN BY GRAPHYCEMS

• Front cover photos: middle-left by kind permission of the Park Hotel, Mulranny, Co Mayo.

WRITTEN BY JOHN MCKENNA

CONTRIBUTING EDITORS:

EAMON BARRETT

KARYN BOOTH

ORLA BRODERICK

SABRINA CONNEELY

CLAIRE GOODWILLIE

VALERIE O'CONNOR

LESLIE WILLIAMS

PUBLISHER: SALLY MCKENNA

EDITOR: JUDITH CASEY

EDITORIAL ASSISTANT: EVE CLANCY

DESIGN BASED ON A STYLE CREATED BY

NICK CANN

ILLUSTRATIONS BY AOIFE WASSER

WEB: FLUIDEDGE.IE

For
Jim and Elspeth Nicholson

THE AUTHORS WOULD LIKE TO THANK

Gillian Bolton, Paula Buckley, Colm Conyngham,
Pat Curran, Sile Ginnane, George Lane,
Bryan Leech, Frank McKevitt, Harry Owens,
Mary and Des Rainey, Miguel Sancho, Hugh Stancliffe

Bridgestone is the world's largest tyre and rubber company.

• Founded in Japan in 1931, it currently employs over 100,000 people in Europe, Asia and America and its products are sold in more than 150 countries. Its European plants are situated in France, Spain, Italy, Poland and Turkey.

• Bridgestone manufacture tyres for a wide variety of vehicles from passenger cars and motorcycles, trucks and buses to giant earthmovers and aircraft.

• Many new cars are fitted with Bridgestone tyres during manufacture, including Ford, Toyota, Volkswagen, Mercedes and BMW. Ferrari and Porsche are also fitted with Bridgestone performance tyres as original equipment.

• Bridgestone commercial vehicle tyres enjoy a worldwide reputation for durability and its aircraft tyres are used by more than 100 airlines.

• In Formula 1 Bridgestone are sole tyre supplier with all the teams now competing on its Potenza racing tyres. Technology developed in the sport has led to increased performance and safety in Bridgestone's road tyres.

• Bridgestone tyres are distributed in Ireland by Bridgestone Ireland Ltd, a subsidiary of the multinational Bridgestone Corporation. A wide range of tyres is stocked in its 6,500 square metre central warehouse and its staff provide sales, technical and delivery services all over Ireland.

• Bridgestone tyres are available from First Stop Tyre Centres and tyre dealers throughout Ireland.

For further information:

BRIDGESTONE IRELAND LTD
10 Fingal Bay Business Park
Balbriggan
County Dublin

Tel: + 353 1 841 0000
Fax: + 353 1 841 5245

websites:
www.bridgestone.ie
www.firststop.ie

How To Use This Book

The Bridgestone Irish Food Guide is arranged alphabetically, by county so it begins with County Carlow, which is followed by County Cavan, and so on.

Within the counties the towns are once again listed alphabetically.

Northern Ireland is listed at the end of the book as a separate entity. Note that this is a sterling currency area, though the euro is often accepted, particularly in the border areas.

Many of the places featured in this book are only open during the summer season, which means that they can be closed for any given length of time between October and March. Many others change their opening times during winter. It is always advisable to check the website or telephone in advance if you are using this book in the countryside, out of season.

Finally, we greatly appreciate receiving e-mails with suggestions and criticisms from readers, and would like to thank those who have written in the past, whose opinions are of enormous assistance to us when considering which people, places and products finally make it into this book.

www.bridgestoneguides.com

The food producers and food providers in this book are a community. They are different yet like-minded people who work in agriculture, speciality food, cookery, and food retailing. What they do is not mainstream, for they are pivotal people who work, by choice, at the margins of the mainstream food industry. Their power comes because they form a meshwork, which the historian Manuel deLanda describes as "an interlocking system of complementary economic functions". Such a system is the antithesis of the pyramidical structure found in the food business world, where one or two powerful groups of figures exercise power. The classic example of a meshwork at work is Farmer's Market, where every trader is equal, but different.

But even within the equality of difference, some people stand out. For these singular talents, we have chosen a trio of Bridgestone Awards:

Our Hands symbol represents Ireland's core artisan food producers.

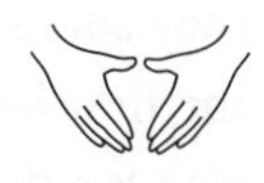

Our Hot symbol represents those people whose talent, at the time of writing, is most exciting.

Our Classic symbol represents those who have contributed enormously to Ireland's food culture.

Introduction

This book is about the different, alternative food chains one can find throughout Ireland. It is about their riches, their culinary vividness, and their charm and culture. It is also a book about the people who man and maintain these valuable alternatives to the blandness that dominates so much modern food production and retailing.

This is the eighth edition of the *Bridgestone Irish Food Guide*. "A directory of sources for lovers of good food and travel" was the sub-title we gave to the first book and we have returned to it after almost twenty years – and in the time that has elapsed since the first edition in 1989, the world of Irish food has turned upside down.

In the Irish agricultural world of the late 1980's, the beef and dairy industries were kings of all they surveyed. Darina Allen could stand up at the first Kinsale Food Forum of 1989, make a plea for there to be support for artisan-scale producers, and find herself shouted down by the beef and dairy barons, who were there to ask deferential questions of Sir Anthony O'Reilly, and who were most decidedly not there to hear about a bunch of hippies in West Cork making cheeses out of raw milk, or planting their spinach leaves according to the phases of the moon.

Whilst this book was in production, we broke off from the grind to speak to a bunch of producers in Northern Ireland at a conference. The room was filled mainly with middle-aged men who sold their wonderful, pasture-reared beef and lamb to the dominant supermarket chain. They were, without question, the most dispirited and disgruntled people we have ever had to address. They were even more dissatisfied than the dairy farmers we meet often, everyone of whom will tell you that the price of milk has not risen in the course of the last twenty years.

We told them that we knew of producers who can haul in three to four thousand euros in the course of a day's trading at a Farmers' market. Not only do they take in a wild amount of money, they also have direct access to – and banter with – happy customers. The Northern Ireland cattle men weren't shocked by this: they were simply mystified. How had the world

"I begin with the proposition that eating is an agricultural act."

WENDELL BERRY, *THE PLEASURES OF EATING*

turned upside down, and how had they found themselves in the underbelly of the beast, being squeezed by all sides to a point of utter dispiritment, whilst the hippies and the moon planters were out there making all the money and having all the craic?

The answer to their mystification is simply the fact that people and producers seek alternatives whenever the prevailing standard is one of bland complacency. They seek organic over-chemicalised agriculture. They seek local rather than internationally-freighted food. They seek the bond of recognition and trust in food relationships, rather than the de-skilled, exploitative mantra of supermarkets. They seek the true creativity in cooking that animates great food, rather than the conformism of chain restaurants.

And so, we have tried, for the eighth time in almost twenty years, to find the alternatives, to track down the food chain that represents Ireland's culture. And we have found it to be in better, ruder health than ever, happy to be "organic and local, biodynamic and slow" as Michael Pollan describes the alternative in his fascinating book. The world of Ireland's food culture has turned upside down, and the right side is now on top.

John McKenna, Sally McKenna
Durrus, West Cork 2007.

"We may need a great many different alternative food chains, organic and local, biodynamic and slow, and others yet undreamed of. As in the fields, nature provides the best model for the marketplace, and nature never puts all her eggs in one basket."

MICHAEL POLLAN, *THE OMNIVORE'S DILEMMA*

Contents

County Carlow

Bagenalstown

Guesthouse

Kilgraney House

Kilgraney is one of the supreme modern country houses, and offers one of the supreme modern country house experiences. Bryan Leech and Martin Marley were ahead of the pack in terms of design, culinary chutzpah and sheer hipness right from when they opened back in 1994, and they have maintained that effortless advantage through the years, as they have developed their accommodation and spa. No one else makes the alliance of the contemporary and the classical feel just so good. In addition to the glam accommodation in the house, there are two suites in the courtyard, and all the rooms are characterised by an electic style collection collated by idiosyncratic and fascinating temperaments. Even without the style, Mr Leech's cooking is reason enough to come to Kilgraney. (Bagenalstown ☎ 059-977 5283 info@kilgraneyhouse.com www.kilgraneyhouse.com)

Ballickmoyler

Country House & Farming

Coolanowle Country House & Health Spa

Organic farmers, marketeers, hospitality providers, spa owners: how do Eddie and Bernadine Mulhall manage to do all they do, and to do it so well, producing work of demonstration quality? The quality of the organic beef they rear and sell at markets is superb, its trueness matched by the exquisite flavour of their own lamb, and they also have one of the coolest market stalls to be found anywhere. The organic dairy herd supplies the Glenisk Dairy, and to see the estate at close quarters you can stay in the farmhouse, or in their self-catering accommodation. Prototypical modern farmers, they are masters of all they do, and all farms should be like this. (Coolanowle House, Ballickmoyler, Carlow ☎ 059-8625176 coolanowle@eircom.net www.coolanowle.com)

Ballon

Coffee Shop

The Forge Craft & Coffee Shop

The Forge is a great wee place. Stone-faced from the outside, it's cosy and unpretentious inside, with a real air of domestic relaxation and true cooking. Mary Jordan has remained committed to her ethos of hand-made food ever since opening in 2000, and it makes The Forge an invaluable place, either for a morning grasp of coffee or a good lunchtime pause for a proper sandwich or something hot, thanks to its location hard beside the N80.
(Kilbride Cross, Ballon ☎ 059-915 9939
theforgekilbride@eircom.net – Open 9.30am-5.30pm Mon-Sun)

Carlow

Butchers Shop

Bosco's

With shops on Tullow Street and in the Fairgreen Shopping Centre, Bosco's is one of the honest, fail-safe reliables of Carlow culinary lore. But don't imagine that age has dimmed their ambitions – not a bit of it, for 2006 alone brought new prizes for their butterfly leg of lamb, their classic spiced beef and the modish rack of lamb with basil and pine nuts. Great service completes the picture.
(132 Tullow Street, Carlow ☎ 059-913 1093 – Open 8am-6pm Mon-Sat)

Brewery

Carlow Craft Brewery

The Irish craft brewing revolution has failed to happen, and the threatened multiplication of artisan breweries throughout the country has yet to materialise. All the more reason then to be grateful for the vivid originality of the three Carlow Brewery beers: the outstanding O'Hara's stout – the best stout not just in these islands but one of the supreme examples anywhere in the world – the excellent, crisp Curim lager and the sweet, moody Molings ale. These brews are superb with food, and they stand alongside pot-still Irish whiskey as the true wine of the country.
(The Goods Store, Station Road, Carlow ☎ 059-913 4356
www.carlowbrewing.com)

Farmers' Market

Carlow Farmers' Market

The excellent CFM takes place on Saturday in the old potato market, now the car park of the Dinn Ri Hotel, and features up to 15 stalls. Alongside such local stars as Carlow Cheese and Coolanowle Meats, look for Newtown Farm meats, Ballycross Juices, the Truffle Fairy, Soul Bakery and Oldtown Mill bakery, Malone Fruit Farm and Ballon free-range eggs, as well as Oracle Farm vegetables from Nurney. A credit to the town. (Potato Market, beside Hadden's Car Park. Sat 9am-2pm)

"For scientists, nothing was more baffling and unscientific than the skill of the cheese makers, who managed to produce savory (Camemberts) without knowing anything at all about microbiology."

PIERRE BOISARD *CAMEMBERT*

Deli and Café

Hennessy's Fine Food Store

Michael and Trish Hennessy's deli and café is down near the courthouse at the end of Dublin Street. A quote from G.B. Shaw on their menu – "There is no sincerer love than the love of food" – lets you know where this dynamic couple are coming from, and their plans to open on Friday and Saturday evenings show a food business that is taking off. There are lots of good treats in store, and great things to eat from breakfast through the rest of the day, whether you enjoy them in the store or take them away. (26 Dublin Street, Carlow ☎ 059-9132849 – Open 8.30am-3.30pm Mon-Sat, summertime 'till 10pm Fri-Sat)

Café Bar

Lennon's Café Bar

That splendid chef, Gail Johnson, has taken up the reins in Sinead Byrne's superb pub, and the earthy, sumptuous deliciousness which was Ms Johnson's trademark when she cooked in Kilkenny hasn't dimmed a jot. Choose Hungarian goulash; liver and bacon with champ; or spinach and feta tart, and all will show confidence and sheer culinary class. The bar will soon be enjoying a makeover, and since they opened in 2000 this key destination hasn't put a foot wrong in offering stylish modern food in an ace space. (121 Tullow Street, Carlow ☎ 059-913 1575 ✉ lennonscafebar@eircom.net – Open for food day-time. Early evening dinner Thurs & Fri. Kitchen closed Sunday & bank holidays)

Clonegal

Restaurant

● Sha Roe Bistro

Henry and Stephanie's SRB is the new star of the county, a place so successful that you need to book weeks in advance in order to get a weekend table. Mr Stone's cooking is rockin' delicious, his menus a masterclass in offering local foods in just the right way: ham shank with cabbage and Pommery mustard cream; hake with parsnip cream; Angus sirloin with pearl onions. He serves Elizabeth Bradley's fine raw milk Carlow Edam as part of a super cheese plate, the puddings are ace, the wine list smart, and prices are very fair for such sassy, contemporary cooking. (Main Street, Clonegal ☎ 053-937 5636 ✉ sha-roebistro@hotmail.com – Open 7pm-9.30pm Wed-Sat, 12.30pm-3.30pm Sun)

Fenagh

Farmhouse Cheese

● Carlow Cheese

Elizabeth Bradley's raw milk cheese uses Edammer culture along with the milk from her herd of Blondes d'Aquitaine, some rennet and salt. The result is a cheese aptly described by Elizabeth as "mellow" – sweet, fudgy, subtle flavours mark out a distinguished new addition to the farmhouse cheese pantheon in Ireland, and it will be fascinating to see this cheesemaker develop. In addition to local farmers' markets, there are also farmgate sales, and do look out for the limited productions of flavoured cheeses – nettle; cumin; chilli; tomato and basil. (Ballybrommell, Fenagh ☎ 087-6124452 ✉ ebradley@gofree.indigo.ie)

Free Range Chickens

Carlow Foods Limited

Bertram Salter's poultry farm produces good quality birds, which exhibit true eating quality and the depth of flavour explained by a 70-day life cycle, of which the last 40 days are spent in mobile sheds when they are fed wheat. In a world where poultry production is little less than a modern atrocity, the Carlow Foods birds are incredibly valuable. Lawlor's butchers in Rathmines is amongst the Dublin stockists. (Kilkea, Fenagh, Carlow ☎ 059-972 7851 carlowfoods@eircom.net www.carlowfoods.ie)

Leighlinbridge

Restaurant & Guesthouse

The Lord Bagenal Inn

James and Mary Kehoe's legendary bar and restaurant has moved into the future, with a massive expansion which has seen their accommodation grown to 39 rooms, whilst George Kehoe has returned home and taken up the reins in the new restaurant kitchen, after years spent working in excellent kitchens in the U.K. and Ireland. The new Lord Bagenal is a powerful attraction and destination in this most charming, characterful village a few miles south of Carlow town, and for Dubliners who want to escape the city and mess about on the river for a night or a weekend the LB is a godsend. Despite the increase in size and capacity, what won't change in the Lord Bagenal will be the graceful, patient, committed hospitality from the owners and staff that has always been the signature of the LB. (Leighlinbridge ☎ 059-972 1668 www.lordbagenal.com)

Cookery School

Tasteworks Cookery School

Christine Jordan's bespoke cookery school is just the right space for this gifted cook to demonstrate not just her culinary skills but also her culinary passions – this is a woman whose childhood holidays in Schull gave her a taste for real bread, farmhouse cheeses, dark chocolate and all the other things that were once exotica back in Ireland's culinary darkness. Ms Jordan's food manifesto, as spelt out on her website, is inspiring stuff, both ambitious and practical, and Tasteworks promises great things. (Rathellin, Leighlinbridge ☎ 059-972 2786 info@tasteworks.net www.tasteworks.net)

Tullow

Cookery School

Ballyderrin Cookery School

Pamela Holligan is one of those mighty women whose skills encompass every desirable discipline. Ballyderrin is a smart house with six rooms for guests, and a cookery school, and a shop selling handmade cakes, chutneys and cookery books. In this regard, it is one of the new generation B&B's, combining comfort with culinary innovation. (Ballyderrin House, Shillelagh Road, Tullow ☎ 059-915 2742
ballyderrinhouse@eircom.net
www.ballyderrinhouse.com – Open all year)

Fruit Liqueurs

Boozeberries

Michelle Power's boozeberry liqueurs are potent, original concoctions, and the latest addition is a wild cranberry Boozeberry to join the blackcurrant and wild blueberry flavours. Ms Power's skills as a herbalist shine through in the balance and vividness of these lovely drinks. (Ballyconnell Lodge, Ballyconnell, Tullow ☎ 059-915 6312
info@boozeberries.com www.boozeberries.com)

Farmhouse Cheese

Knockeen Diary

Tom and Fiona Burgess make Coolattin mature cheddar, which is ready after one year, whilst the semi-hard Ring of the Rath is ready after one month. Both are raw milk, agrestically pleasing thanks to granitic soils, and resplendent, brilliant new cheeses from imaginative farmers. (Knockeen, Tullow ☎ 059-915 6189 tofiburgess@eircom.net)

Butcher's Shop

Laz Murphy

Four generations of the Murphy family have plied their trade in the centre of Tullow, buying stock from farmers from within a seven mile radius, dealing with the same farms year after year, exhibiting the skills and artistry of classic Irish charcuterie. The shop has expanded to include a deli, wine shop and hot food bar. Precious. (Church Street, Tullow ☎ 059-915 1316 jimmurphy12@eircom.net)

County Cavan

Cavan

Bailieboro

Wholefoods & Café

Planet Earth

Diane Crook's shop is a wee beauty. Smack in the centre of the village, it is a fine wholefood shop with a great range of organic veg and farmhouse cheeses. But its real secret is the café and bakery, where their own breads form the star turn, along with great salads, juices from their own fruit, organic soups and good sandwiches. Like others of the new generation of wholefood stores, PE is a model of endeavour, and a model of forthright culinary goodness. (Lower Main Street, Bailieboro ☎ 042-966 5490 ✉ dibob@planet-earth.ie 🖱 www.planet-earth.ie)

Belturbet

Farmhouse Cheese

Corleggy Farmhouse Cheese

Silke Cropp is one of the small handful of culinary pioneers whose lifetime's work has created a working definition of Irish artisanship. She has remained faithful to raw milk cheese production for her cow's milk cheeses, she has pioneered farmers' markets both locally and in Dublin, and her children now have a culinary presence to rival that of their talented Mum – daughter Tina is one of the foremost crêpe concocters at farmers' markets. Throughout a long career, Ms Cropp has remained youthful, spirited and focused, first and foremost a cheesemaker of great skill, whose Corleggy and Drumlin cheeses are sui generis in Ireland. Look out for fresh cheeses at the markets, and for the soft Quivvy cheese preserved in olive oil, and do keep some of the Corleggy cheese until it hardens, at which time it is one of the best goat's milk cheeses to grate. (Belturbet ☎ 049-952 2930 ✉ corleggy@eircom.net 🖱 www.corleggy.com)

Crepes

Crêpes in the City

Tina Cropp and Oisin Healy's world-conquering crêpe enterprise is one of the great farmers' market stalwarts, feeding the frenzied masses at Temple Bar, Dun Laoghaire, St

Anne's Park in Raheny, at Farmleigh and Brooklodge in deepest Wicklow. Tina and Oisin will also travel to your party or anniversary bash and cook up a storm for all your family and friends, and they also feed teenage music heads at festivals such as Electric Picnic. Great crêpes, made with fab ingredients. (Coragh, Belturbet ☎ 049-952 4861 crepesinthecity@hotmail.com www.crepes.ie)

Blacklion

Restaurant with Rooms

MacNean Bistro

Neven Maguire is cooking the food of his life right now. His cooking is so structured and so elemental that it reminds us of the great Spanish chef Andoni Luis Adurriz, of Mugarritz in San Sebastian. There is the same control balanced by the same wild expression. There is the same vividness, and the same modesty. There is the same questing, and the same sense of completion. But, Mr Maguire is nobody's man but his own, and comparisons are, ultimately, misleading. His cooking now belongs in the pantheon of great contemporary Irish culinary experiences – Roscoff in 1991, Truffles in 1995, Chapter One in 2006, Shanks in 1997, Shiro in 1989, L'Ecrivain in 2002. The MacNean, with its smart new rooms, is right up there creating new definitions of what contemporary Irish cooking is, and setting out what contemporary Irish cooking can be. (Blacklion ☎ 071-985 3022 – Open 6pm-9pm Wed-Sun; 1pm & 3pm Sun)

Duck and Geese Farm

Thornhill Ducks

Ken Moffitt's ducks and geese form a staple of many of the signature dishes in the nearby MacNean Bistro, which is the sort of acclaim this talented producer deserves for his super birds. (Thornhill Farm, Thornhill, Blacklion, ☎ 071-985 3044 thornhillfarm@eircom.net)

Cavan

Butcher

Barry John Crowe

BJ Crowe is an ambitious young man, and he has brought the creative, competitive sausage mania which is such a feature of the leading butchers in Northern Ireland south of the border to Cavan. He now has no fewer than 19 styles of sausage, encompassing every style you can think of, all showing the same acute sense of balance and culinary kno-whow. Last time out we predicted that everyone would be hearing a lot more about Mr Crowe, but that seems to have been understating this young man's drive and ambition to be one of the master charcutiers. (2 Connolly Street, Cavan ☎ 049-436 2671 – Open 8am-6pm, till 7pm on Fri)

Farmers' Market

Cavan Farmers' Market

It's still early days for the Cavan FM, but it is proving to be a good resource for organic vegetables and jams and chutneys and baking. Look out also for a market planned sometime soon for Belturbet. (Saturday morning, McCarron's Meat Centre)

Restaurant

The Oak Room

Norbert Neylon is a talented cook, and he is producing some tasty food upstairs in The Oak Room – duck confit spring roll with chilli jam; chicken hot-pot with fresh tarragon; sirloin with onion marmalade; banana tarte tatin – food with good flavours and precise techniques, and he isn't going to stay a secret for much longer. Early bird is great value, weekends are busy on both floors of the dining room. (62 Main Street, Cavan ☎ 049-437 1515 info@theoakroom.ie www.theoakroom.ie – Open Dinner Tue-Sat from 5.30pm. Bank hol Sundays open 6.30pm-9.30pm)

Cloverhill

Restaurant with Rooms

Olde Post Inn

You get two things in Tara McCann and Gearoid Lynch's OPI. First off, Ms McCann and her team deliver some of the very best service you will find anywhere: swift, informed, solicitous, and very, very witty. Second, from Mr Lynch you get some of the best modern Irish cooking you can find. Put the two together and it is a mighty combination, which will be even more attractive when the new conservatory is up and running and the bedrooms get a needed make-over.

The cooking shows true accomplishment, married to a real sense of maturity. Pheasant is cooked on the bone; snipe and quail are beautifully handled, the fish cookery is precise and soulful, and right through the exposition of an entire meal, flavours and – above all – textures are highlighted and maximised, one after the other. This is a powerful kitchen, and a sublime concoction. (Cloverhill, Butler's Bridge ☎ 047-55555 ✉ gearoidlynch@eircom.net 🖱 www.theoldepostinn.com – Open 6.30pm-9pm Tue-Sat, 12.30pm-3pm, 6pm-8.30pm Sun)

Cootehill

Tea

SIP

Sean Moran's SIP teas push out the linguistic envelope just as much as they push the taste envelope. Lover's Leap Garden; Smoky Jo's; Buddha's Tears – man, we are a long way from Lyon's green label here. These exotic brews from Sri Lanka, India, China and South Africa can be enjoyed in boutique hotels such as The Clarence, The Morrison, The K Club and in the Leon chain of patisseries. (Bellamont Forest, Cootehill ☎ 086 8156369 ✉ sip_tea@hotmail.com. For more information see 🖱 www.odaios.com)

Killeshandra

Boxty

Drummully Boxty

Paul Farrelly's boxty owes its splendidly different taste and texture thanks to a mixture of cooked and raw potato, boiled together, then fried, in the Cavan style. Boxty has become too under appreciated in Ireland in recent times, which is a great pity as it is a signature of this Border region and an utterly distinctive and – at its best – delicious food. (Drummully, Killeshandra ☎ 049-433 4626)

Virginia

Preserves

Govender's

Jane and Dion Govender make excellent relishes, the sort of echt Indian foods – though the couple hail from South Africa they are of Indian descent – that show what a bland travesty so many ethnic ingredients sold in Ireland actually are. What Jane and Dion do is to introduce you to the chutneys, pickles, relishes and true tastes that you would find

Cavan

on the sub-continent. Their mango and almond chutney, for instance, seems to bundle up the essence of its ingredients into a mighty taste cascade, whilst the aubergine pickle again delivers the essence of aubergine in its alternately bold-yet-bland paradox. Brilliant stuff. (Ryefield, Virginia ☎ 087-975 6554 sales@govenders.com www.govenders.com)

Sauces

● Jill's

Jill Wright's excellent sauces and relishes are the real thing, fresh and true tasting, tactile and quite delicious, and their usefulness in cooking, aside from being excellent condiments, makes them a store cupboard stand-by of great merit. (Ballaghanea, Virginia ☎ 049-854 8234)

"But when from a distant past nothing subsists, after the people are dead, after the things are broken and scattered, taste and smell alone, more fragile but more enduring, more unsubstantial, more persistent, more faithful, remain poised a long time, like souls, remembering, waiting, hoping, amid the ruins of all the rest; and bear unflinchingly, in the tiny and almost impalpable drop of their essence, the vast structure of recollection."

MARCEL PROUST,
À LA RECHERCE DU TEMPS PERDU

County Clare

Ballina

Restaurant

The Cherry Tree

Harry McKeogh's smart, modern restaurant, right at the water's edge, has an angular, attractive room that is both formal and informal at the same time. The same formality-informality is the signature of chef Mark Anderson's cooking, which works best when flavours are directly stated – salmon with pea and mint purée; grilled rump of lamb with confit shoulder; organic berries with champagne sabayon – and when too much elaboration is avoided. But when on song, this kitchen makes for mighty music, and food that can be a pure thrill. (Lakeside, Ballina, Killaloe ☎ 061-375688 www.cherrytreerestaurant.ie – Open 6pm-10pm Tue-Sat, 12.30pm-3pm Sun)

Ballynacally

Farmhouse Cheese

Bluebell Falls Goat's Cheese

Paul Keane's delicate, fresh goat's cheese is a favourite with many chefs on the west coast and further afield, but don't overlook its appeal as part of a cheeseboard, where its liveliness and open flavours contrast well with more mature, washed-rind cheeses. (Ballynacally ☎ 065-683 8024 bluebellfalls@eircom.net)

Ballyvaughan

Farmhouse Cheese and other produce

Aillwee Cave

Most folk come to Ballyvaughan to walk deep into the inners of the Aillwee Cave. But, when you are doing that, don't on any account miss the excellent shop and cheesemaking plant run by Ben Johnson. Ben's cheese, Burren Gold, is a beaut; a raw milk, Gouda-style which comes plain and in five flavoured varieties, but you won't find it much outside of the Aillwee shop. Aside from the cheese, the shop has a brilliant array of other local foods, and a great selection of Ben's honeys. (Aillwee Cave, Ballyvaughan ☎ 065-707 7036 www.aillweecave.ie – Open 10am-5pm Mon-Sun)

Cafe

An Fear Gorta

The great stalwart of good eating in busy Ballyvaughan, Catherine O'Donoghue's tea rooms always feels like the perfect place, especially after a morning's flora spotting in the Burren. It's a modest, feminine room, with lovely sweet baking, splendid service, and it's a wee treasure. (Pier Road, Ballyvaughan ☎ 065-707 7023 – Open daytime. Open in high summer only)

Clare

Farmers' Market

Ballyvaughan Farmers' Market

The BFM has now developed from a summer market to one that is open in the winter months also. (St John's Village Hall, Ballyvaughan. Saturdays 10am-2pm)

Shop, Café and Hampers

Burren Fine Food & Wine

Cathleen Connole has astutely developed her lovely stone cottage business, which started selling a selection of wines from Galway's The Noble Vine, and some interesting crafts, into a delightful space and place in which to enjoy a glass of wine and some smart food: smoked fish platter; warm chicken salad; ham and mushroom pizza; chicken and roast vegetables in pitta. She has also developed a successful hamper business, which comes into its own towards the end of the year, after the summer cooking has ceased for the year. (Corkscrew Hill Road, Ballyvaughan ☎ 065-707 7046 info@burrenfinewine.com www.burrenfinewine.com – food served 11am-5pm)

Accommodation & Restaurant

Gregan's Castle Hotel

The Haden family's hotel has been in business for over thirty years, and Simon's Haden's stewardship has brought new energy to this handsome place, which enjoys a stunning location on Corkscrew Hill in the heart of the Burren. Gregan's really looks to be going places. (Ballyvaughan ☎ 065-707 7005 stay@gregans.ie www.gregans.ie – Open 16 March-27 Nov, Restaurant open 8am-11.30pm, 12.30pm-2.30pm, 6.30pm-8.30pm)

Bar

O'Loclainn's Bar

Peter O'Loghlen's bar is the bar your mind sees when it thinks of a classic, traditional Irish bar, with a mind-expanding selection of great whiskeys waiting to be enjoyed, and with an air not just of timelessness, but of time seemingly having been stopped. And that is even before you have a sip. This is one of the classic Irish pubs, and the real thing in all its glory. (Ballyvaughan ☎ 065-707 7006 drink@irishwhiskeybar.com www.irishwhiskeybar.com)

Clare

"Good cooking is not fantasy, it is reality. It's not theatre, it is life."

MARCELLA HAZAN

Shop

The Village Stores

A buzzy, busy shop in buzzy, busy Ballyvaughan, the Village Stores mixes a good gifts and craft section with lots of good foods.(Ballyvaughan ☎ 065-707 7181 villagestores@eircom.net – Open 9am-8pm Mon-Sun)

Carron

Café & Perfumery

The Burren Perfumery

"I like fresh food, so everything in the tearoom is organic – the butter, the milk, the bread and everything, but it's just really simple nice food." That's what Sadie Chowen told Betsy Klein, in the book *Cottage Industry*, when she was talking about her exceptional perfumery and tea-room. "What it's become is a vehicle for an expression of who I am," she elaborated, which gives a clue to the aesthetic of this perfume creator, who is intent on "making a little world where everything is beautiful". Amen to that. To see that beauty, tour the herb garden, then enjoy a glass of organic wine with some lovely simple cooking, and all will be revealed. (Carron ☎ 065-708 9102 burrenperfumery@eircom.net www.burrenperfumery.com – Perfumery open all year. Tea rooms open Apr-Sept, 10am-5pm Mon-Sun)

Clare

Pub

Cassidy's Croide na Boirne

Turn up at Cassidy's on a Friday night and you are in time for their seafood special. In July and August they like to have barbecues, so there is a lot more to this imposing-looking stone-faced pub than just pints of beer, though anyone who has been on a 20km trek through the limestone will surely be looking forward to one of those. Utterly amazing views come for free. (Carron ☎ 065-708 9109 ✉ info@cassidyspub.com 🖱 www.cassidyspub.com – Food served day-time and early-evening)

Cratloe

Farmhouse Cheese

Cratloe Hills Sheep's Cheese

Sean and Deirdre Fitzgerald have been winning deserved awards for their mature Cratloe Gold sheep's milk cheese in recent years, returning home from the British Cheese Awards with gold medals on an almost annual basis. It is a particularly fine cheese, especially when grated when it adds a piquancy and edge to any food that might traditionally welcome some grated Parmesan. You will find it in good cheese shops and delis. (Cratloe ☎ 061-357185 ✉ cratloehillcheese@eircom.net)

Doolin

Preserves

The Clare Jam Company

"Quaint, unique" are terms folk have used to describe David and Vera Muir's jam shop, inspired to such adjectives, perhaps, by coming across the shop whilst walking the Burren Way, and picking up the scent of sweet fruits and sticky sugars cooking away in the kitchens as the Muirs make their latest batch of hand-made goodies. "People are convinced they can smell whatever type of jam or marmalade we are making on a particular day," says Vera. You can buy the complete range of jams at the shop, and have a cup of coffee, but even if you aren't trekking in County Clare, the superb jams are worth hunting down in good delis. (Lough North, Doolin ☎ 065-707 4778 ✉ christinemuir@eircom.net)

Restaurant & Guesthouse

Cullinan's Restaurant & Guest House

James and Carol Cullinan run a sweet restaurant with rooms, and they do it with that quiet, demure style that is characteristic of so many of the best places to eat and stay in the county. The house has a cottage style, though it was purpose-built back in 1994, and since then James has beeen creating happy food in the kitchen: Aran scallops with cucumber dressing; turbot with caramelised onions; Burren lamb with mint pesto. Cullinan's is one of the original d'n'd's – dinner and duvets – and this hard-working couple and their crew are dedicated and creative people. (Doolin ☎ 065-707 4183
✉ info@cullinansdoolin.com
🖱 www.cullinansdoolin.com – Open Easter-October 6pm-9pm Mon-Sat, closed Wed)

Café

Doolin Café

The DC is an ever-popular, sort-of-left-field-kind-of place, but we have enjoyed consistently tasty, simple cooking in these low-ceilinged little rooms over the years, and it remains a good destination for hungry souls who want something nice to eat. Just don't try to get a table during the Willie Clancy festival. (Doolin ☎ 065-707 4795 – Open Feb-Dec, 12.30pm-2.30pm, 6pm-10pm Fri-Wed, open Mon & Tue during high season)

Restaurant

Doolin Crafts Gallery & Restaurant

Adrienne Doolan and Jan Wagensveld have taken over this beautiful crafts gallery, one of the best in the West. There is a small café in the building for those who are browsing and those who are exploring beautiful Doolin. (Ballyvoe, Doolin ☎ 065-707 4309 ✉ info@doolincrafts.com
🖱 www.doolincrafts.com – Open day-time)

Doonbeg

Wine Importer

Doonbeg Wine Imports

John and Dan Mulhall's wine company specialises in French wines, in particular some very interesting wines from the Loire Valley. John and Dan distribute locally to restaurants, shops and private customers. (Doonbeg ☎ 065-905 5334)

Gastro Pub

Morrissey's Pub

Hugh McNally has created one of the County Clare runaway success stories in Morrissey's. He has done it by steadily transforming this celebrated bar into a pair of beautiful dining rooms, by cooking seriously fine food, and by putting some slick, stylish rooms in upstairs, above the pub. As a d'n'd – dinner and duvet – Morrissey's is one of the very best, and the combination of great food and great rooms makes for a dream getaway. Our children complained long and loudly after we last stayed here, arguing that one night simply was not enough. They were absolutely right. (Doonbeg ☎ 065-905 5304
hughmcnally@hotmail.com
www.morrisseysdoonbeg.com – Open 12.30pm-3pm, 6pm-9pm Mon-Sun)

Ennis

Asian Store

Baraka

"African, Asian, Mediterranean, Eastern European, Turkish". Those are all the places from which Baraka sources its foods, so if you seek anything from the greater Mediterranean area, then you know that this is the place to find it. We like the Gazi yogurt and the feta, and the packed-to-the-rafters, souk-like, feel of the shop. (Mill Road, Ennis ☎ 065-689 1766 – Open 11am-9pm, Mon-Sun)

Chocolate Shop

Chocolat

"This shop is so cute", said our friend, Sile. As cute as Johnny Depp, then? Well, Mr Depp may have been in the movie but he isn't in store, but they have chocs from Wilde's, Cocoa Bean, Cherub, Cluizel and Valrhona, the powerhouse heavyweights of the chocolate world. Cute. (Barrack Street, Ennis ☎ 065-686 8599
chocolatennis@eircom.net – Open 10am-6pm Mon-Sat)

Pie Shop

Cornish Pasty Co.

Pasty lovers will travel any distance to get a great pie, and great savoury pies is what you will get in the CPC. The lamb and mint pasty is ace, the peppered steak just as good, and there is even a pasty for vegetarians. Each one is a meal in itself, whether you sit down at the few tables or take one home for dinner. Decent coffee also, and some smoothies. (Market Place, Ennis ☎ 065-686 4021)

Farmers' Market

Ennis Farmers' Market

The EFM doesn't have the greatest location, but it has some cracking food, and is especially fine in the summer months when a bounty of organic produce is available from local farmers, supplementing West Coast specialists such as the superb Gourmet Tart Co. and the Sunflower Bakery. Happily, Clare County Council, back in 2004, abolished a by-law which had heretofore made anyone selling "untrimmed vegetables with clay, soil or dirt" on them liable to a fine of up to 1,275 euro. As farmers' representative Tom Brooks told the environmantal committee, "People believe that vegetables are fresher with earth on them and that carrots, for instance, taste much nicer if they are bought with earth". Good man yourself, Tom.(Upper Market Street Car Park, Friday 8am-2pm ennisfarmers@eircom.net)

Shop & Café

Ennis Gourmet Store

Anne Leyden's shop is a tiny space that is jam-packed with all the good foods of the area, and it is also a great place to enjoy good coffee and nice deli foods. (1 Barrack St, Ennis ☎ 065-684 3314, gourmetstore@eircom.net www.ennisgourmetstore.com – Open 10am-7pm Mon-Sun. In summer open 10am-9pm on Thur & Fri)

Fishmonger

The Fish Market

Val Egan's Fish Market is a comprehensively stocked local shop in Ireland's first technology town, and it sells a fine variety of Atlantic fish and shellfish. (19 Lwr Market Street, Ennis ☎ 065-684 2424 – Open 9.15am-6pm Tue-Fri, 9.15am-1.30pm Sat)

Traiteur

The Food Emporium

Just across from the convent, the 'Emporium is a charming, home-style traiteur with good foods-to-go, and if that 50th birthday or christening bash is looming, then do the smart thing and take advantage of TJ's catering. (8-9 Francis St, Ennis ☎ 065-682 0554 – Open 9am-6pm Mon-Sat)

Café

Food Heaven

Noirin Furey does simple dishes really well – this girl can cook a smoked chicken, pear and blue cheese tart that hits the spot, or fire out a banoffi pie that hits the sugar barometer, or rustle up a mushroom and thyme omelette that will set that hangover to rights in two shakes. There is a daily hot pot, good wraps, and a just-arrived salad and sandwich bar in this hip and vital address. (21 Market Street, Ennis ☎ 065-682 2722 – Open 8.30am-6.30pm Mon-Sat)

Clare

Café

Glor

The café of the theatre in Ennis is a good spot for coffee and light lunches. (Friar's Walk, Ennis ☎ 065-684 3103 - info@glor.ie www.glor.ie – Open daytime – Open 10am-5pm, lunch served noon-5pm)

Café

Henry's

Henry Benagh's iconic eating house does the right stuff, and has been doing the right stuff for many a year now. Food lovers gather here to polish off excellent cold ice creams, excellent hot sandwiches, and good, punky pizzas. (Abbey Street Car Park, Ennis ☎ 065-682 2848 – Open 8.30am-6pm Mon-Sat)

Butcher

Derek Molloy

Derek Molloy has just opened a second butcher's shop, in the Roslevan Shopping Centre, which will bring the noted charcuterie skills of this talented butcher to a new audience. The modern style of the new shop is a nice contrast to the utterly charming traditional shop in the centre of town. The dry-cured bacon Mr Molloy prepares is especially fine. (Abbey Street, Ennis ☎ 065-682 3296 – Open 9am-6pm Mon-Sat and Roslevan Shopping Centre, Tulla Road, Ennis ☎ 065-686 8350 molloybutchers@eircom.net – Open 9am-7pm Mon-Fri, 9am-6pm Sat)

Hotel

The Old Ground Hotel

Every town used to have an hotel like The Old Ground: family-run, where the staff remember your name and remember your favourite room, and even remember what you like to drink. The replacement of these old coaching hotels with charmless, bland, chain-run bed factories makes the Old Ground even more precious. A darling address. (O'Connell St, Ennis ☎ 065-682 8127 reservations@oldgroundhotel.ie www.oldgroundhotel.com – Open mid Jan-end Dec)

Clare

Wholefood Shop

Open Sesame

A first port-of-call for excellent local foods from the area as well as vital wholefoods, Open Sesame has long been a trailblazer in Ennis, and stays right up to the mark with every passing year. (35 Parnell St, Ennis ☎ 065-682 1480 opensesame@eircom.net www.opensesame.ie – Open 9am-6pm Mon-Sat)

Fish Monger

Rene Cusack

Locals positively rejoiced when Rene Cusack decided to open a branch of the much-respected Limerick fish mongers operation in Ennis, and the Ennis store has lived up to expectations of stellar piscine standards. (Market Street, Ennis ☎ 065-689 2712 – Open 9am-6pm Mon-Sat)

Restaurant

The Town Hall Café

The THC is a bistro related to the excellent Old Ground Hotel, and its funky style is a pleasing contrast to the more formal manner of the hotel. Good tasty cooking punches above its weight, the staff have energy and the room has great character and verve. (O'Connell Street, Ennis ☎ 065-682 8127 www.flynnhotels.com – Open 10am-noon for coffee, noon-5pm lunch, 6pm-10pm dinner)

Wine

The Wine Buff

Paddy O'Flynn's chain of wine shops is expanding steadily and decisively throughout the country, and Eamonn Cagney is doing a fine job in a compact, atmospheric shop in the market area in the centre of town. The wines are characterful and quirky, value is excellent and service is courteous and helpful. (Market area Ennis ☎ 065-684 2082 www.thewinebuff.com – Open 10.30am-7pm Mon-Thur, 10.30am-9pm Fri, 10.30am-8pm Sat)

Restaurant

Zucchini

Colm and Jane Chawke are just finding their culinary feet in the old Halpino's restaurant, in the centre of town, and are beginning to attract an enthusiastic audience of locals. (7 High Street, Ennis ☎ 065-6866 566
reservations@zucchini.ie www.zucchini.ie)

Clare

Ennistymon

Restaurant with Rooms

Byrne's Restaurant & Townhouse

A handsome old building in pretty Ennistymon, Byrne's offers the modern d'n'd, dinner and duvet mix, with smart, good value rooms and a popular bistro-style restaurant. (Main Street, Ennistymon ☎ 065-707 1080
byrnesennistymon@eircom.net
www.byrnes-ennistymon.com – Open 6.30pm-9.30pm Mon-Sat, reservations recommended)

Restaurant

Holywell

The Ennistymon Holywell is the echo of the original restaurant in Ballyvaughan, so it serves pastas, pizzas, and the most stunning ice creams. This is Tyrolean cooking, so it is hearty, rich, and marvellously delicious, and Wolfgang and Sibylle Dietl manage to get every element of the restaurant to chime just so, so everyone loves it to bits. So, three Margaritas for the McKenna children, please, Calzone for Sally and a Montanara for John. Are we happy? Indeed we are. (Ennistymon ☎ 065-707 7322 – Open 11am-11pm)

Farmhouse Cheese

Mount Callan Cheddar

In common with many of the newer generation of Irish farmhouse cheesemakers, Lucy Hayes hit the ground running with her Mount Callan cheddar, and, right from the release of the first cheeses, made as recently as 2000, this was always a singular and distinguished cheese. Lucy uses raw milk, from her herd of Montbelliard cows, the cheese is pressed in 4kg and 15kg truckles, and matured on wood in a stone house after being wrapped in cheesecloth. The cheeses are only made with summer pasture milk, and the result of all this care is a wonderfully complex, buttery, rich and full cheese, particularly with the cheeses matured to 18 months. Quite how Mrs Hayes, a self-taught cheesemaker, managed to make such a complete and polished farmhouse cheese right from the start is destined to become the stuff of legend. Mount Callan is also a member of the Irish raw milk cheese presidium in Slow Food Ireland. (Drinagh, Ennistymon ☎ 065-707 2008 ✉ mtcallan@oceanfree.net)

Clare

Fishmonger

● Sea Lyons Seafood Sales

Gearoid Lyons's Sea Lyons company specialises in fresh crab and crab claws, and also wild salmon in season. (Main Street, Ennistymon ☎ 065-7072444 – Open 10am-6pm Tue-Sat)

Bakery

● Unglert's Bakery

Mr Unglert has been baking good bread and cakes for a long time now – he has been in the *Bridgestone Guides* ever since the first BIFG back in 1991. Recently, he has reduced the extent of the confectionery offer in order to concentrate on those good breads, so snap up the very fine rye bread, made in the Continental style – and the chewy wholemeal. (Ennistymon ☎ 065-707 1217 – Open 9am-6pm Tue-Sat)

Fanore

Restaurant

● Holywell Trattoria

Wolfgang and Sibylle Dietl are taking over the west coast with their expanding chain of delightful Holywell restaurants. Two County Clare operations have been joined by a third outlet, in Galway city, and all three of them are sure-fire successes. In the trattoria, unlike the Italian restaurant in Ennistymon, there are meat dishes – pasta with ragu; turkey cacciatore; grilled meats with potato croquettes; spezzatino – but the formula is one of concision and precise execution, apart from the portions, which are huge. The ice creams are amongst the very finest on the planet, never mind the county, and all-day opening means that Holywell is well-nigh indispensable. (Fanore, ☎ 065-707 6971 – Open 11am-11pm, evenings only off season)

Flagmount

Confectionary

Bizzy Lizzy Ltd

Helene Goomans's meticulously crafted and superbly packaged European-style confectionary is found in many good delis and speciality shops. (Lakefield Lodge, Cahermurphy, Flagmount ☎ 061-921900)

Clare

Inagh

Brewery

The Biddy Early Brewery

Niall Garvey's little brew pub and craft brewery, hard by the side of the road in Inagh, is one of the best known Irish craft breweries, and indeed was one of the pioneering craft breweries, opening back in 1995 when there was only the Hilden Brewery in Northern Ireland at work. They have four main beers – the excellent Black Biddy stout; Red Biddy ale which uses bog myrtle to impart its herbacious flavour; Blonde Biddy lager, and Real Biddy, which is a cask conditioned ale. The beers are fined with Carrrageen, an ancient practice now abandoned by commercial brewers but kept alive here, and using these ancient practices explains why the Biddy Early Brewery is a member of the Slow Food movement. You will find the brews in good wine shops in the vicinity but, to be honest, there is no experience quite like a tour of the pub and brewery, and a comprehensive tasting, in situ. (Inagh, Ennis ☎ 065-683 6742 feedback@beb.ie www.beb.ie)

Farmhouse Cheese

Inagh Farmhouse Cheeses

Siobhan ni Ghairbhith's organic goat's milk cheeses represent a continuum that goes back to the earliest days of farmhouse cheesemaking in Ireland. Siobhan learnt her craft in the late 1990's from Meg and Derrick Gordon, who had created the goat's milk cheeses more than 20 years before. Since taking over as cheesemaker, Siobhan has broadened the range of cheeses, which now includes fresh St. Tola's sold in oil, and small St. Tola's sold as crottins. These complement the classic St. Tola goat's log, and the sweetly agrestic St Tola hard cheese. The Inagh cheeses have long been amongst the most distinguished and singular farmhouse cheeses made in Ireland, with the goat's log, in particular, one of the most mesmerising cheeses, as it transforms from a smooth, subtle mild cheese when young into a richly flavoured riot of pungent, flinty flavours. Sublime. (Inagh ☎ 065-683 6633 info@st-tola.ie www.st-tola.ie)

Kilfenora

Gastro Pub

Vaughan's Pub

Vaughan's is famed as a music pub, but it deserves an equal reputation as a gastropub, for the cooking here is sound, imaginative and uses well-sourced ingredients, and the good food is congratulated by tranquil, polite service. (Kilfenora ☎ 065-708 8004)

Kilkee

Restaurant

Murphy Blacks

Cillian Murphy's restaurant is rather good. "Our business ethos is very simple," says Cillian. "Buy it fresh, cook it simply and serve it well". They score on all counts: baked St Tola with tomatoes and basil pesto is ace, Carrigaholt crabmeat tartlet with chilli and lime is super, mains of monkfish scampi and sirloin with garlic butter are right on the money, and vegetable cookery is as strong as the excellent puddings. This restaurant is one of the best in the county, yet remains something of a West Clare secret. Great staff, and a really promising culinary adventure that deserves to be – and will be – much better known. (The Square, Kilkee ☎ 065-905 6854 murphy-blacks@iol.ie – Open 6pm-9.30pm Tue-Sun from Easter-end Sept)

Bistro and Shop

The Pantry Shop & Bakery

Imelda Bourke's café and bakery has to be seen to be believed in summertime, because at busy weekends there are so many people eating and shopping in here that it would take your breath away. Imelda takes it all in her stride, however, somehow managing to cook, bake, serve, clean and generally run the entire operation that is The Pantry with indefatigable skill and energy, even after 25 years in the heat of the kitchen. That background as a home economics teacher has stood her in good stead

over the years, and despite the hordes The Pantry is always calm and collected. The food is good comfort country cooking – sirloin with whiskey sauce; cod Dijon; chicken stuffed with Clonakilty black pudding – but even if you aren't eating, the shop is an invaluable resource for superb breads and cakes and much, much more. (O'Curry Street, Kilkee ☎ 065-905 6576
info@thepantrykilkee.com
www.thepantrykilkee.com)

Clare

Hotel

Stella Maris Hotel

The Haugh family's family-run hotel is one of few examples of a small resort hotel left in Ireland, and is all the more valuable for that. Hospitality here is expressed as a way of life – generous, thoughtful, patient, timeless – and it makes for an excellent, modest destination that is charm-filled. (Kilkee ☎ 065-905 6455
info@stellamarishotel.com
www.stellamarishotel.com – Open all year)

Kilkishen

Bakery

Sunflower Bakery

Breads, cakes, pastries, and gingerbread men are all made using organic ingredients, "by hand, with care", as the girls say. You will find these lovely treats in the Grainey health food shop, in Scarrif, on Thursday, Friday and Saturday, and look out for the Bakery's ever-popular stall at the Limerick milk market on Saturdays. (Cappalaheen, Kilkishen ☎ 061-367924 macmcmanus@eircom.net)

Killaloe

Farmers' Market

Killaloe Farmers' Market

It is hard to credit today that there were no farmer's markets in County Clare five years ago. Since then, markets have begun in towns throughout the county, and the local Slow Food group has sent marketeers to Salone del Gusto to help the producers realise that they are "part of a worldwide movement to protect and recover local, wholesome and traditional foods", as local activist Michael Gleeson has written. So, get those local, wholesome and traditional foods at Killaloe, from producers such as Blue Moon Farm who sell here, and who also operate a box system via their company Golden Goose Green Grass. (Between the Waters, Sunday 11am-3pm) .

Clare

Kilnaboy

B&B

● Fergus View

Mary Kelleher runs a cosy, domestically meticulous B&B, a mile or so outside Corofin and just at the foot of the Burren. Fergus View makes a perfect base for anyone exploring the limestone, the hazel and the flora, and Mrs Kelleher is a genial hostess. (Kilnaboy, Corofin ☎ 065-683 7606 ✉ deckell@indigo.ie)

Kilrush

Bakery

● Considine's Bakery

An ageless, old-style bakery on the main street. (Francis Street, Kilrush ☎ 065-905 1095 – Open 8am-5pm Mon-Sat)

Farmers' Market

● Kilrush Farmers' Market

Local Slow Food powerhouse Michael Gleeson is the organiser of the market in Kilrush (The Square, Kilrush, Thursdays 9am-2pm Michael Gleeson ☎ 087-227 2115 ✉ michael.gleeson@eiri.org)

Lahinch

Seafood Restaurant

● Barrtra

Paul and Theresa O'Brien's Barrtra is one of those places that seems to exist just as much in your dreamscape as your reality. If you are going to be in Clare, on the western seaboard, your mind really wants to find a little seafood resaurant, maybe one that is actually part of the owner's house. Well, here it is. Smashing service, lovely cookery, and views out across Liscannor Bay. No, you aren't dreaming, it's for real. (Barrtra, Lahinch ☎ 065-708 1280 ✉ barrtra@hotmail.com – Open 5pm-10pm Mon-Sun in July & Aug, Tue-Sun summer, limited hours off-season)

Farmhouse Cheese

● Kilshanny Cheese

Peter Nibbering's gouda-style Kilshanny cheeses aren't seen much away from the West coast – you will find them in markets in Clare and in Limerick on Saturday, and this cheesemaking operation has always remained small-scale and local. But don't imagine that such modesty reflects on the cheese, for these are beautifully crafted, raw milk cheeses, whether you choose the subtle, buttery plain or any of the five flavoured varieties. Aged to about 18-months, Kilshannycheeses are superb. (Derry House, Kilshanny ☎ 065-707 1228)

Clare

Local Speciality
SEAFOOD CHOWDER

Guesthouse

● Moy House

"One of the nicest country houses I have ever been to." That's what our distinguished editor, Elizabeth Field, wrote to us after a few days in County Clare, staying in Moy House, walking in the wild and the wet, and having a fine old time. But that's the sort of spell that Moy can cast on the visitor, thanks to the magisterial views across the bay, thanks to the lovely cooking, and the plush comfort, not to mention the excellent bathrooms which are some of the best in the west. (Lahinch ☎ 065-708 2800 moyhouse@eircom.net www.moyhouse.com – Open Feb-Dec)

Guesthouse

● Vaughan Lodge

Michael and Maria Vaughan have stuck to their guns in providing creative food and excellent accommodation in Vaughan Lodge, even though the market in Lahinch can tend more towards the beer'n'chips brigade. But they do the good stuff here: seared scallops with butternut squash; hot smoked mackerel with pickled vegetables; coq au vin with potato purée; Angus beef with fondant potato; Burren lamb with mint pancakes. A friend put it well when she said that Michael and Maria and their crew "have a lovely way about them". Indeed they do, and it makes Vaughan Lodge rather special. (Ennistymon Road, Lahinch ☎ 065 708 1111 info@vaughanlodge.ie www.vaughanlodge.ie – Open Apr-Oct)

Liscannor

Café & Shop

Liscannor Rock Shop

A sister outfit to the ultra-professional Aillwee Caves in Ballyvaughan, folk come here to learn all about the beautiful Liscannor stone, and to enjoy some simple but tasty day-time cooking. (Dereen, Liscannor ☎ 065-708 1930 – Open 10am-6pm Mon-Sun)

Clare

Lisdoonvarna

Smokehouse

The Burren Smokehouse

Peter and Brigitta Curtin are amongst the most important food producers on the west coast of Ireland. Their fish smokery, their shop, their pub, are powerhouses of activity, manned with unflagging energy ever since we first encountered this talented pair back in the late 1980's, when Lisdoon had little more than a curious matchmaking festival and when the smokehouse was just about to commence smoking. Today, the serious attraction in the town is focused more on the stomach than the heart, for their visitor centre attracts 30,000 food lovers every year, folk who can buy the Burren smoked fish – eel, trout, organic salmon, Arctic char – along with lots of other great foods from near and far. The Curtins are visionary folk, and their success is testament to determination, hard work, and skilful fish smoking. (Lisdoonvarna ☎ 065-707 4432 info@burrensmokehouse.ie www.burrensmokehouse.ie)

Miltown Malbay

Restaurant

The Black Oak

Bernie and Tom Hamilton's restaurant is one of the little-known Clare champions, those good places that do the good thing and do it quietly and efficiently. This is the sort of restaurant where people go back, time and again, and eat the very same thing they had the last time; the seafood pot, or the crab cakes with horseradish, or the good sirloin steak or the ginger pudding. It is, therefore, a local favourite, which means it is the sort of place visitors should not miss, even if the design is a long way from the cutting edge. (Rineen, Miltown Malbay ☎ 065-708 4403 🖱 www.blackoakclare.com – Open 6pm-10pm Tue-Sat)

Fishmonger

● Malbay Fish

You can buy fresh crab meat here, from the factory, during the season. (Malbay Industrial Estate, Ballard Road, Miltown Malbay ☎ 065-708 4888 – Crab season runs from Mar-Dec)

Clare

Mountshannon

Cafe

● An Cúpan Caife

Dagmar Hilty is the new owner of this cosy little café in lovely Mountshannon and is just setting out her stall as we write. (Main Street, Mountshannon ☎ 061-927 275 ✉ dhilty@eircom.net – Open noon-3pm, afternoon bites 3pm-6pm, dinner 6pm-9pm)

Scarrif

Seed Savers

● Irish Seed Savers Association

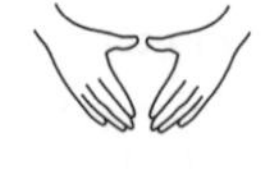

"What if 90% of your country's vegetable varieties became extinct within 100 years... well, they have."

The Irish Seed Savers Association pulls no punches with that explosive line from its brochure, stating the cold, hard truth about what has happened to seed varieties during the course of the 20th century. Established in 1992, ISSA has collected almost 200 varieties of native apple, almost 50 varieties of grain, and has over 350 rare and commercially unavailable seeds in its vegetable bank. This is, truly, a priceless heritage, and it deserves everyone's support, for without it we are truly diminished. Look out for their excellent bio-diversity days in Scariff, with potato tastings, working with draught horses – the farm horse is coming back! – rare poultry breed workshops and much, much more. ISSA work is inspirational work, and they aim to double their membership of 2,500, so please, please do sign up, and sign up all your friends. (Capparoe, Scarrif, Co Clare ☎ 061-921866 ✉ info@irishseedsavers.ie 🖱 www.irishseedsavers.ie)

Sixmilebridge

Deli & Cafe

● Barrell of Grapes

Anyhow, whenever our friend Sile goes to an auction in Sixmilebridge – as you do – she always stops at Barrell of Grapes, because the coffee is good, the lunches tasty, the wines interesting and there is always some nifty jar or other that will have her name on it. Jacques Hubert brings in little-known wines from France, and you can enjoy them by the glass in the shop with a plate of cheese or charcuterie or some salad or quiche. Now, are you ready to do some, like, serious bidding? (Sixmilebridge ☎ 061-368 915/087-9832 640 ✉ info@barrell-of-grapes.com 🖱 www.barrell-of-grapes.com – Open noon-late Tue-Sat)

Clare

"In food - simplicity."

MAURA FOLEY

Shannon

Farmers' Market

● Skycourt Farmers' Market

A gaily colourful outdoor market with everything from bakes to crafts to plants to some interesting queer gear from local producers. (Skycourt Shopping Centre, Friday 12.30pm-7pm)

Tuamgraney

Chocolates

● Wilde's

Patricia Farrell's chocolate company produce organic chocolates of impeccable provenance, made carefully by hand so that they are in control of every aspect of flavour, consistency and uniqueness. This painstaking approach makes for fabulous chocolates with a real signature style unique to Wilde's. (Unit 6, Enterprise Centre, Tuamgraney ☎ 061-922080 ✉ wildeirish@eircom.net)

County Cork

CORK CITY CENTRE

Cork Central

Bakery

Arbutus Bread

Declan Ryan's pioneering bakery is one of the most important artisan businesses in Ireland. Everything Mr Ryan has done has been singular, distinctive and daring. He switched people onto sour-dough bread when there was none in the market, and as such he deserves a place in the pantheon of great baking pioneers alongside Lionel Poilane and Steve Sullivan of California's Acme Bread Company. Just as importantly, the quality of Arbutus Breads has never dipped ever since Mr Ryan first fired up his ovens, and today the range has expanded to include a great pain au chocolat, new Turkish flat breads and pitta breads and a pain au raisin. The stuff of culture and the staff of life. (Rathdene, Montenotte ☎ 021-450 1113 arbutus@iol.ie)

Tea

Barry's Tea

We remain daily devotees of Barry's Classic Blend tea, for our money the best blend on the market and a peerless everyday libation. If we lived away from Ireland this is the drink we would want shipped over from home. Their Earl Grey is also very fine and but it remains better than any other brand. (Kinsale Road, Cork ☎ 021-491 5000 www.barrystea.ie)

Asian Foods

Mr Bell's

Driss Belmajdoub runs two pell-mell stalls in the English Market, their shelves groaning with good things from the east and all points in between, a taste of the souk in the centre of Cork. Several years back, for the Cork Free Choice Group, Driss made a Moroccan version of Irish Stew. Now, that is a dish we should love to taste! (The English Market, Cork ☎ 021-488 5333 – Mr Bell's produce is available in gourmet stores throughout Cork)

Tapas Bar

Boqueria

A gorgeous bar whose Spanish name indicates its Iberian emphasis, Boqueria offers classic tapas (chick peas and black pudding; stuffed piquillo peppers; potato tortilla) but transforms them into Irish artisan dishes by offering Belvelly smoked fish and West Cork charcuterie, and even Macroom Oatmeal for breakfast. The room is politer than the sort of bustle you might recall from bars in Barcelona and San Sebastian, the staff a little hesitant at times, but on a good night it's a fun space. (6 Bridge Street, Cork ☎ 021 455 9049 tapas@boqueriasixbridgest.com www.boqueriasixbridgest.com – Open 8.30am-11.30pm Mon-Thur, until 12.30am Fri & Sat)

Cork Central

Cookware Shop and Cookery School

Brennan & Co

The shelves of Brennan's cook shop are stuffed with everything you might ever need in the kitchen. The staff are unbelievably helpful, and their Cook School is a busy, happy place where courses book out quickly. They particularly specialise in baking, but if you are seeking anything for the kitchen, then this is your first port of call. (7 Oliver Plunkett Street, Cork ☎ 021-427 8273 letscook@brenco.ie www.brenco.ie)

Butcher

Michael Bresnan's

The Bresnan family can trace their involvement in the meat business back to 1898, and after almost 110 years they continue to do what they have always done: raise Hereford and Angus stock on their farm and process them in their abattoir and then sell them in the Market. The beef is superb, but so is their lamb, and at the right time you can even get lamb's sweetbreads here, nowadays a product that has all-but-vanished. (The English Market, Cork ☎ 021-427 1119 – Open 9am-6pm Mon-Sat)

Wine Merchant

Bubble Brothers

Billy Forrester's wine company is one smart operation. They began bringing in bubbly several years back – hence the name – but have long-since expanded into covering the vinous globe, whilst remaining true to their artisan champagne producers. Aside from the shop in the English Market, you will find their wines, arranged with great style, in cutting-edge shops like URRU and The Stuffed Olive. Mr Forrester favours easy-drinking, rather serene wines, often characterised by an overall sense of sweetness, whether you are trying the Brightwater sauvignon blanc or the Domaine de Lalande Macon. Splendidly efficient service squares the circle on a fine wine company. (Wine Depot, Marina Commercial Park, Centre Park Road, Cork ☎ 021-484 5198 info@bubblebrothers.com www.bubblebrothers.com)

Café

Café Gusto

Marianne and Denis have just opened a second Gusto, on the Boardwalk at Lapp's Quay, spreading their message of intricately thought-through coffee and foods. Java Republic beans are the basis for their coffee expertise, and they are assured baristas. The care taken with the coffee is shown also in their sandwiches, made using Alternative Bread Co. breads and rolls: sandwich fans who remember the pioneering sandwiches of Iago will feel right at home in Café Gusto. (3 Washington Street, Cork & The Boardwalk, Lapp's Quay, Cork ☎ 021-425 4446 info@cafegusto.com www.cafegusto.com)

Vegetarian Restaurant with Rooms

Café Paradiso

Asparagus gratin with hazelnuts and capers in a mustard cream sauce. Gratin of aubergine, crushed potato and Bluebell Falls goat's cheese with a watercress cream, braised lentils and green beans with marjoram. Some chefs have such an individual style that you only have to spell out a couple of dishes for everyone to say: "That's a Denis Cotter invention!"And of course the two courses we ate on our last visit to Café P were quintessential Denis Cotter – involved yet pure, complex yet chaste, roundabout yet direct. No one else cooks like this, no one else thinks about food like this, and that is why Café Paradiso is so singular. Not cooking with meat has proven to be the greatest creative springboard for this chef. Note there are three chic guestrooms upstairs. (Lancaster Quay, Cork ☎ 021-427 7939 info@cafeparadiso.ie www.cafeparadiso.ie – Open noon-3pm, 6.30pm-10.30pm Tue-Sat

Market

The Coal Quay Market

The Saturday CQ Market is the city's farmers' market, and has grown to a healthy trestle-table-count of up to 16 stalls. Expect fabulous organics from pioneering growers such as Caroline Robinson, great breads and comestibles from Mark Hosford, the brilliant Flores foods, and there are lots of good things to graze on and to feed the kids. (Coal Quay, Saturdays 9am-4.30pm Contact Caroline Robinson carolinerobinson@eircom.net
☎ 021-733 0178)

Cork Central

Coffee Shop

Coffee Central

Mary Rose used to sell pork and bacon in the market, continuing the family tradition, but switched her trade back in 2001 to open Coffee Central. Today, the stall is one of the Market's key meeting places, with smashing coffee and great things to eat. (The English Market, Cork
☎ 021-427 1999 – Open Mon-Sat 9am-5pm)

Coffee Roasters

Cork Coffee Roasters

Anna and John Gowan's CCR produce superbly roasted coffees. Pick any of their blends, from Morning Growler to Rebel City Espresso, from Summerhill Blend to Earlybird Fairtrade – and you get coffee roasting that extracts and states the essence of the bean and the roast: this is seriously skilful and talented coffee roasting, and the CCR blends can stand alongside any of the great Irish-produced drinks. An icon in the making. (Summerhill, Cork ☎ 087 776 6322 johngowan@gmail.com
www.corkcoffee.com)

Restaurant

Crawford Gallery Café

The loveliest café in Cork, and probably the loveliest café in Ireland. The Crawford is serene, polite, and has politely delicious food whose consistency never wavers, whether you nip in for coffee and a freshly baked biscuit, or gab over a lazy lunch with your mates, or wander in after a stroll around the galleries to enjoy the art on the plate that is the Crawford's signature. (Emmet Place, Cork
☎ 021-427 4415 – Open 10am-4.30pm Mon-Sat)

Market

The English Market

"The most remarkable thing about Cork's English Market, beyond its diversity – which is on a par with any French market you have idled through in envy – is its intrinsic regionalness. Preserving its own ancient traditions seems to have emboldened Cork to espouse those of its nearer neighbours."

The food writer Tamasin Day-Lewis wrote that, back in 2000, and it's a spot-on summation of what makes the English Market special. Diverse. Regional. Traditional. Yet open to its neighbours and their traits and products and ways of working. The EM is a meshwork for foods, by which we mean that one stall – and they are stalls, not shops, another key characteristic – supports the others in terms of the overall offer. Shopping here, you ping-pong between one stall and another, so that should you want to cook the recipe for salsify scallops that appeared on the same page of *The Daily Telegraph* as Ms Day-Lewis was writing, you get your fish in one side of the market and your salsify at another end and your butter elsewhere, and you buy all these things from Different Stalls run by Different People who may be different but who share high-level Skills and Expertise in their special area. The English Market is, mercifully, The Anti-Supermarket. It is the antithesis of supermarket blandness. It is the Soul of the City.

Along with other stalls specifically mentioned elsewhere on these pages, in the market you will discover · The Alternative Bread Company (☎ 021-489 7787) · Joup (☎ 086-8776450) · The Chocolate Shop · Iago (☎ 021-427 7047) · The Meat Centre (☎ 021-427 7085) · The Organic Shop (☎ 021-427 9419) · Linda's Flower Shop (☎ 021-427 6917) · Fruit Boost (☎ 021-435 8467) · Superfruit (☎ 021-427 5721). And across from O'Connell's fish stall there are two fine fishmongers, one an outpost of Ballycotton Seafood in Midleton. This company is new to the market, and intends producing cooked seafood to go, as well as a great selection of fish. The other is known as "the fish shop on the corner" and has no name, but many loyal customers.

Chocolates

Eve Chocolate Shop

A chocolate shop in a wee industrial yard?! Only in Cork. And you will find Eve St. Leger's stunning chocolates only in Cork. Ms St Leger never intended to have a store – it just sort of happened as a result of having a little chocolate production unit. But devotees of the utterly unique Corkies – the best Irish chocolate, we think – or the sublime Crunchies and the kid-inspiring Metre-of-Chocolate happily make their way to Magazine Road. Eve is one of the great Cork companies, and she shows exactly how Cork has a food culture that everyone else envies: she is more original, more creative, but she is also bespoke in scale, luxury brand in style, cult in character. (College Commercial Park, Magazine Road, Cork ☎ 021-434 7781 eve@evechocolates.ie www.evechocolates.ie– Open 9.30am-6pm Mon-Fri, 9.20am-1pm Saturday plus extra hours for Christmas, St Valentine's Day, Mother's Day and Easter)

Cork Central

Sweets

Exchange Toffee Works

Remember clove rock? Remember that vibrant, hallucinogenic burgundy-surrounded-yellow-centre. Imagine clove rock that, instead of that deadly concoction of additives and whatnots, was made with good ingredients? Well, that is what the Linehan family do in The Exchange Toffee works. Real clove rock. Real acid drops (groovy man!) Real bull's eyes. Charlie and the chocolate factory away with ye! ETW is where it's at. (37a John Redmond Street, Mulgrave Road, Cork ☎ 021 450 7791 – Open 9am-6pm Mon-Fri)

Pizza

Fast Al's

Alan Goulding does the good thing by pizza. Hand-rolled dough. Only a few varieties. Sold by the slice when it is ready. This is proper pizza, with a crisp crust and a pizza maker who understands the culture of his calling: this poor man worries about the quality of his dough, and Al's worries are your guarantee of the best slice in Cork city. (3 Paradise Place, Cork ☎ 087-609 9544 Al is open until 6pm daily, then re-opens from 9.30pm-3.30am on Fridays and Saturdays.)

Restaurant

The Farmgate Café

Kay Harte is a passionate woman. She needs to be in order to persist in serving what some regard as "traditional" Irish dishes – tripe and drisheen; corned beef with colcannon; Irish stew; macaroni cheese;

breadcrumbed lemon sole. But, of course, like those other great County Cork women whose culinary work has no truck with fashion, Ms Harte simply does what she does best, and the result is some of the best eating in Cork city, which means some of the best eating in Ireland. The Farmgate states the case for our traditional foods with more eloquence than anywhere else, because it renders these dishes with such exactitude, and because they deliver such pleasure. One of the great Cork addresses. (Old English Market, Princes Street, Cork ☎ 021-427 8134 – Open day time)

Dips and Marinades

Flores

Miriam Flores worked as a personal chef in the US and Mexico, where she hails from, and she has also worked with Seamus O'Connell in The Ivory Tower. Miriam has now started her own company, selling fresh salsas, fajitas, dips and marinades in some of the markets around Cork. These include Mahon Point, Kinsale and the Coal Quay Market. These are wickedly fine products with razor sharp taste definitions, and it is amazing how the hot chilli sauce is as precise as the Mediterranean Pesto. Flores foods are some of the most exciting new products we have enjoyed recently. (14 Pope's Hill, Cork ☎ 085-139 4037 rojocatering@yahoo.com)

Brew Pub

Franciscan Well Brew Pub

Blarney Blonde. Rebel Red. Shandon Stout. Do these guys know how to give a drink a name, or what? Give them a job in a branding agency. Actually, do nothing of the sort. Cork needs these really fine brews, and it needs this riverside brew pub, facing the river on the North Mall. These are some of the best micro-brews made in Ireland, and yet they remain little known. No trip Leeside is complete wiithout getting up close, and personal, with a Blarney Blonde. (14b North Mall, Cork ☎ 021-439 3434 – Open 3pm-11.30pm Mon-Wed, 3pm-midnight Thur, 3pm-12.30am Fri & Sat, 4pm-11pm Sun)

Wines & Spirit Shop

Galvin's Wines & Spirits

Galvin's import and distribute a wide range of popular brands of wines, beers and spirits, so if you seek anything from a bottle of Beringer to Choya saki, they are the man. (Washington Street, Cork ☎ 021-427 6314 info@galvinswines.com www.galvinswines.com)

B&B

Garnish House

Hansi Lucey's excellent B&B offers swaddling maternal care, and one of the biggest and best breakfasts in the land. No wonder every guest is a regular. (Western Road, Cork ☎ 021-427 5111 info@garnish.ie www.garnish.ie)

Restaurant

Les Gourmandises

Pat and Soizic Kiely are talented professionals, and they run a blissfully professional restaurant. If Mr Kiely cooked in Dublin, he would never be out of the media, but Cork's high standards mean that his high standards simply get taken to be part of the fabric of the city. His work is cheffy – some would say the complexity of the dishes can be fussy – but the fact is that he makes everything work, from ravioli of goat's cheese with celeriac and marinated salmon to red mullet with pink grapefruit to caramelised passion fruit custard with passion fruit granita. (17 Cook Street, Cork ☎ 021-425 1959 info@lesgourmandises.ie www.lesgourmandises.ie – Open 6pm-9.30pm Tue-Thur, 6pm-10pm Fri & Sat, and open Fri lunch)

Patisserie

Heaven's Cake

Joe Hegarty's cake company has begun to work markets away from his base in the English Market, good news for cake lovers away from the city. HC brings a professional finish to domestically inspired baking, making for a treasurable series of cakes and patisseries. (English Market, Cork ☎ 021-422 2775 – Open 9.30am-5.30pm)

Café

Idaho Café

Mairé and Richard Jacob's café is a wee beauty. It is, in fact, extremely tiny, but the only scale they worry about is the extent of the deliciousness of the dishes they serve, and by that standard they deliver in gargantuan terms, and that is why it is so difficult to get a seat here at any time of the day. Waffles with maple syrup to start the day, risotto with basil and bacon for lunch, then tea and a slice of

Cork Central

orange and almond cake to while away the afternoon. Small, yes, and perfectly formed, and all-round bliss. (19 Caroline Street, Cork ☎ 021-427 6376 – Open 8.30am-5pm Mon-Thu 8.30am-6pm Fri & Sat)

Restaurant

● Isaac's

Isaac's is one of the great and enduring Cork brasseries, and Michael Ryan and Canice Sharkey have run this big room with unflagging energy and skill right from the start. In many ways, Isaac's is the Cork equivalent of Roly's Bistro in Dublin; a big, handsome, energised room, with full-on-flavour food and all the pleasures of great classic dishes delivered with panache. (48 MacCurtain Street, Cork ☎ 021-450 3805 isaacs@iol.ie – Open Lunch & Dinner Mon-Sun)

Cork Central

Restaurant

● The Ivory Tower Gastrological Restaurant

Back in 1994, the brilliant food writer Emily Green wrote of Seamus O'Connell, "he is a jazzy character who scats along, whether in a frantic New York restaurant or the pressurised, formal kitchen of a Michelin three-star. This requires stamina and a healthy rebel streak".
Well, all these years later, Mr O'Connell has the stamina and rebel streak, both present and correct. His work remains off-kilter with what other chefs of his generation cook and how they work. He makes us think of the composer Morton Feldman – out there, way out there. So, if you don't mind a Bohemian setting, and you do fancy food that is ravishing in its uniqueness, then the Icarus of the kitchen is the man for you. (Exchange Buildings, Princes Street, Cork ☎ 021-427 4665 – Open noon-3pm, 6.30pm-10pm Tue-Sat)

Restaurant

● Jacob's on the Mall

We have eaten some of the best dishes of our lives in Jacob's, thanks to Mercy Fenton's brilliant cooking skills and the talents she has inculcated in her crew. Salad of flat bread, chicken and carrots in 1998; salmon with noodles and Chinese greens in '99; venison with celeriac and parsnip purée in 2001; cod with champ and green beans in 2004, and we could go on and on. The food reads simple, yet it eats spectacular, and it is food that is full of goodness.

(30a South Mall, Cork ☎ 021-425 1530
✉ jacobsonthemall@eircom.net
🖱 www.jacobsonthemall.com – Open 12.30pm-2.30pm, 6.30pm-10pm Mon-Sat)

Restaurant

Jacques

In a few years time, Jacque & Eithne Barry's restaurant will celebrate thirty years in business. That is several lifetimes in the cooking trade, yet these girls work away as if they were fresh out of college and looking for the right challenge to master. They spin out new ideas endlessly, they remain as excited by food as ever, and their energy is addictive and intoxicating, as addictive and intoxicating as their food. So, Gubbeen pork with gremolata, lamb's liver with sherry, shallots and raisins, and rhubarb and custard tart to follow. That will do nicely. (9a Phoenix Street, Cork ☎ 021-427 7387 ✉ jacques@eircom.net
🖱 www.jacquesrestaurant.ie – Open 6pm-10pm Mon-Sat; 5pm-9pm Sun)

Cork Central

Cafe & Wholefood Store

Joup

Joup is not just a place to eat, it is also a place to absorb Rachael Connolly's food philosophy, which espouses sound eco-slow-food principles which are steadfastly right on! So, get your jaws around good smoothies, good soups, fair trade drinks, artisanal baking and healthy salads. Aside from the English Market, you will find them in farmers' markets and on the Ballinlough Road. (City End, Ballinlough Road, Cork, Unit 4B Grand Parade, Old English Market, Cork ☎ 086 8776450
✉ rachaelconnolly@ireland.com 🖱 www.joup.org
– Open 8am-5.30pm Mon-Sat)

Chipper

Jackie Lennox

Whilst Jackie is now frying at that great hot counter in the clouds, everything in Lennox's remains true to their mantra of fresh food, fried properly; the staple diet of generations of UCC students and ordinary decent people. The chips – they use, believe it or not, as many as 20 to 40 different types of potatoes through the year – are wickedly good and thunderously consistent. (137 Bandon Road, Cork ☎ 021-431 6118 – Open noon-1.30am Mon-Sun)

Coffee Roasters

Maher's Coffee

Maher's has been doing a great job of roasting and selling coffee from the days long before the drink's current cult status, quietly getting on with being very good at what they do and not making much of a fuss about it. We like the understatedness of the shop, and the quiet subtlety of their roasts and blends. (25 Oliver Plunkett Street, Cork ☎ 021-427 0008 – Open 9.30am-5.30pm Mon-Sat)

Farmers' Market

Mahon Point Farmers' Market

Mahon Point is an awesome farmers' market, with an atmosphere unlike any other market. All the finest Cork artisans are here every Thursday and the food to eat is as outstanding as the food to buy and fill up your bags. The produce of Cork for the people of Cork is their logo, and being surrounded on all sides by bland, commercial shopping emporia makes the energy and Cork character of the market even better. To understand the avant garde of Cork artisanship you only need to come to Mahon Point. (Thursdays, 10am-2pm Contact: Rupert Hugh-Jones ☎ 021-464 6601 rupert@ballycottonorganics.com)

Restaurant

Nash 19

If Isaac's is Roly's Bistro by the Lee, then Nash 19 is Avoca for Cork food lovers. Swish, busy, assured, and with food that punches above its weight in terms of flavour, Nash 19 is a fail-safe, sure-bet, supremely-organised food operation. Care and attention to detail are evident in every detail of this pristine food concept. (19 Princes Street, Cork ☎ 021-427 0880 info@nash19.com www.nash19.com – Open 7.30am-4.30pm Mon-Sat (4pm close Sat)

Wholefood shop, bakery and café

Natural Foods

NF is a diminutive wholefood shop with a fine bakery. They produce no fewer than eight different types of bread, and there is also a lovely range of healthy sweet things to enjoy. Their new bakery complex means that these great breads will now be more widely available. (26 Paul Street, Cork ☎ 021-427 7244 orlaobyrne@yahoo.com roddyhenderson@hotmail.com)

Chocolates

OConaill Chocolates

Casey OConaill covers all bases. Chocolate producer, chocolate café owner, farmer's marketeer, he is a dynamic guy, restless, self-critical, supremely amiable, hard-working. Everything he does is signed with a signature of true goodness. (16 French Church Street, Cork ☎ 021-437 3407)

Fishmonger

Kay O'Connell Fishmongers

Pat and Paul O'Connell have an entire corner of the market these days, all the better to accommodate their enormous fish business. But they have done more over the last years than simply grow their business to the size it is now. They have also flown the flag for superb fish, skillfully served, and in doing so have made their product hip and fashionable. They have done it via the oldest and simplest method: sheer bloody hard work, driving hither and thither to get the best fish, then selling it with great energy all day long in the Market, and they have done it by consistent innovation and improvement. And they haven't stopped yet, you know: on our latest visit, Paul was too coy to tell us just what was planned with the stall, but something was afoot. As ever. (The English Market, Cork ☎ 021-427 6380 www.koconnellsfish.com)

Wine Merchant

O'Donovan's

Gary O'Donovan's chain of wine shops are popular addresses dotted throughout the city and its environs. (St Patrick's Woollen Mills, Douglas ☎ 021-436 4799: also at Ballincollig; Bishopstown; Blackpool; Summerhill; Oliver Plunkett Street; Shandon Street; Main Street, Midleton; and Riversdale, Midleton)

Butcher

O'Flynn's

The O'Flynn brothers have gone back to their old habitat, opening a gourmet sausage stall in the English Market, where their father, Jackie Sam, first opened a stall as long ago as 1927. Simon and Patrick remain best known as the luminary butchers of Marlborough Street, having moved just out of the market in the early 1980's. They are pioneering charcutiers, men who understand the culture of charcuterie, its creative edge, its challenge, and they are amongst the most significant and important of the Cork culinary specialists. (36 Marlborough Street, Cork ☎ 021-427 5685 – Open 9am-5pm Mon-Thur, 8am-5pm Fri, 8am-4pm Sat)

Butcher

On The Pig's Back

Isabelle Sheridan "believes her stall reflects the best elements of the Market as it has developed since the 1990's: the old alongside the new, the Irish and the international, the gourmet with the plain". That's how the brothers Ó Drisceoil describe Isabelle's stall in their lovely book on the English market, *Serving a City*, and it's spot on. Here you will find great breads and terrines, cheeses in immaculate nick, lovely fresh sausages and preserves, and a whole host of good things. Brilliant. (The English Market, Cork ☎ 021-427 9232)

Cork Central

Drisheen and Tripe

O'Reilly's

Stephen O'Reilly's stall sells tripe and drisheen, the Cork speciality made with sheep and beef blood. Tripe and drisheen. Nothing else. Now, that's what we call niche marketing. Genius. (The English Market, Cork ☎ 021-496 6397)

Greengrocer

Organic Garden

Donal O'Callaghan's stall has excellent organic produce, feathery-fine salad leaves and sparkling fresh vegetables, and do look just down the row for Paradise Garden which has lots of fine exotica. (The English Market, Cork ☎ 021-427 2368)

Patisserie

Petits Fours

Christine Girault sells classic artisan French produce in this petite patisserie on Washington Street, including tarte tatin, almond croissants and, of course, petit fours. Opera is their signature cake and they will produce any of the range to order. (27 Washington Street ☎ 021-480 6530 petitefours@gmail.com www.petitsfours.ie – Open 10.30am-5.30pm Tue-Fri, 11am-4pm Sat. See also Sugar, her café a few doors up the street)

Wholefood Shop and Self Service Restaurant

The Quay Co-Op

The QC remains best known for its up-the-stairs whole-food café, but the star of their show, for us, is actually their shop, which is a brilliant repository of essential things to eat, cook and use. The vegetarian dishes in the café are hearty wholefood offerings, and they have a devoted audience who enjoy both their flavour and their value. (24 Sullivans Quay, Cork, ☎ 021-431 7026 quaycoop@eircom.net www.quaycoop.com – Open 9am-9pm Mon-Sat)

Olives and Sandwiches

The Real Olive Company

Back in 1993, Toby Simmonds used to be asked "what class of grapes" he was selling, as bemused Corkonians tried to get their heads around this young bloke selling a dozen varieties of olive. Today, the Real Olive is one of the stalwarts of the Market, and an example of how change, development and innovation has become a key element of what makes the Market work. The ROC has expanded to open a very fine sandwich store just behind the olive stall itself. (The English Market, Cork ☎ 021-427 0842)

Restaurant

Star Anise

This quiet little star of Cork's restaurant circle has settled in nicely over the last couple of years. They do the essential things well, so the room and the staff are welcoming, and the food is just-what-you-fancy: the signature slow-cooked lamb in filo; galette of hummus, mushrooms and brie; tempura of tiger prawns; roast pork belly with Chinese-spiced cabbage; roast duck with an unusual orange and tomato sauce; star anise dessert plate. Modest and meticulous. (4 Bridge Street, Cork ☎ 021-455 1635 staranise@eircom.net www.staranise-cork.com – Open noon-2.30pm Tue-Fri, 6pm-10pm Tue-Thu, 6pm-11pm Fri & Sat)

Bread Mixes

Sowan's Organic Bread Mix

Never mind what is in Louise Delaney's excellent bread mixes. It is what is NOT in them that is perhaps of even greater import – no chemical flour "improvers"; no bulking agents; no artificial colours; no artificial flavours; no preservatives; no additives; no sugar; no yeast. In other words, none of the gunk that you get when you buy standard bread or bread mixes. Louise's four mixes couldn't be easier to use: mix in milk to your chosen mix, put in a tin which you put in an oven for 60 minutes and voila! fresh organic bread made with your own fair hands. There are two spelt varieties, a sunflower seed mix and a wheat and rye mix, and Louise has just introduced catering-sized mixes. (Mount Verdon House, 15 Wellington Road, Cork ☎ 087 662 3998 louise@sowansorganic.ie www.sowansorganic.ie)

Cork Central

Café

Sugar

Soups, salads, ciabattas and rolls, and good cakes make up a very nifty lunch offer in Christine Girault's bright café on Washington Street. But the speciality of the house must be the traditional French breakfast of home-made brioche and almond croissants. (27 Washington Street ☎ 021-480 6530 petitefours@gmail.com www.petitsfours.ie – Open 8am-5pm Mon-Fri. See also Petits Fours, her shop a few doors down the street)

Restaurant

Table

Domini and Peaches Kemp have steered Itsabagel to success, followed by Itsa4, and have now set their sights on Cork city, opening up Table, upstairs in Brown Thomas. These sisters know what people like to eat: buttermilk chicken goujons with aioli; soy-marinated chicken salad with buckwheat noodles; Thai fish cakes with chilli and ginger dip; char-grilled burger with Swiss cheese; apple, cinnamon and walnut cake. It reads like Bill Granger food, and it looks as slick and hip as Bill's. Happily, it's in Cork rather than Sydney. (Brown Thomas, 18-21 Patrick Street, Cork ☎ 021-427 5106 www.itsabagel.com – Open 9am-7pm Mon, Wed & Sat, 9.30am-7pm Tue, 9am-8pm Thur, noon-6pm Sun)

Soup and Sandwich Bar

Wildways

Maura Roche's soup and sandwich bar is hip and chipper, a smart outfit that makes delicious organic soups and delicious organic sandwiches and serves them with charm and efficiency. (21 Princes Street, Cork ☎ 021-427 2199 info@wildways.net www.wildways.net – Open 7.45am-5pm Mon-Fri, 9am-4pm Sat)

Wine Merchant

● The Wine Buff

Barry Acheson runs the Cork branch of the 14-branch chain supplied by Paddy O'Flynn from his base in Bordeaux. The wines are good, the service is good, there is genuineness and typicity in what they sell and the way they sell it, and the individual stores all have the enthusiasm and energy of their owners as an added bonus. (4 Washington Street, Cork ☎ 021-425 1668 ✉ barry@thewinebuff.com 🖱 www.thewinebuff.com)

CORK CITY OUTSKIRTS

Cork Central

Ballincollig

Greengrocer

● Eco Harvest

Catriona Daunt is best known for her lovely organic vegetable stalls at the various farmers' markets around Cork. Recently she opened this shop with Willie Doherty, selling her trademark vegetables, plus goods from the Olive Stall and a selection of wholefoods. You can find Catriona's stalls at Midlelton Market on Saturday, Macroom and Kinsale markets on Tuesdays, Mahon Point on Thursdays, and Bantry on Fridays. Catriona will have exceptional quality organic fruit and vegetables, both Irish produced and imported, and there are teas, blueberry tonic and other good things. (The Old Village Shopping Centre, Ballincollig ☎ 086 362 2918 – Open 10am-5.30pm)

Butcher

● Michael O'Crualaoi

O'Crualaoi's is both butcher and deli, fresh meat shop and cooked food shop, specialist for the domestic market and – via its sister company Ballyburden Meats – supplier to food service throughout Cork and Kerry. It is the most humungously successful enterprise, with some of the very best staff working in any food destination. Their success is based on a simple premise; they do the good thing, and they look after their customers, which is why the company will celebrate 50 years in business in 2007. If you seek good meats, good cooked food, even kid's party food, you will find it all here. (Ballincollig ☎ 021-487 1205 ✉ info@ocrualaoi.com 🖱 www.ocrualaoi.com – Open 7am-6.30pm Mon-Thu, 7am-7pm Fri, 7am-6pm Sat)

Blackpool

Fishmonger

Dennehy's Seafood

Tom Dennehy runs the shop his father, Tom Dennehy senior, opened more than 60 years ago, and he still buys all the fish himself from Union Hall. "I sell the ordinary everyday fish, like whiting, plaice, sole, cod and haddock, rather than the prime fish, and I find there's a great demand for it." (96 Great William O'Brien Street, Blackpool ☎ 021-430 2144 – Open 7.30am-5.30pm Tue-Fri, 7.30am-3pm Mon & Sat)

Blarney

Guesthouse

Ashlee Lodge

A wonderful mix of B&B comfort with country house grandness and hotel professionalism, Ashlee Lodge is powered by Anne and John, a dynamic couple who work extra hard, and who are amongst the most helpful hosts we have ever encountered. Recently, Anne has begun to cook for non-residents on Thursday, Friday and Saturday evenings, which is a brilliant boost for Blarney, which has few fine places to eat. Whatever you might expect, simply expect this couple to exceed your expectations. (Tower, Blarney ☎ 021-438 5346 info@ashleelodge.com www.ashleelodge.com)

Gastro Pub

Blair's Inn

A riverside pub with good cooking – and some traditional music – is just the ticket, and so it is in John and Anne Blair's bar and restaurant. Care in the sourcing and care in the cooking makes for good eating. (Cloghroe, Blarney ☎ 021-438 1470 info@blairsinn.ie www.blairsinn.ie – Food served in bar 12.30pm-3.45, 4pm-9pm. Restaurant opens at 6pm)

B&B with Restaurant

Phelan's Woodview House

Billie Phelan's highly-regarded cooking, enjoyed in this simple, domestic house, is a valuable antidote to touristy Blarney. (Tweedmount, Blarney ☎ 021-438 5197 www.phelanswoodviewhouse.com)

Carrigaline

Country Market

Carrigaline Country Market

Carrigaline hosts a legendary country market every Friday morning, so get there early. (Carrigaline GAA Pavilion, Fridays 9.30am)

Farmhouse Cheese

Carrigaline Farmhouse Cheese

The quintessential him'n'her artisan cheese, Pat and Ann's Carrigaline is mild and smooth with a pleasingly yielding texture. Pat not only makes it, he also drives it around the county to the many shops where you will see its distinctive label. A brand new edition to the plain and flavoured Carrigalines is a lightly smoked cheese. (The Rock, Carrigaline ☎ 021-437 2856 www.carrigalinecheese.com)

Cork Central

Fishmonger

Good Fish Processing

A thriving retail shop has developed out of Denis Good's fish processing business in Carrigaline, with the shop offering a really fine choice of sparklingly fresh seafood. (Carrigaline Industrial Park, Crosshaven Road, Carrigaline ☎ 021-437 3917 – Open 9am-5.30pm Mon-Fri, 9am-2pm Sat)

Wine Importer

Karwig's Wines

Joe Karwig has added an on-line shopping service via his website, good news for those of us who seem to always get lost when making our way to the shop. But, getting lost makes the pleasure of finding so many wonderful wines at the end of the journey even more pleasurable. Mr Karwig has patiently and expertly built his list over more than 20 years of selling wines in Ireland, and the list is idiosyncratic, informed and personal – Joe loves Rieslings and he also loves good, big Italian wines. (Kilnagleary, Carrigaline ☎ 021-437 2864 www.karwigwines.ie)

Wine Importer

Kevin Parsons Wines Ltd

Kevin Parsons has long been one of the most distinguished figures in the Cork wine firmament, a superb taster, a fine educator, a man whose grasp of the culture of wine is unerrring and illuminating. (21 Liosbourne, Carrigaline ☎ 021-437 3237)

Douglas

Butcher

Liam Bresnan

A member of the luminary Cork butchering family, Liam Bresnan's beef and lamb come from the family farm and are shown appropriate respect by this skilled charcutier. (Douglas Village Shopping Centre, 021-489 1009)

Restaurant

Citrus

Cork Central

A smart, glass-walled room, smart food, smart customers, that's the Citrus spin, a little taste of Bill Granger style just south of Cork. Harold Lynch cooks reliably and well and there is a very strong sense in Citrus that Mr Lynch cooks what he likes to eat – char-grilled brill; seared beef with blue cheese; chicken curry with chutneys – and the boutique polish and presentation completes a chic outfit. (Barrycourt House, East Douglas Village, Cork ☎ 021-436 1613 – Open noon-3.30pm, 5.30pm-10pm Mon-Sat, 5pm-9pm Sun)

Farmers' Market

Douglas Farmers' Market

This thriving food market was set up in 2004 and features a number of the artisans mentioned on these pages. (Douglas Community Park, Saturdays)

Traiteur

Billy Mackesy's Douglas Village Foods

Billy Mackesy is a real professional: he makes it well, he makes it look good, he knows how to make buying it enjoyable, even if everything is packed away in freezers. The shop is a whirligig of activity as Douglas residents decide what BM speciality they want for tonight's dinner. (1 Tramway Terrace, Douglas ☎ 021-489 0060 – Open 8am-6pm Tue-Fri, 8am-4.30pm Sat)

Fish and Chips

KC's Fish & Chip Shop

Wes Crawford is a witty, sharp bloke, and he runs an ace outfit in K.C's. "All information seems correct at time of press but we have been known to make mistakes (thinking that having a chipper was easy work for instance...").

Well, having a chipper is easy if you do it the lazy way, but Wes does it the hard way: fresh ingredients, skilful cooking, imaginative new combinations. Yes, it's fast food, but only inasmuch as it comes at you quickly. But, to tell the truth, this is gourmet fast food, so abandon any snobbery and order up a meat pattie, a Rhode Island Red and a Vampire. (Douglas, Cork ☎ 021-436 1418 ✉ wesc@eircom.net – Open 12.30pm-2pm Wed-Fri, 6pm-12.45am Wed, 9.30pm-12.45am Thu, 5pm-1.30am Fri & Sat, 5pm-12.45am Sun)

Rochestown

Traiteur

● Cinnamon Cottage

Carol Murphy and Kieran Corcoran's traiteur was the original Cork cooked-food-to-go shop, and over the last few years its success has been phenomenal, with the premises having to be constantly extended on an almost annual basis. An army of chefs fire out delicious food, executed with sure skill and true care – chicken and pasta gratin, peppered beef in Murphy's stout; lamb tagine; white chocolate and raspberry trifle – and there are constant new additions and exciting new creations, which underlines CC's creative animus. (Monastery Road, Rochestown ☎ 021-489 4922 – Open 9.30am-6.45pm Tue-Fri, 10am-5.30pm Sat)

"It is an historical place that refuses to stagnate and a cultural space that mocks pretension, a jewel of shabby charm and a bulwark against the vulgar tide of homogenising commercialisation."

DIARMUID O DRISCEOIL AND DONAL O DRISCEOIL, *SERVING A CITY: THE STORY OF CORK'S ENGLISH MARKET*

Buttevant

Fish Smokehouse

Old Millbank Smokehouse

Geraldine Bass smokes organic salmon using beech and oak, and the result is very fine indeed. The smoke notes are very subtle and delicate, more like a halo of flavours rather than anything direct, and it allows the piscine flavours greater prominence and makes for a salmon that is superb served as sushi. This is very fine work indeed, and Old Millbank fish deserves a place up with the best-known Cork fish smokers. You will find these delicately smoked and hand-sliced fish for sale at local farmers' markets in north Cork and in good shops in Cork – it's for sale in mywine.ie in Mallow. There is also an old Millbank smoked trout, and some fine fish cakes and terrines. (Willow Pond, Buttevant ☎ 022-23299 bass3@indigo.ie www.theirishsmokehouse.com)

Castlelyons

Country House

Ballyvolane House

Ballyvolane enjoys a reputation so stellar that folk virtually swoon when they talk about staying and eating in Justin and Jenny Greene's house. There is an elegance, a welcome, a sassy stylishness that means that Ballyvolane defines what we mean by the Country House Experience. In this regard, it solves all the paradoxes: it is grand but intimate. It is ancient yet avant garde. The food is domestic yet the polish of its presentation is professional. It is not your house but you feel right at home. The other guests are strangers, yet in five minutes they are your new best friends. Truly, this place casts a spell, right from that first rhubarb martini made by Justin, through the course of a superlative dinner, through to a fabulous cheeseboard offering Durrus, Gubbeen, Beenoskee, St. Tola and Maighean. The old kitchen has been converted into a smart new drawing room, restoring the fundamental structure and organisation of the house, and this is one red-hot address. (Castlelyons, Fermoy ☎ 025-36349 info@ballyvolanehouse.ie www.ballyvolanehouse.ie – Open all year apart from Christmas)

Charleville

Farmhouse Cheese

Clonmore Goat's Cheese

Clonmore is a difficult cheese to get your hands on, as it tends to sell out as soon as it is ready and mature. Tom and Lena Biggane only make Clonmore using summer goat's milk, and after two months the cheese is ready to go, though a further month best expresses its sweetness. (Clonmore, Newtown, Charleville ☎ 063-70490)

Coolea

Farmhouse Cheese

Coolea Farmhouse Cheese

Dick Willem's cheese is one of the classic Irish farmhouse cheeses, a Gouda-style cheese that looks like the classic Dutch goudas but which is not as sweet and is much creamier than its Dutch cousins. The creaminess expresses itself as butterscotch and soft caramel, but the fresh acidity of the cheese keeps everything in balance, making for one of the most satisfying Irish cheeses, especially if allowed to mature to 24 months when it packs an awesome flavour punch. Again, it seems to us that the superb old north Cork pastures are a vital ingredient in Coolea, along with the cheesemaking skills handed down to Dick by his parents. (Coolea ☎ 026-45204 cooleacheese@eircom.net)

Fermoy

Restaurant

La Bigoudenne

Rodolphe and Noelle Semeria's creperie and restaurant has been working away happily in Fermoy since 1991, offering Rodolphe's quirky take on French classic dishes – tomato stuffed with crab; cod en papillote; chicken breast with apple and liquorice; venison medallions with red wine and mushrooms; pheasant with Madeira. This is pleasingly rural cooking, and the simplicity of execution, and the simplicity of service is charming. Crêpe lovers can enjoy those fine specialities on Thursdays and Saturdays when the restaurant opens for lunch. (28 McCurtain Street, Fermoy ☎ 025-32832 – Open 12.30pm-3.30pm Thurs-Sat, 5.45pm-9.30pm)

Farmhouse Cheese

● Fermoy Natural Cheeses

Frank and Gudrun Shinnick are seriously talented cheesemakers, and their little flotilla of cheeses – the raw milk St. Gall, the pasteurised St. Brigid, and the fresh cheeses Cais Dubh and Cais Rua – are beautifully made farm cheeses, distinctively piquant, with notes of hazelnuts and a sherry-like astringency to be found in the mature St. Gall. The Shinnicks were inspired by Swiss cheesemaking techniques, but, as with so many other Irish artisan cheesemakers, the original influence has long been transcended and replaced by something distinctively original and of-its-place. (Strawhall, Fermoy ☎ 025-31310 ✉ gudrun1@eircom.net)

Café

● Munchies

Munchies is old-fashioned, and really rather nice. The room hasn't been designed to within an inch of its life, and the cooking is real and enjoyable. Jason and Fiona Hogan fire out a good shepherd's pie, Thai fish cakes, homemade beefburgers, garlic bread, and they serve this good, tasty food to droves of happy customers every day, from breakfast through lunch and on into the afternoon. (Lower Patrick Street, Fermoy ☎ 025-33653 ✉ munchiesfermoy@eircom.net)

Restaurant

● Thai Lanna

Brendan Moher's restaurant has been open since early 2005 and has won an audience for accessible and enjoyable Thai cooking in an intimate room. There are some concessions to conservative Irish tastes, but otherwise menus are refreshingly concise and focused on classic Thai cuisine. (McCurtain Street, Fermoy ☎ 025-30900 ✉ bmoher@eircom.net 🖱 www.thailanna.net – Open 5.30pm-10.30pm Mon-Sat, 12.30pm-2.30pm Thur & Fri, 4pm-10pm Sun)

Kanturk

Farmhouse Cheese and Milk

● Ardrahan Farmhouse Cheese

Mary Burns made the first Ardrahan cheese back in 1983, but the secret of the powerful, distinctive taste of the cheese goes back to 1925, when the late Eugene Burns' father, Eugene senior, first started the Ardrahan herd of pedigree Fresians. No other Irish cheese matches Ardrahan for totality of flavour, a fact that can be attributed to the ancient and grass-diverse pastures in this part of County Cork, pastures which create a milk that has been referred to as "white gold". Preserving this white gold in a washed-rind cheese makes for a farmhouse cheese of uniquely agrestic character. Mary and her family also produce the splendid Lullaby milk, made using only the morning milk from the herd, and thereby rich in melatonin, which helps aid sleep. Lullaby is also interesting in that it is not homogenised, so it has that lush, lush texture of milk of old. And how wonderful to see a new cheese emerging from the dairy: the brand-new Duhallow Farmhouse Cheese is made in a style reminiscent of Port Salut, so it offers a milder alternative to the Ardrahan. (Ardrahan, Kanturk ☎ 029-78099 ardrahancheese@tinet.ie www.ardrahancheese.ie)

Butcher

Jack McCarthy

North Cork pancetta. Whiskey-cured bacon. Guinness and cider spiced beef. Chilli and coriander sausages. Spiced rashers. Is there another butcher with the ferment of imagination that Jack McCarthy and his crew enjoy? This man spins out new products with seeming ease, and no matter what innovation he delivers, it will be distinguished by great flavour, texture and brilliantly realised culinary practicality. Mr McCarthy is a fifth-generation butcher, and there seems to be a motherlode of tradition behind everything he creates. The good news for folk who don't live near Kanturk is that you can get a hamper of these superlative McCarthy meats delivered to your door. (Main Street, Kanturk ☎ 029-50178 jackmccarthy@eircom.net www.jackmccarthy.ie – Open 8.30am-6pm Mon-Sat)

Kilavullen

Market

Kilavullen Farmers Market

Now in it's fifth year, the Kilavullen market was begun by a group of like-minded locals who wanted to bring their produce to market, and it's been a roaring success, so much so that during the summer they also hold extra markets on Friday evenings. Geraldine Bass brings her wonderful fish, Thomas Hueneberg will be up from Cobh with his splendid breads – and will have a big queue ready to snap up everything he brings. Peter and Mary Raftery have plants, Gudrun Shinnick has her magnificent cheeses, Isabelle has her wines, Olive and John have their organic meats – don't miss it! – there are candles from Castlekevin, eco-products, home crafts, patisserie from Carmel Carroll, whilst Claire and Paul from Essink restaurant in Mallow will have soups, pates and lots more. "It's a social market" says Mary Raftery, and any aspiring producers who want to get in on this sublimely social act should contact Mary. (Nano Nagle Centre, Sat 10.30am-1pm fortnightly, details from ☎ 022 26470)

Macroom

Cheesmonger

Fiona Burke

Fiona is one of the great Cork marketeers, known most of all for selling artisan Irish and French cheeses, but look out also for country butters, eggs and other precious foods. (Macroom ☎ 026-43537)

Farmhouse Cheese

Carraig Goat's Cheese

Apart from Organico in Bantry, we aren't aware of anywhere else you can find Aart Versloot's ace goat's milk cheese. Reader, that is reason enough to go to Bantry, for Carraig is one of the best, hard, mature goat's milk cheeses made in Ireland. (Ballingeary ☎ 026-47126)

Preserves

Folláin

Peadar OLionaird began Folláin back in 1983, making a 100-year-old recipe for chunky marmalade into his first successful product. Over almost 25 years, Folláin has developed and prospered, its quality consistent throughout the entire range of jams, relishes, chutneys and new salsas. The latest development has been a speciality gift range for hampers. The Folláin products are widely available, but don't confuse them with mass-market jams and preserves, for these are the pure, natural thing, and as such they are beacons of culinary goodness. (Cuil Aodha, Maghchromtha ☎ 026-45288 www.follain.ie)

Bakery

Lynch's Bakery

Humphrey Lynch's bakery has fine, old-style breads, and is highly regarded for a proper traditional brack amongst other hand-made sweet confectionery. (South Square, Macroom, ☎ 026-41084 hlynch1@eircom.net – Open 9am-6pm Mon-Sat)

Oatmeal

Macroom Oatmeal

Donal Creedon is celebrated as the maker of the unique Macroom Oatmeal, a porridge quite unlike any other produced today. But he also mills a very fine, extra-coarse wholewheat flour, which he reintroduced after a lapse of production of 50 years. The flour is just as ruddy and real as the oatmeal; its secret lies in the hand-controlled roasting which Donal judges by smell, appearance and feel: experience tells this man when the oats are ready. Donal also feels that roasting concentrates the flavour of the oats, and that flavour is so profound that it has made Macroom Oatmeal one of the cult Irish foods, sold by luminary stores such as Zingerman of Ann Arbor, Ian Mellis in Scotland and Neal's Yard in London. Boutique porridge, then? Luxury brand oats? That's right. (Kanturk ☎ 026-41800)

Mallow

Country House

Longueville House

William O'Callaghan is a chef who is working his way back to the primary source of food. His walled garden produces everything he needs for the kitchen at Longueville, one of the most stately of Irish country houses, and so he has taken to making compotes, chutneys and condiments, including a particularly fine basil vinaigrette. He uses his venison to make sausages. He makes a (very rare) mushroom powder, a result of his interest in the mysterious fungi. He produces the most superb spice mixes. There is also an apple brandy, honey from their hives, and his own smoked salmon. These are superb products, and reason to call into Longueville even if you aren't eating or staying. But aside from his skills as an artisan, Mr O'Callaghan's skills as a chef are undoubted, and dishes in

Longueville can make your jaw drop with their artfulness. Aisling O'Callaghan oversees the house and the beautiful Turner conservatory dining room. (Mallow ☎ 022-47156 ✉ info@longuevillehouse.ie 🖱 www.longuevillehouse.ie – Open Dinner & Lunch for groups)

Wine Shop & Deli

mywine.ie

Isabelle O'Driscoll's little wine and speciality shop imports French wines from producers whom Isabelle herself visits regularly, "which ensures a very strong connection from the producer to end user". You will find wines from the Rhone Valley, Burgundy, the Languedoc, Gascony and elsewhere, and there is true interest in every bottle. Isabelle also sells Irish foods such as Old Millbank smoked salmon, and she creates beautiful hampers of wines and food that make terrific gifts. Delightful. (72 Davis Lane, off Main Street, Mallow ☎ 087-903 9396 ✉ info@mywine.ie 🖱 www.mywine.ie)

Market & Free Range Eggs

Nano Nagle Centre

It's the lovely brown eggs from the Nano Nagle Centre that you are most likely to encounter. They are sold in markets up and down the county, but the sisters also sell garden produce at the fortnightly market that is held in the centre every second Saturday. (Ballygriffin, Mallow ☎ 022-26411 ✉ nanonaglecentre@eircom.net 🖱 www.presentationsistersunion.org)

Delicatessen & Café

URRU

Tucked into a courtyard just off the main street, Willie and Ruth Healy's second URRU store is in a smartly refurbished building, which houses a bright, busy shop on the ground floor and tasting rooms and an exhibition space upstairs. The new shop is bigger than the Bandon pioneer, and the mix of good things, selected and presented with an unerringly exact eye, is as dazzling as ever. URRU has all you need: it is as simple as that. (URRU House, Bank Place, Davis Street, Mallow ☎ 022-53192 ✉ ruth@urru.ie 🖱 www.urru.ie)

Mitchelstown

Delicatessen & Cafe

O'Callaghan's

There is a bypass around Mitchelstown now, but devotees of Mary and Pat O'Callaghan's deli and café won't bother with that new slip of tarmac. For them, Mitchelstown means a stop in O'Callaghan's, whether it is for tea and a sausage sandwich for breakfast, or for a nice savoury lunch – shepherd's pie; some roast chicken; a good salad plate; their signature steak sandwich with mushrooms and salad – and then some nice O'Callaghan food to take away: fresh breads and scones, a pot of well-made jam, a few dishes to slip into the freezer; a coffee cake, and perhaps some of their gluten-free products. Nice place, nice staff. (19 Lr Cork Street, Mitchelstown ☎ 025-24657 ✉ ocalhansdeli@eircom.net 🖱 www.ocallaghans.ie – Open 8.30am-5.30pm Mon-Fri, 8.30am-5pm Sat)

"No matter how successful your country is, it's useless unless you've got quality food".

PAT O'DOHERTY

Newmarket

Organic Meats

Knockatullera Farm

The first bite we ever had of the organic pork reared by Olive and John Forde – shoulder chops, brushed with oil and grilled on a cast-iron pan – we said "Wow!". And we then said "Wow!" about twenty times more. We also said: "If this is Irish pork, whatever is everyone else selling?". The last time we ate pork so fine, as dark coloured as lamb, as tender as the tenderest beef, it had been two years previously, when we tried cul noir pork in the Dordogne, in France. And now, here in North Cork, is quality every bit as fine as that rarest of breeds. The Knockatullera meat is procesed by T.J. Crowe of Cahir, and the farm grows their own fodder beet and oats, which goes some way to explaining ths unbelieveable quality. You will find Olive and John selling it, along with their beef, bacon and lamb, at Kilavullen, Douglas and Kanturk markets. Do not miss it! (Newmarket, ☎ 029-60079)

Local Specialities
SPICED BEEF
DRISHEEN & TRIPE
BOILED SWEETS

Rathcormac

Delicatessan & Café

Posh Nosh

Catherine Hickey and Elieen O'Leary are food pioneers in the burgeoning, much-extended metropolis of Rathcormac. Posh Nosh is a cafe, a deli and a traiteur, and they look after you everywhichway. There is a takeaway menu – Thai chicken; smoked salmon and potato gratin. There is a sit down menu – home made salads of potato, couscous or pasta, good coffee. Or you can buy from their shelves – Taste a Memory pies, G's Jams, Country Choice preserves, O'Flynn's sausages and puddings, Corrin Hill Ice cream. Posh Nosh is unquestionably the epicentre of Rathcormac. (4 Riversdale, Rathcormac ☎ 025-37595 poshnosh@eircom.net – Open 10am-6pm tue-sat)

Fruit Farm

Rathcormac Fruit Farm

John Howard's fruit farm sells its fine produce at the Saturday Midleton market, but you can also buy from their farm shop, between June and September. Look out for fresh tayberries, blueberries, strawberries and rhubarb. They also sell freshly frozen fruit. (Rathcormac ☎ 025-36253 – Open Mon-Sun in the fruit growing season)

Watergrasshill

Traiteur

Taste A Memory

Anne Bradfield's simply packaged pies and pasties are pie heaven. "Real Pie" it says on the label, but that doesn't hint at the skill this pie maker brings to the noble craft of pie making. The traditional pasties are superb – in fact, for us they are the best pies made in Ireland – the chicken pasty is nice and hot with jalapenos, the seafood pies are almost as good. The secret? Great pastry, which is light and delicate yet satisfying. Get them from URRU, from Posh Nosh, and from the Bandon Market on Saturday morning, where they sell as fast as...hot pies, actually. (Rolls House, Watergrasshill ☎ 086-868 2201 ✉ anne@tasteamemory.ie)

Whitechurch

Farmhouse Cheese

● Hegarty's Farmhouse Cheddar

Dan and John Hegarty's territorial-style cheese is made from the milk produced by their herd of Friesians when out on spring and summer grass. The cheeses are made into 20 kilogram truckles, wrapped in cloth and matured for a minimum of 12 months. Hegarty's is a very accessible and pleasing Cheddar, with hints of toasted nuts and a full, open creaminess. (Ballinvarrig, Whitechurch ☎ 021-488 4238)

"Milk was not some ordinary substance to be bought and sold in the usual way. It was an intimate material and closely linked to the place where it was produced. Dairy cows were cherished domestic animals, not anonymous producers."

PIERRE BOISARD, *CAMEMBERT*

Ballycotton

Organic Vegetables

Ballycotton Organics

Rupert and Lydia produce organic vegetables and salad leaves, and they are also the organisers of the Thursday farmers' market at Mahon Point. (Ballycotton, ☎ 086-168 5312 rupert@ballycottonorganics.com)

Potatoes

Willie Scannell

"He remarked that the farmers' market has put the fun and enjoyment back into farming and has enabled farmers and food producers to get viable prices for their produce so they can continue to live and farm on the land they love." Darina Allen's Slow Food profile of Willie Scannell, Ballycotton potato grower and Midleton market hero, really hits the nail on the head in that paragraph. Consider the language: fun; enjoyment; viable prices. All the things that elude so many farmers were rediscovered by Mr Scannell when he began to sell his floury Home Guard, British Queens, Kerr's Pinks and Golden Wonders from his trailer at the market. Lovely spuds. Lovely story. (Ballytrasna, Ballycotton ☎ 021-464 6924/086-830 3625)

Carrigtwohill

Farmhouse Cheese

Ardsallagh Goat's Cheese

Jane Murphy is one of the true food heroes. She makes her goat's milk cheeses spoonful by spoonful, taking four hours to complete the process, which she compares to "emptying a bath with a teaspoon". Then she drives off to work at farmers' markets, and to deliver her cheeses to good shops, and to some multiples with whom she deals "on my terms". Her children all assist her in covering the markets, whilst Ger Murphy minds and milks the 500 goats. And she is always cheery, calm, creative, despite this massive workload, and keen to experiment with new ideas, which most recently has meant smoking cheeses using beech wood. There is also an Ardsallagh goat's milk, and a sharp, fresh yogurt,

and small production of an excellent hard goat's cheese. (Woodstock, Carrigtwohill ☎ 021-488 2336
✉ jane@ardsallaghgoats.com 🖱 www.ardsallaghgoats.com)

Vegetables and Plants

Ballintubber Farm

David and Siobhan Barry bring the produce of Ballintubber Farm to Midleton farmers' market, and they also have a farm shop (open on Friday afternoons 4pm-7pm). Look out for early spuds, Peace peas, Hallowe'en pumpkins and even Xmas trees. Much of the produce is grown chemical-free. (Carrigtwohill ☎ 021-488 3034/086-823 8187)

Castlemartyr

Greengrocer and Takeaway

The Village Greengrocer

The VG has grown over the years, and is now a capacious store with a great array of good things on the shelves, and lots of prepared foods and some nice breads and cakes to take away. (Main Street, Castlemartyr ☎ 021-466 7655 – Open 8am-7pm Mon-Fri, 8am-6pm Sat)

Cloyne

Deli & Bakery

Cuddigan's Foodstore

Siobhan Cronin and her crew produce a mighty array of cooked foods in this tiny little shop. Everything from daily breads and cakes to cottage pie, carbonara sauce and traditional Irish stew is available, and they will also prepare special orders, and offer ready-to-go dinners that are both fresh and frozen. It's a hectic mix and a busy, busy shop. (Cloyne ☎ 021-465 2762 – Open 7.30am-6pm Mon-Sat)

Honey

Lisanley Honey

Lisanley is a particularly fine honey, collected by Samuel Leslie Kingston, which you will find for sale in the Ballymaloe Shop and other nearby outlets. And every time you dip a honey dipper into a fine pot of Irish honey, do take a second to reflect on Albert Einstein's scary, profound, observation: "If honey bees become extinct, human society will follow in four years". (Cloyne ☎ 021-465 2627)

Cobh

Fish Smokehouse

Belvelly Smokehouse

"To be a success, we've got to make sexy food", Frank Hederman told Colman Andrews of *Saveur* magazine. Well, smoked fish doesn't get slinkier or sexier than Belvelly Smokehouse fish. The use of beech wood gives the smoked salmon and smoked mackerel an aura of smoke that is more akin to a dressing, an essence, as fine as Loro Piana Highlander wool, as opposed to clumsy cashmere or vicuna. It is this fineness that makes Belvelly fish the boutique product it is, and that applies whether Mr Hederman is smoking brown trout from Lough Neagh or humble haddock. Everything has an aura of wellness that makes the eater feel fortunate to be alive and eating these precious, precocious foods. (Belvelly, Cobh ☎ 021-481 1089 ✉ shipping@frankhederman.com 🖱 www.frankhederman.com)

Fish and Shellfish

Peter Kidney & Laura Thorington-Jones

Peter sells fish and shellfish, and runs the Friday morning Cobh market, whilst Laura uses the seafood to make interesting pies, fishcakes and dressed crabs. (Rushbrooke Commercial Park, Cobh ☎ 021-481 4617 ☎ 086-815 3922)

Guest Accommodation

Knockeven House

John and Pam Mulhaire's house is a design head's treat, but the hospitality exceeds the style by a comfortable margin, making this one of the best new arrivals in the Cork hospitality scene. Breakfasts are just ace. (Rushbrooke, Cobh ☎ 021-481 1778 ✉ info@knockevenhouse.com 🖱 www.knockevenhouse.com)

Bakery

T. H. Continental Bakery

Thomas Hueneberg sells his continental-style breads at farmers' markets, so look out for rarities such as pretzels, brioche and good croissants. (Cork Dockyards, Rushbrooke Industrial Estate, Cobh ☎ 087-693 2194 ✉ thecontinentalbakery@eircom.net)

Killeagh

B&B with Restaurant

● Ballymakeigh House

Margaret Browne's famous B&B is comfortable and welcoming, and distinguished by her fine, considered cooking. That cooking is on show both during the lingering, lazy breakfasts and also throughout the confident, five-course collation that Margaret offers for dinner. (Killeagh ☎ 024-95184 ✉ ballymakeigh@eircom.net 🖱 www.ballymakeighhouse.com)

Cork East

Midleton

Organic Chickens

● Dan Ahern Organic Chickens

We ordered Dan Ahern's chicken at Otto Kunze's restaurant one evening, and to tell you the truth we still haven't gotten over it. The flavour! The texture! The satisfaction! It was an awesome experience to eat this bird, so savoury, the skin so crisp and textured and real, the flesh so juicy, so profoundly delicious. These are extraordinary birds, and they make for extraordinary eating. What is the secret? A happy healthy life, which lasts fully for 11 weeks, lots of fresh grass, lots of room to roam. In other words, Dan's chickens get what every chicken should get, but doesn't get. Dan also rears organic beef and lamb which is sold frozen at farmers' markets. Dan's brother, JJ, also produces superb birds at Dungourney, and collaborates with Paul Crotty of Waterford to rear the Born free poultry. (Ballysimon, Midleton ☎ 021-463 1058/086-165 9258)

Fishmonger

● Ballycotton Seafood

The Walsh family's seafood company is in expansionist mode these days, and has just taken over the old Bandon Fish stall in Cork's English Market. (Stall 40 ☎ 021-427 2093). They have also developed a large cooked seafood side to the business in recent years, with all the cooking being done in the Midleton premises, whilst the filleting of the fresh fish is done down at Garryvoe. (46 Main Street, Midleton ☎ 021-461 3122 ✉ ballycottonseafood@eircom.net 🖱 www.ballycottonseafood.com)

Delicatessen and Restaurant

The Farmgate

Last time we met up with Richard Corrigan, he was just back from having lunch at Marog O'Brien's Farmgate restaurant. "Fantastic food. Just brilliant" said Richard. And the lady hackette from *The Observer* agreed (Richard seems to trail journalists around with him, but it doesn't seem to get him down). And so did *The Observer's* photographer. Local foods, cooked with timeless techniques by Marog, and if it's good enough for Richard it's sure good enough for us. There is a fine shop out front of the restaurant. (Coolbawn, Midleton ☎ 021-463 2771 – Open 9am-5pm Mon-Sat, 6.45pm-9.30pm Thur-Sat)

Cork East

Restaurant

Fire & Ice

Gary Masterson and Winnie Lynch are doing the good thing in Fire & Ice, and are quickly gearing themselves to pole position in East Cork. They are a talented pair, and they have an openness to new ideas and experiences which is truly admirable – you are likely to find Mr Masterson over at Slow Food's Salone del Gusto in Turin when he has a moment, and they are keen Slow Food supporters. That philosophy translates into real cooking – roast duck broth with soba noodles and vegetables; a pure, unmessed-with Caesar salad; coconut-poached chicken with sweet chilli; pan-fried salmon with grilled lemon. This is cooking with verve and culinary savvy. (The Courtyard, 8 Main Street, Midleton ☎ 021-463 9682 fireandice@eircom.net www.fireandicecafe.ie – Open Mon-Sat 9am-5pm & Sat dinner from 6.30pm)

Local Speciality

SMOKED MUSSELS
SHRIMPS
IRISH WHISKEY

Honey

Glenanore Apiaries

Michael Woulfe's superb honey can be found in shops in Cork, Midleton, and as far away as Galway and Limerick Market. Michael also teaches honey workshops at the Ballymaloe school. (Railway House, Midleton ☎ 021-463 1011)

Bakery & Café

● The Granary

Eleanor O'Sullivan's much-respected shop has lots of expertly prepared foods to go. "As good as the best home-made; first-class execution," say Midleton locals, as they hoover up the sweet brown soda bread, good quiches and nice puds. (6 Coach Horse Lane, Main Street, Midleton ☎ 021-461 3366)

Bread vendor

● Mark Hosford

Our favourite bread seller, Mark Hosford chases all over Cork during the week, working markets at Kinsale on Tuesday, Ballincollig on Wednesday, at the bustling Mahon Point on Thursday, and in the centre of the city at Coal Quay on Saturday. Mark sells all the Arbutus breads as well as the superlative R-GL patisserie. (6 High Range, Rostellan, Midleton ☎ 086-6351954
markscheese@yahoo.ie)

Farmers' Market

● Midleton Farmers' Market

We were there on the first day of the Midleton market, back in 2000, when Myrtle Allen snipped the ribbon. It was obvious even then that this market would be a fulcrum for the town, for there was an energy about it from day one that was irresistible. In the intervening years, it has matured, developed, and become even more essential as a statement of the merits of farmers' markets, not to mention an asset to this bustling town. What it offers are foods that are local, artisan, and Slow. You can buy organic chickens from Dan Ahern (you've tasted nothing like them). You can get Ireland's most acclaimed artisan breads, and its most acclaimed smoked fish. There are goat's cheeses from just down the road, and blueberry tonic from County Offaly. The Ballymaloe stall has everything from superb local ducks to tomatillos. There are chocolates and cakes and, guarding the entrance with his trailer and his sign and his table and scales, is Willie Scannell and his Ballycotton potatoes, a man who has come to signify the ability of farmers' markets to transform the practices and finances of a farmer and food producer. Keep it local. Take it slowly. (www.midletonfarmersmarket.com)

Butcher

Frank Murphy

Murphy's is a traditional butcher's shop in the very best sense, which is to say there is a small display of meats, and Frank will happily prepare whatever you require whilst you stand and wait, and chat about the weather and those poor people up in Dublin in the traffic jams, God love them. The meat comes from the family farm, with Angus-Hereford cross as the beef of choice. (79 Main Street, Midleton ☎ 021-463 1557 – Open 9am-6pm Mon-Sat)

Restaurant

O'Donovan's

Cork East

Ian Cronin heads up the kitchen in Pat O'Donovan's modest and professional restaurant. We have described Mr Cronin's cooking as calm and measured, an antidote to the all-too-frequent trait of male chefs to overwork their dishes past the point of logic. But Mr Cronin always knows where to stop, and his work is refreshingly savoury and complete, whether it is something as simple as Ballycotton mackerel with chive hollandaise, or a powerful dish of lamb's kidneys with mushrooms. Out front, Mr O'Donovan is as measured and polite as one could wish for in a host. (58 Main Street, Midleton ☎ 021-463 1255 – Open 6pm-9.30pm Mon-Sat)

Wholefood Shop

Well & Good

Jill Bell's shop is one of the most respected Cork wholefood shops, and as such operates as a first port-of-call for interesting local foods, as well as a fount of information and knowledge on the specialist food culture of the county. (Broderick Street, Midleton ☎ 021-463 3499 – Open 9.30am-6pm Mon-Sat)

Shanagarry

Cookery School

Ballymaloe Cookery School & Gardens

Darina Allen has moved from being a hard-working teacher and cook, into being a hard-working activist on behalf of good food. Her move towards polemics, as she has grasped and grappled with the issues surrounding not only Irish food but also global food issues, has been a good fit for the Ballymaloe school, where the education begins with respecting the elements from which we create good food. "Our food should be our medicine", she told Denise Dubé in *Intermezzo* magazine. "The reality is, nowadays food is doing us damage rather than nourishing us." That powerful realisation is the modus operandi of the Ballymaloe school, and not just for the 12-week certificate students who want a job in the food business. It also shines through in everything Mrs Allen teaches, whether it's a day's course on keeping chickens or a couple of fun days spent absorbing hints and recipes for entertaining. (Shanagarry ☎ 021-464 6785 www.cookingisfun.ie)

Restaurant and Country House

Ballymaloe House

Both the vanguard and the avant garde of Irish cooking, Myrtle Allen's house, and her work over the last forty three years, deserve a book unto themselves, and not merely a section in a guidebook such as this. But we can at least ask how Ballymaloe made its international reputation, coming as it did out of the dark days of Irish food. And the answer seems to us to be because Myrtle Allen is, above all, defined by two things. She is a democrat – Ballymaloe is for all people, not just the wealthy. And, perhaps more importantly, Mrs Allen is a modernist. She is rooted in the particular, but she is comfortable with abstract ideas. Ballymaloe, then, is neither fixed nor fixated in a particular time, it is not wedded to particular fashions of thought or style. Yes, it is grand and comfortable and ancient, but it is not conservative in any way. In many ways, what Ballymaloe is about is timelessness: what you eat here is something you might have eaten a century ago, or a century hence. In that regard, Ballymaloe House fulfills Claude Levi-Strauss's famous old dictum: yes, this is food that is good to eat. But it is also food that is "good to think". (Shanagarry ☎ 021-465 2531 info@ballymaloe.com www.ballymaloe.com – Restaurant Open 7pm-9.30pm Mon-Sat, 7.30pm-8.30pm Sun)

Kitchen Shop and Café

Ballymaloe Shop & Café

Ballymaloe is all about wise choices – what to cook, what to eat, what to buy – and none more so than Wendy Whelan's shop and café. Every item in the shop has an aesthetic and a function. Every single thing offered in the café has a sound culinary reason to be there. Mrs Whelan manages to make your choice of goods feel like a necessity, rather than an indulgence, a masterly aspect of the retailer's art: it's not that you want these things, it's really, actually, truthfully, unequivocally that you need them! Nowhere else gives your conscience such a free ride, which is why it is such potent pleasure to shop and eat here. (Ballymaloe House, Shanagarry ☎ 021-465 2032 www.ballymaloe.ie – Open Day-time Mon-Sun)

Smoked Salmon

Casey's Smokehouse

Cork East

Bill Casey's smoked salmon is the fish you will enjoy at Ballymaloe House, and with 20 year's experience of fish smoking, Mr Casey has a sure, veteran's hand that makes for a lightness in his use of oak and beech wood with the fish. (Shanagarry ☎ 021-464 6955 smokiec@gofree.indigo.ie)

Ready Meals

Cully & Sully

Our kids love the Cully & Sully brand. They like the flavours, and they like the funkiness, the witty, Innocent-style packaging. We like the C&S brand because we want to see these blokes grow bigger, because then they can have a greater impact on prepared foods, to which they have already brought an epicurean dimension that is utterly absent from most processed foods. They have the energy, and they are masters at promotion, so Denis Brosnan should watch his ankles. Carefully. (The Hen House, Shanagarry ☎ sully 086-6058471/☎ cully 086-6076030 sully@cullyandsully.com www.cullyandsully.com)

Spice Mixes

Green Saffron

Arun Kapil makes exceedingly fine spice mixes, sold in little sachets under the Green Saffron label at the Kinsale and Mahon Point markets and in Cork and Waterford stores. Arun also imports spices directly from India, and organises curry nights when he and Ivan Whelan demonstrate curry technique and tips. The freshness and balance of the spice mixes is absolutely pukka, and they are an invaluable aid for food lovers. (Unit 4, The Gallery Workshops, Shanagarry ☎ 087-672 7188 arun@greensaffron.com www.greensaffron.com)

Whitegate

Butcher

Day's of Whitegate

The shop doesn't look like much, just a standard issue small supermarket, but at the back of the shop the talented Kevin Day plies his butchering trade, preparing top-class meats from his own farm: sweet lamb, good beef, and charming service. (Whitegate ☎ 021-466 1223 – Open 7am-10.30pm Mon-Sun)

Youghal

Restaurant and Guesthouse

Aherne's

There isn't a more professionally-run operation in the whole of Ireland than the Fitzgibbon family's restaurant, bar and accommodation, at the eastern end of Youghal town. It's a place where you can have seafood chowder or hot-buttered lobster in the bar, enjoy a terrific value dinner of Youghal Bay smoked salmon followed by chargrilled swordfish with vegetable compote and shellfish bisque in the restaurant, and then sleep in a fine, comfortable, altogether plush room upstairs, before enjoying a sterling breakfast cooked with just as much precision as last night's dinner. Doing the good thing and the right thing explains, in the simplest, most honest way, how this family business rides the years, astutely creating its own fashions, staying ahead of the posse by doing their own thing with amiable resolution. (163 North Main Street, Youghal ☎ 024-92424 www.ahernes.com – Open all year except Christmas. Bar open noon-10pm, Restaurant open 6.30pm-9.30pm)

Traiteur

Le Gourmet

Jean-Francois Bernard's shop is the star of the unprepossessing River Gate Mall, in the centre of Youghal. Excellent breads, stylish food-to-go for dinner and for the freezer, good sweet baking and good lunch treats make for a really valuable shop for busy people, and their catering service, which will take care of any and every occasion, is slick, professional and hard-working. (5 River Gate Mall, Youghal ☎ 024 20000/087-231 9210
legourmet@eircom.net – Open 9am-6pm Mon-Sat)

Cork East

Baker

Oonagh Poynton

Fast becoming a popular baker at farmers' markets, and about to start selling at Dungarvan Market, Oonagh is a Ballymaloe graduate, with a nice selection of savoury and sweet baking. (Tourig Lodge, Rincrew, Youghal ☎ 087-689 9861)

Fishmonger

Yawl Bay Seafood Shop

David Brown's seafood shop has developed out of a fish processing business, and offers an excellent arry of fresh fish on ice, along with a freezer section and fresh shellfish from southerly ports, (Foxhole Industrial Estate, Youghal ☎ 024-92290 yawlbay@indigo.ie – Open 9am-5pm Mon-Fri, 10am-2pm Sat, closed for lunch Mon-Thur)

"The case for animal liberation is very simple. It's that animals can feel and have interests. There is no reason why we should give less consideration to their interests than we give to similar interests of members of our own species."

PETER SINGER

Local Specialities
SMOKED BACON
SMOKED CHEESE
SMOKED CHICKEN
SMOKED EEL
SMOKED SALMON
SMOKED SAUSAGE
SMOKED TUNA

WEST CORK

Ballinspittle

Butcher

Lordan's Family Butcher

Donal Lordan's shop, in the centre of the village, is renowned for particularly creative sausage-making and the shop is a vital resource, both for prime raw ingredients and for ready-to-cook prepared meats. (Ballinspittle ☎ 021-477 8226 – Open 8.30am-6pm Mon-Sat)

Ballydehob

Restaurant

Annie's

Enduring and unchanging and always enjoyable, Annie and Danno Barry's restaurant is one of the West Cork icons. The cooking is classic cordon bleu – mussels with garlic and bread crumbs; duck liver pâté with Cumberland sauce; fillet steak medallions with peppercorn and brandy sauce; scallops with white wine and garlic; hot chocolate fudge cake – but the hospitality is pure West Cork, and that is the secret of their success. (Main Street, Ballydehob ☎ 028-37292 – Open 6.30pm-10pm Tue-Sat)

Gourmet Catering

Food For Thought

Stephen and Sarah Canty's catering company has been

winning plaudits ever since they began to cater for groups, functions, parties, bashes and whatnot in 2004. Efficient and smart, they are also prominent Slow Food supporters, proof of their astute culinary philosophy. Look out for their sushi and noodles in the Schull Sunday market. (Ballydehob ☎ 087-752 8945/752 8940
sarah@foodforthoughtwestcork.com
stephen@foodforthoughtwestcork.com)

Wholefoood Shop and Café

Hudson's

Cork West

Gillian Hudson's wholefood shop is admirably eclectic, a genuinely left-field treasure trove of good things to eat and cook. We love their smart wraps – quite different from what anyone else does – and there are lots of good choices in the little café at the back of the shop. Their breads are a particular signature, and the shop also acts as a great focus for lots of the best West Cork foods. (Main Street, Ballydehob ☎ 028-37565 – Open 9.30am-6pm Mon-Sat)

Free-range Ducks

Skeaghanore Ducks

Eugene and Helena Hickey's Skeaghanore ducks are one of the best known West Cork brands, and a blessing for so many chefs who value the taste, texture and cooking qualities of these happily reared birds. The domestic cook will also value the easy-to-cook duck breasts which are available, along with the whole duck, but we like to make a big casserole with the duck legs, which are also brilliant value for money. (Skeaghanore, Ballydehob ☎ 028-37428 skeaghanoreduck@eircom.net)

Café Bar and Cookshop

SummerSalt Culinary Emporium

Summersalt has a top notch kitchenware shop set beside the tables, and down in the basement of the shop that forms the dining area of this corner site in Ballydehob. The food is casual, modern and tasty, featuring local producers such as Gubbeen smokehouse and Sonia's pickles, and this is a promising newcomer to the village and to West Cork. (Main Street, Ballydehob ☎ 028 37139
summersaltcookshop@hotmail.co.uk – Open 9am-9pm Mon-Sat, noon-5pm Sun in summer, 9am-5pm Mon-Sat in winter)

Baltimore

Farmhouse Cheese

● Ardagh Castle Goat's Cheese

One of the rarest West Cork cheeses – only Carraig Goat's cheese is harder to find – Judy Wootton's raw goat's milk cheese – from a tiny herd of eight goats – is a beauty, with a freshness and nuttiness that is only excellent. Judy also make gjetost, a Norwegian-style cheese made using the whey from the cheese making, quite unique in Ireland, and she also has some yogurt. You will find them at the Saturday Skibbereen market, and you can also buy from the farm, where there is also a cottage to rent. (Ardagh South, Baltimore ☎ 028-20547 jwotton@eircom.net www.ardaghcastle.com)

Cork West

Fishmonger

● Baltimore Fresh Fish

Alan Hassett's pier side trailer sells the classiest fish from a man who really knows his stuff, thanks to a previous career as a trawler man. Mr Hassett buys from day boats to ensure optimum freshness, and he matches this quality with great preparation skills. (Main Shop is at 27 North Street, Skibbereen ☎ 028-40924)

Café and Gardens

● Glebe House

Jean Perry is one of those people who makes you wish that you were as cool as Jean Perry is. She has a sort of engaged sang-froid – yes, we know that's a contradiction, but when you meet her you will understand – that touches everything she puts her hand to – her atypical garden, and above all her quirky, funky restaurant. Rebuilding during the winter of 2006 will see the restaurant move out of the house into the gallery, and there will be a cool verandah and a courtyard and, best of all, extended opening hours as the Glebe will be opening at weekend evenings. So far, Glebe cooking has been distinguished by a simplicity and purity that has been utterly winning, so expect this to become even more well-defined in the new restaurant space. (Glebe Gardens, Baltimore ☎ 028-20232 glebegardens@eircom.net www.glebegardens.com – Re-opening June bank holiday '07 after refurbishment. Open 10am-6pm Wed-Sun, 6pm-10pm Thur-Sat)

Self-Catering Accommodation & honey

● Inis Beg

The Boat House at Inis Beg, designed by architect Tony Cohu, has become a famous piece of modernist Irish architecture, sitting proud out on the water on the Inis Beg estate, Frank Lloyd Wright meets Glen Murcott on an island off the coast of – where else? – West Cork. Aside from the Boat House, there are lots of other superbly comfortable cottages to rent in Paul and Georgie Keane's complex of rental properties, and there is also the terrifically delicious Inis Beg honey to be enjoyed. (Inis Beg, Baltimore ☎ 028-21745 bookings@inishbeg.com www.inishbeg.com)

Cork West

Restaurant

● The Mews Bistro

Denis Connolly's restaurant is housed in one of Baltimore's prettiest buildings, tucked into a side street as you head down the hill, and the warm design and the intimacy of the room makes an ideal location for a good evening's eating, for this owner-chef has won much local acclaim from food lovers. (Baltimore ☎ 028-20390 – Open 6pm-10pm, May-Sept)

Country House

● Rolf's Country House

The builders have been busy in Baltimore – well, yes, for some years now – and in addition to work at The Glebe, Rolf's has been undergoing a major transformation from its previous life as a nice-but-simple hostel, to a country house and restaurant. Johannes Haffner and his crew cover almost all bases, from the smart everyday food in the café to the grander cuisine offered in the restaurant, and their can-do attitude has always been a tonic. It's smashing to see a 20-year-old business transforming itself with such imagination, and with such hunger for the future. (Baltimore ☎ 028-20289 www.rolfsholidays.com – Open Lunch & Dinner)

B&B

● The Slipway

A favourite little water's edge B&B, with lovely breakfasts. Should you be planning a long boating stay in Baltimore, do note that they also offer self-catering. (The Cove, Baltimore ☎ 028-20134 theslipway@hotmail.com www.theslipway.com)

Bandon

Farmers' Market

Bandon Farmers' Market

We actually cut the ribbon – metaphorically speaking – to open the first Bandon market, back in April 2006. The day was an amazing success, with stall holders and punters having a mighty time of it, and the gentle precipitation was positively refreshing. By 11am there wasn't a Taste a Memory pie to be had, and the Six Ladies of Ballinascarthy hadn't a slice of quiche or a free-range egg left, and were utterly exhilarated by the thrill of it all. All they had was a box full of money. The Old Market Area had been brought back to its original incarnation, as a trading market, home now to URRU, Baltimore Fish, Gwen's Chocolates, Valley View eggs, Beechwood Farm foods, Ummera smoked fish, Mellas' fudge, Sonia's Inner Pickle, Krawczyk salamis, Baking Emporium breads and cakes, Travara Lodge baking from Brendan and Richard, J.D Organics, Martin Carey's sausages, Finder's Inn seafood pies, Gairdin Eden salads, Coachford vegetables, Ballycotton veg, and Heavenly Cakes. The late Peter Crowley, whose idea it was to start the market, would have been pleased as punch. (Old Market Garden – car park at the back of the New Spar, Friday 10.30am-1pm)

Cork West

Butcher

Carey's Butchers

"Martin Carey's shop is the Lidgate's of Ireland". That's how a food-loving friend described Carey's of Bandon, and it seems to us to be just right. Like the legendary London butcher, Martin Carey is a creative, artistic charcutier, whose meticulous sourcing makes for some of the most superlative meat you can buy. It is impossible to sing the praises of this butcher too highly, for there is no challenge he does not relish, no new idea he isn't ready and willing to experiment with. He is blessed with a great team in the shop, allowing him to practise his craft at stratospheric levels. (82 South Main Street, Bandon ☎ 023-42107 mcarey-ie@yahoo.com – Open 9am-5pm Mon-Sat)

Butcher

Maloney's Meat Centre

Choose the "pan-fried T-bone served with its own gravy, mushrooms, onions and garlic butter" in Otto Kunze's

Dunworley restaurant, and that T-bone will have been "well-hung in Dan Maloney's cold room". It would be hard to find greater praise for butchering skills and technique than that accolade from one of West Cork's pioneering chefs. The Angus and Hereford beef comes from Dan's brother's farm, and lamb is sourced locally also, being finished in their own abattoir. (25 Sth Main Street, Bandon ☎ 023-44206 – Open 9am-5pm Mon-Sat)

'Fish is a gift, not a commodity.'

MARTIN SHANAHAN.

Cork West

Gastro Pub

● The Poacher's Inn

Barry McLaughlin cut his teeth working with Martin Shanahan in Fishy Fishy in Kinsale, and he has brought some of the master's touch and ideas to this sweet little pub on the Clonakility Road just outside Bandon. Working with his wife, Catherine, he serves bar food each day and opens the restaurant above the bar at weekends. John dory with parsnip purée and curry oil and roast cod with creamy leeks show Fishy Fishy influences, and he has abetted these classics with good comfort dishes such as chicken stuffed with basil and cheese; spaghetti with broccoli and cashel Blue, Thai crab cake with rocket crème fraiche, and there are nice simple puds. Barry and Catherine are a hard-working team, and the potential in The Poacher's is infinite. (Clonakilty Road, Bandon ☎ 023-41159 McLaughlinbc@hotmail.com – Open for bar lunch Mon-Sat. Restaurant open Thur-Sat diner & Sun lunch)

Organic Growers

● Eddie and Caroline Robinson

The Robinsons are amongst the finest organic growers in West Cork, producing vegetables and salad leaves that are as beautiful to admire as they are to eat. But what distinguishes this couple is the fact that they farm eight acres. That's right: eight acres. From that, they feed droves of people at the markets in Coal Quay and in Macroom. So, we have to ask the question: if what Caroline and Eddie are doing is agriculture, and if they can run a hugely successful, distinctive, agri-business from eight acres, what on earth are the farmers of Ireland, with their capacious acreage, well, just what are they doing? (Parkmore, Templemartin, Bandon ☎ 021-733 0178 carolinerobinson@eircom.net)

Delicatessen

URRU

With a brand new URRU having opened in Mallow at the end of 2006, Ruth and Willie Healy are on the march, and we shouldn't expect that they will stop at a pair of the smartest stores in Ireland. Indeed, a decent government would decree that there should be an URRU in every county, at the very least. Why? Because we all need the glamour, the pzazz, the verve and the intelligence this brother and sister have brought to retailing. The Healys' signature is that they themselves don't produce. What they do is to select, they edit, from the masses of food out there, and they bring you only the best, in the swishest stores, making every URRU experience an oasis of pleasure. Interestingly enough, they have opened in two conservative towns, and taken them both by storm. The rest of the country needs them. (The Mill, McSwiney Quay, Bandon ☎ 023-54731 info@urru.ie www.urru.ie – Open Mon-Sat 9.30am-6.30pm)

Cork West

Wholefood Shop

An Tobairin

Mary Wedel's wholefood shop is a beauty. You will find local organic vegetables, lots of delicious things in the fridge, and bread from the brand-new Natural Foods Bakery, who have started distributing to shops beyond their own store in Cork city, so it's cherry buns for West Cork food lovers from now on. Mary and her team know all you could possibly need to know, and this is a benchmark destination in Bandon. (79 South Main Street, Bandon ☎ 023-52985 well@antobairin.com)

Bantry

Cookware Shop

Bantry Cookware Company

A couple of doors up from The Stuffed Olive, and tucked down a small walkway, Maria & Andrew Campbell's Cookware Store has lots of severely covetable kitchen goodies, so whether you are whisking, chopping, shredding, grating or folding in, you will find the essential, shiny piece of kit in here. They also operate a knife-sharpening service with local knife-maker Rory Conner. (New Street, Bantry ☎ 027-55651 – Open 10am-6pm Mon-Sat)

Cork West

Farmer's Market

Bantry Friday Market

Yes, that is us over there, with the wheely shopping bag, filling up with salads from Urs and Rosie's stall, and getting some kid meat from Martin, and Gubbeen salami from Wally on the Gubbeen stall, and some Mella's fudge, and hummus from Shiela and salad plants from Paul Schultz and smoked sausages from Frank Krawczyk and a melting Cooleeney from Fiona Burke and olives from Seanie and organic fruit and veg from Catriona Daunt. It's what we do on a Friday morning. Bantry Fair Day was once the fourth largest market in Ireland, and it's a pity local officials don't make more of this singular West Cork institution. (Bantry Town Centre, Fridays, with enlarged market on first Friday of the month when you can buy live chickens and guinea fowl and even donkeys along with other paraphernalia)

Fishmonger

Central Fish Market

Colman Keohane's fish shop is a West Cork star, offering superb fresh fish selected by the man himself with precise skill and expertise. Mr Keohane was the herald of new things in Bantry, setting the standard in a town which now boasts many other funky food and design outlets. (New Street, Bantry ☎ 027-53714 – Open 9am-6pm Tue-Fri, Sat 10am-5pm, Mon 9.30am-5.30pm)

Bakery Café

Floury Hands

Mary Kelleher's bakery and café is a Bantry classic, and in Floury Hands she continues the great tradition of baking begun by the Cotter family decades ago. (D Cotter Building, Main Street, Bantry ☎ 027-52590 floury@eircom.net – Open 8am-5.30pm Mon-Sat)

Organic Growing Supplies

Fruit Hill Farm

Manfred Wandel sells the sexiest garden tools you can buy, whilst his wife Eddie shows just how to use those sexy tools to produce some of the very best West Cork organic produce. Eddie's produce can be found in the local SuperValu in Bantry (locals call it the VG, by the way) and also at the Peppermint Farm stall at the Friday market. (Bantry ☎ 027-50710 www.fruithillfarm.com)

Nursery

Future Forests

As funky, left-field and out-of-the-box as a garden centre can be, FF is a sport of nature, and a thing of beauty. This is where you go if you want to plant a fruiting hedgerow, or purchase bare-rooted native woodland plants. At summer weekends it gets crazy busy, so be patient as the wait will be lengthy. Meanwhile, the crazy piecemeal wooden structure that houses the centre has become as much of a curiosity as the nature of the plants they stock. (Kealkill, Bantry ☎ 027-66176 futureforests@eircom.net www.futureforests.net)

Cork West

Knife maker

Hand-Crafted Knives

For us, Rory Conner is one of those people who encapsulates the West Cork zeitgeist. He does something unusual – he is a hands-on knife maker, making individual, bespoke knives to order – and he does it superbly, producing world class artefacts, and he takes his time about it, which is also that West Cork thing. It means his knives are more than just implements; they are works of art, the works of an artist. (Ballylickey, Bantry ☎ 027-50032 handcraftedknives@eircom.net)

B&B and Restaurant

Larchwood House

A quirkily domestic setting for a restaurant – in the dining room of Aidan and Sheila Vaughan's house – and with good cooking from Sheila, a woman with a sure touch for flavours and textures. Garden lovers should note that the gardens, maintained by Aidan, are celebrated throughout West Cork. (Pearsons Bridge, Bantry ☎ 027-66181)

Local Shop

Manning's Emporium

Val Manning is entitled to take things a bit easy at this stage of his career - he varies his winter opening hours "depending on weather and form", as he says. But his honest form created the right conditions for many West Cork artisans, who made Manning's Emporium their first port of call whenever they had a new food or a new idea. Summertime suits Val more, and his fantastic annual food fairs at the height of summer are days to be treasured. (Ballylickey, Bantry ☎ 027-50456 – Open 9am-6pm summer. Check off season)

Maughnasily Organic Farm

Martin and Yvonne O'Flynn are amongst the great characters of the Friday Bantry Market. Their beautiful basketry is arranged in front of their old Land Rover, and their freezer box holds all the goodies you seek: the best beef and pork, hard-to-find kid meat and in the summertime they have superb vegetables. Everything is produced to organic standards, but the O'Flynns transcend the concept of standards to produce foods that are sublime in and of themselves, none more so than their Xmas turkeys, which simply cannot be compared to what anyone else produces. They are purveyors of foods that encapsulate sheer, elemental goodness, foods that express the force of nature. (Maughnasily, Kealkill, Bantry ☎ 027-66111)

Restaurant

O'Connor's Seafood Restaurant

Peter and Anne O'Brien have gifted O'Connor's with a spanking new, nautical livery, turning it into one of West Cork's smartest rooms, and they have notched up the food offer as well, delivering their simpler, signature dishes such as mussels, battered fish, local lamb and Skeaghanore duck with sharp precision. A calm professionalism marks out this Bantry address, making it a sure thing. (The Square, Bantry ☎ 027-50221/51094
oconnorseafoods@eircom.net
www.oconnorseafood.com – Open Lunch & Dinner)

Wholefood Shop, Bakery and Cafe

Organico

Rachel and Hannah Dare's Organico is top notch, 24-carat, top-of-their-game. Pioneers in Fair Trade goods. A superb bakery. Brilliant organic vegetables arranged like a still life. Great wines. A lovely café with an ever-changing roster of local artists, plus lots of PCs so you can gab away with your friends wherever they currently are. If you are currently hunting down Aart Versloot's Carraig goat's cheese, one of Ireland's best – and rarest – cheeses, then you will find it here, just as you will find other local cheese innovators whose efforts may or may not prove enduring. Organico is not just a shop: it is a hub of energy, and a hive of activity, and it is one of the stars of the West Cork firmament. (2 Glengarriff Road, Bantry, shop ☎ 027-51391 cafe ☎ 027-55905 www.organico.ie – Open 9.30am-6pm Mon-Sat)

Nursery

Peppermint Farm

Doris and Achim Hoffman will sell you superb herbs, brew you great herbal teas, make you a staircase or a kitchen, and sell you a greenhouse or a polytunnel, perhaps one you will have seen when having a tour of their celebrated herb garden. Hard working people, and there is an impressive fastidiousness and dedication to all their work. (Toughraheen, Bantry ☎ 028-31869
www.peppermintfarm.com)

Home Store

Roost

Hilary Rahr sailed – literally – into Bantry from America, and opened Roost in a little back street of the town. Roost is a home store, and we've not been surprised, after carrying various kitchen items from the groovy store in Fundacion Joan Miro in Barcelona, to find the very same items in Roost when we got home. Hilary's flair for choosing items makes this shop as good as any international Home Store, and on a par with the very best in Ireland, such as Avoca. (5 Barrack Street, Bantry
☎ 027-55500 hilary@roost.ie www.roost.ie
– Open 10am-6pm Mon-Sat)

Hotel

Sea View House Hotel

A classic country hotel, all politesse, discretion, peace and quiet. Do our mothers love to be brought to Sunday lunch here? Dead right they do. Once upon a time all hotels were like Kathleen O'Sullivan's gracious lodgings, but whilst others have failed to survive or have been reborn as "boutique" hotels, Ms O'Sullivan does what she has always done and does it superbly. And what do the mammies like for Sunday lunch? Pâté maison with melba toast. Leek and potato soup. Supreme of salmon, hollandaise sauce. Desserts from the trolley. Ah, yes. (Ballylickey
☎ 027-50073 info@seaviewhousehotel.com
www.seaviewhousehotel.com)

Pub

The Snug

Early Friday evening, and with all the tables taken in The Snug it's a seat at the bar, and a steak forestiere with fries and vegetables, and a large piece of fresh hake with lots of garlic. And what lovely cooking this is, as consistent, reliable and delicious as Maurice and Colette O'Donovan's bar food has always proven to be. Small wonder all the tables are taken. So make sure to get there early and soak up the calm charm of the bar. (The Quay, Bantry ☎ 027-50057 – Food served noon-8.45pm)

Delicatessen

The Stuffed Olive

Trish and Marjorie's Stuffed Olive is the store Bantry has always needed, and locals have responded with alacrity and acclaim to this fab store, which means you have to fight to get a seat at many times of the day. Arbutus breads, RGL patisserie, West Cork cheeses, Flores syrups and pestos and oils, Green Saffron mixes, Caherbeg pork, Glen Ilen yogurts, Gwen's chocolates, Cork coffee Roasters brews, Bubble Brothers wines, and lunchtime sandwiches that are the best in the region. That is one mighty mix, and explains why the SO has opened with a bang. (New Street, Bantry ☎ 027-55883 – Open 9am-6pm Mon-Sat)

Cork West

Restaurant

Willie Pa's

Pulling in an audience from Drimoleague to Durrus to Bantry, Willie Pa's is the local favourite for Friday night steak dinners and all the communion lunches, baptism bashes and whathave you. They source their fish and shell-fish from the Central Fish Market in Bantry, so the prawn cocktail and the scampi are very good, and properly cooked meats are a satisfyingly reliable choice. For some reason they ask you to choose from the menu whilst waiting in the bar, but this distraction aside, there is ambition and intent here. (Colomane Cross, Bantry ☎ 027-50392 – Open 6pm-10pm Tue-Sat, 12.30pm-4pm Sun. Open bank holiday Mondays)

Castletownbere

Fishmonger

Castletownbere Fishermen's Co-op

A fine fish shop that sells the fish landed from the many boats that dock at busy Castletown, so don't make up your mind what you want to cook until you see what is freshest on the ice slab. (The Pier, Castletownbere ☎ 027-70350/70045 ✉ ctbfishcoop@eircom.net – Open 9am-5pm Mon-Fri. Note: closed 1pm-2pm for lunch)

Bar

McCarthy's Bar

When writers describe certain Irish pubs as "atmospheric", they mean places like McCarthy's, places where shelves groan under the weight of geegaws and bottles and the light always seems to be 4pm on an April afternoon. Just the right time to have a drink, then. (The Square, Castletownbere ☎ 027-70014 adrimac22@yahoo.com)

Shop

Taste

Ciannait Walker has had four years of success in Taste, and now it's time to expand Castletown's own deli and wholefood store, with plans to open a new café, Taste at the Pier, in summer 2007. You can expect the same savvy discrimination in the Café as you will find in the shop, with good salads, pancakes, smart pizzas with local cheeses and ace coffees and drinks. (The Square, Castletownbere ☎ 027-71842)

Cork West

Castletownshend

B&B

Bow Hall

So, which room is it to be? The Oak Apple Room? The Apricot Room? The Toffee Room? To be honest, we would be happy to sleep on the floor in Barbara and Dick Vickery's unique B&B, just to get a taste of this amazing lady and her fabulous skills as a hostess, and her fabulous muffins at breakfast and her demon home-made sausage, and her beautiful Shakerish house. But, if you're asking, we'll have the Oak Apple Room, please. (Main Street, Castletownshend ☎ 028-36114)

Gastropub

Mary Ann's

There is a lovely photograph of Trish O'Mahony of Mary Ann's in the 2007 West Cork Arts Centre calendar. Laughing uproariously, with a black apron on over a white t-shirt and holding a big spatula, it's a delightful portrait, by Bridget Tiernan, full of energy and joie de vivre. Trish's contribution to the calendar, entitled "Recipes for Renewal", is a recipe for lobster salad with Union Hall mixed salad leaves and lemon and dill mayonnaise, and we would be happy to eat that in Mary Ann's every day of the week, and happy to soak up that energy and joie de vivre as we enjoy the lovely cooking. (Castletownshend ☎ 028-36146 ✉ maryanns@eircom.net – Open noon-2.30pm, 6pm-9pm Mon-Sun. Closed Mon off season)

Smokery

Woodcock Smokery

Sally Barnes won the Supreme Award at the Great Taste Awards in 2006. That tells you all you need to know about the distinctiveness, deliciousness and utter singularity of this most gifted fish smoker's levels of creativity: line the Woodcock smoked fish, whether haddock, tuna, sprats, salmon, whatever, up alongside 4,500 other artisan foods and the simple, pure magic of Sally's wild smoked salmon will put everything else in second place. Woodcock is the quintessential artisan, Slow Food, hand-made, West Cork food, a true icon. (Gortbrack, Castletownsend, ☎ 028 36232 ✉ sallybarnes@iolfree.ie 🖱 www.woodcocksmokery.com)

Clonakilty

Gastro Pub

An Súgán

The O'Crowley's pub and restaurant has been serving fresh fish dishes to the punters for more than two decades, and has grown to accommodate both a stylish B&B next door to the bar, and self-catering accommodation. Professionalism and consistency are their trademarks. (41 Wolfe Tone Street, Clonakilty ☎ 023-33825 ✉ ansugan4@eircom.net 🖱 www.ansugan.com – Open 12.30pm-6pm Mon-Sun)

Farmers' Market

Clonakilty Market

So good they have to run it twice a week – on Thursdays and Saturdays – the 'Clon market is a beauty, with its strong Thursday food offer abetted by craft sellers on Saturday. (McCurtain Hill, Clonakilty, Thur & Sat 10am-2pm)

Restaurant

Deasy's Harbour Bar

Billy Blackwell's restaurant and bar in little Ring, a couple of miles east of Clon, has been attracting attention from other talented local cooks, always a sign of merit. It's a typical West Cork address, with interesting and unusual food served in a simple premises, making the experience of discovering it all the more special. (Ring Village, Clonakilty ☎ 023-35741 – Open 6pm-9.30pm Wed-Sat, 1pm-3pm Sun)

Restaurant

Gleeson's Restaurant

Robert Gleeson's cooking has won awards and admirers since the restaurant opened in 2003, and his hard-working style of classic food – salmon and crab fish cake; foie gras, chicken liver and skeaghanore duck in a terrine; halibut with pak choi and shiitake; beef fillet with oxtail and herb roulade – has classy finish and a polished professional sheen. He uses many local foods – Gubbeen bacon with calves' liver; Woodcock smokery haddock in a tart, and of course Clonakilty pudding with poached egg, lardons and shallot vinaigrette – and for such thoughtful and accomplished cooking, Gleeson's offers very keen value for money. (3-4 Connolly Street, Clonakilty ☎ 023-21834 gleesonrestaurant@eircom.net www.gleesons.ie – Open 6pm-9.30pm Tue-Sat, closed 10pm Sat)

Coffee Shop

Hart's Coffee Shop

Hart's is a great spot, with hearty savoury cooking that speaks of food cooked from the heart. There are droves of places offering something similar to Aileen Hart's café, but this one is special. (Ashe Street, Clonakilty ☎ 023-35583 – Open 10am-5.15pm Tue-Sat)

Shop & Bakery

Lettercollum Kitchen Project Shop

Lettercollum was one of the West Cork pioneers, garnering a reputation for fab cooking and a left-field style way back when it was a restaurant in an old convent in Timoleague. Now, the project is both a food store with quite the most delicious foods-to-go, and a wandering cookery school, which takes classes of cookery students to different locations in the Mediterranean, all the better to immerse them in the cooking and the culture. This is an inspirational kitchen project. (22 Connolly Street, Clonakilty ☎ 023-36938 info@lettercollum.ie www.lettercollum.ie)

Craft Shop

Etain Hickey

A gorgeous craft shop, run by the ceramicist Etain Hickey, and which sells many of the products produced by the West Cork Craft Guild, an inspiringly talented cross-section of producers. (40 Ashe Street, Clonakilty ☎ 023-21479 ✉ etainhickey@eircom.net)

Craft Shop

Michelle Mitton Design Gallery

Clonakilty's Style Central, and what a funky store! You need only look in the window to see just what an expert, professionally focused eye Michelle Mitton has: the way this woman can dress a window is breathtaking, and it means you just want to buy everything she has sourced and arranged with such precision and artistic chutzpah. MM is a shop that is a luxury brand all by itself. (28 Pearse Street, Clonakilty ☎ 023-35412 – Open 10am-5.30pm Mon-Sat, note, closed lunch 1pm-2pm)

Cork West

Local Speciality
BROWN CRAB

Delicatessen

Olive Branch

Look out for the marvellous organic produce from Narmada Organics, amongst other local specialists, in this excellent wholefood shop, tucked at the end of Spiller's Lane, a wonderful warren of alternative shops. The OB is literally choc-a-bloc with good things. (Spiller's Lane ☎ 023 35711 – Open 9am-6pm Mon-Sat)

Bar & Bistro

Richy's Bar & Bistro

Not many chefs away from the big cities have published a cookery book of their recipes, but Richy Virahsawmy has, and it's a mark of the singularity of this guy. His bistro offers nachos and garlic bread and cod and chips, but you will also find specials such as samphire being cooked here, and there is lots of ambition which gives Richy's an edge. We'd love the room to be a little brighter, and the staff are excellent. (4 Wolfe Tone Street, Clonakilty ☎ 023-21852 ✉ richysbarandbistro@hotmail.com 🖱 www.richysbarandbistro.com – Open noon-2.30pm lunch, 6pm-10pm Dinner)

Supermarket

Scally's Supervalu

Scally's is a local legend. Yes, it's a supermarket. But, like Field's of Skibb or Ardkeen of Waterford, it is much more than that: it is both a reflection of the food culture and the zeitgeist of the food culture. Scally's has, for instance, a superb fish counter. It has real butchers behind that butcher's counter. It has all the local foods worth eating. It is a true community shop, and yet it is also a huge supermarket. "We see ourselves as a local independent store", they say, and it is no idle boast. (Six Bridge, Clonakilty ☎ 023-33088 – Open 8.30am-9pm Mon-Fri, 8.30am-8pm Sat, 9am-6pm Sun)

Butcher's Shop

Edward Twomey

In 1989, on the first day spent researching our first book in West Cork, Eddie Twomey led us on a whirligig tour of Clon, along with Tom O'Donovan of O'Donovan's Hotel. Eddie's pride in his town and his product went beyond infectious: it was irresistible, and it was also intertwined. He was making Clon famous for the right reasons because of Clonakilty Black Pudding – the Kinsale Food Forum at which we had met was a huge boost for his product, which was taken into the stratosphere the following year when Gerry Galvin cooked it for the first Irish Euro-toques dinner – but Clon also made him. As such, Eddie was the quintessential example of a West Cork artisan archetype: the individual in his place, his town, his land, with food and brand and person all in one. Edward Twomey passed away in 2005. (16 Pearse Street, Clonakilty ☎ 023-33365 - Open 9am-6pm Mon-Sat)

Courtmacsherry

B&B and Catering

Travara Lodge

Brendan Murphy and Richard May run one of the best B&B's, on the waterfront in Courtmac. Mr May is a master of hospitality whilst Mr Murphy's cooking is especially fine. If you would like to get a taste of it away from Travara, then take yourself to the weekly country market and join the enormous, good-tempered queue that awaits Brendan each week as he sets up his bakes and savoury specialities. In 20 minutes, everything is gone! (Courtmacsherry ☎ 023-46493 ✉ travaralodge@eircom.net)

Crookhaven

Gastropub

The Crookhaven Inn

Emma Jepson & Freddy Olsson have been working away quietly in this waterside pub for several years, but a rejigging of their food offer has meant that the Crookhaven Inn has leapt well up the culinary ladder. The lunchtime dishes are very fine – smoked salmon and crab quiche; Oriental lamb burger; fusilli with chicken and pesto – but Freddy really gets creative with dinner – red wine braised lamb shank; beef and ale stew; salmon fish cakes; apple and blackberry crumble. And, if you are off to the beach at Barleycove, call in and take away a bag of their fantastic crab sandwiches. (Crookhaven ☎ 028-35309 crookhaveninn@eircom.net – Open 12.30pm-9pm Mon-Sun, check off season. Closed Oct-Easter)

Cork West

Pub

O'Sullivan's Bar

A popular, characterful pub, O'Sullivan's becomes Dublin 4 à la mer in summertime, packed with wealthy boating types enjoying pints and sandwiches. (Crookhaven ☎ 028-35319 o'sullivans@crookhaven.ie)

Drimoleague

Dairy

Glenilen Dairy

We have been eating and enjoying Alan and Valerie Kingston's dairy products ever since Valerie began to sell at the Bantry Country market in the late 1990's. Since those modest beginnings, they have powered their way to stardom. Phillipa Davenport of the *FT* says the Glenilen butter is the best you can buy. Their yogurts with fruit purées are peerless. Their sundaes are sublime. The cheesecakes are fab. And they keep experimenting, trying new things, trying new ideas, gaining in confidence all the while. They show how artisan dairy production is the only way forward for dairy producers, they reveal the art and the craft – and the congratulation – of artisanship. (Drimoleague ☎ 028-31179)

Dunmanway

Bakery

The Baking Emporium

Bandon, Skibb, Douglas and Bantry are the latest farmer's markets where the innovative Baking Emporium now bring their speciality breads, whilst the bakery in Dunmanway continues to supply the retail trade and the catering industry throughout West Cork. The new breads introduced via the markets – spelt breads, farmer's breads, traditional soda, butter toast, gluten-free and a range of pretzels – show the growth and imagination that fires up this impressive and ingenious bakery company. (Dunmanaway ☎ 023-45260 info@bakingemporiumltd.com www.bakingemporiumltd.com)

Cork West

Quail Eggs

Coturnix Quail

Brendan Ross's company produces splendid quail's eggs, sold in handsome jars, cooked and peeled, and in tiny little boxes which cradle these precious, beautiful things. (Droumdrastil, Dunmanway ☎ 087-206 5067)

Patisserie

Richard Graham-Leigh

Richard Graham-Leigh is a superlative patissier. "His patisseries are perfection", the food writer Clodagh McKenna has written, and indeed they are. But even more than perfection, they are consistent perfection – we have been eating Richard's apricot frangipane bars since 2003 when he first began to bake and sell, and they have never, ever diverted from that perfection of execution – and that applies to everything this gifted man creates, from his seasonal fruit pies and tarts to carmelitas. "In bakery, precision is all", Richard has said, and his work proves it. (Maulanimirish, Dunmanway ☎ 086-086 8183 jandrgrahamleigh@eircom.net)

Beef

Kinrath Dexter Beef

Paul Johnson is following the example of other beef specialists by selling his Dexter beef privately, via a box scheme from the farm. Dexter beef is as rare in Ireland as Belted Galloway, and we hope this imaginative endeavour, following on from other farmers who have begun to do the same such as Joe Condon's omega beef and Maurice Kettyle's beef from Fermanagh, will lead to a situation where food lovers will in future order beef according to breed. (Kinrath House, Dunmanway ☎ 023-55710)

Durrus

Wine Importer

● Albatross Enterprise

Harro Federsen's little wine company imports a small selection of wines from Europe, mainly from Mr Federsen's native Germany, and he holds extremely jolly tastings every so often in his shop-cum-tasting room just across from the neat little cottage which is also available for rental. New wines are consistently added to the list, and it's a most jolly enterprise, so when you see the sign as you are driving down to Ahakista, make sure to turn up the lane and buy a few bottles. (Ahakista, Durrus ☎ 027-67248)

Farmhouse Cheese

● Durrus Farmhouse Cheese

"When you see an artisan cheese maker at work in the dairy or in her maturing rooms you will understand the craft. Instinctive decisions are made in response to ever-changing subtleties of the raw materials. The curd is held between the fingers or tasted to determine timing; the smell and feel of the rind governs decisions on temperature and humidity. There is no rigidity of technological systems but rather the intuition of the crafts person assisted by technology. The crafts person lives on the land that produces the milk and experiences the weather that shapes its subtleties: these are the connections that link the land to the food." Kevin Sheridan and Fiona Corbett of Sheridan's Cheesemongers wrote that in the Slow Food magazine, *Seilide*, and the paragraph ran across from a photo of Jeffa Gill's Durrus cheese. It would be impossible to better describe the practices and skills Ms Gill has mastered ever since she made her first cheese back in 1979. Durrus is a washed-rind raw milk cheese that seems to us to be the product of sheer intuition, the triumph of art over the blandness of technology. Durrus is one of the world's greatest raw milk cheeses, a cheese that trusts to instinct. (Coomkeen, Durrus ☎ 027-61100 info@durruscheese.com www.durruscheese.com)

Restaurant and Cookery School

Good Things Café & Cookery School

Carmel Somers' restaurant has become such an icon address in West Cork it comes as a shock to realise that she only opened in April 2003. But within four years she has become the most admired and original cook in West Cork, and the orchestrator of a cult series of cookery classes, held in the café during the year.
She has done it by cooking local ingredients in season, and by bringing to these foods a vivid technique and a true flair for flavour. Lamb's kidneys with coriander and lime butter takes simple offal into the taste stratosphere, whilst her signature dishes such as Sugar Club beef or Durrus and spinach pizza are contemporary classics. The cookery classes are distinguished by the same original flair and energy, and do note that Good Things is also a most excellent food store. (Durrus ☎ 027-61426
info@thegoodthingscafé.com
www.thegoodthingscafe.com – Open 11.30am-4pm (lunch served from 12.30pm-3pm), 7pm-8.30pm Thu-Mon. Open Easter, bank holiday weekends and from 21 Jun-1 Sep)

Cork West

Local Specialities

MILK
COUNTRY BUTTER
DOUBLE CREAM
BUTTERMILK
YOGURT
WHEY-FED PORK
WASHED-RIND CHEESE

Enniskeane

Farmhouse Cheese

Round Tower Cheese

Nan O'Donovan's mild and sweet cheese is found throughout County Cork, in good stores and shops, and it has always been a most enjoyable food, made with considerable care. (Enniskeane ☎ 023-47105)

Eyeries

Farmhouse Cheese

Milleens Farmhouse Cheese

The first Milleens cheese, made by Veronica and Norman Steele, was sold in 1978, establishing a new way of making Irish food – the ancient way – and, just as importantly, spelling out a new way of doing business. Norman and Veronica didn't just create like artisans, they did business like artisans. "You must believe in the food," Norman once told us. "It simply will not work for a small business if you do not believe in it as a high quality food that will win respect". Milleens won that respect, and created a stellar reputation, and established a precedent that has had a cataclysmic effect on Irish food ever since. And so, with the cheese's thirtieth anniversary looming, let us think of ways to honour this couple and their work. Honorary doctorates from the N.U.I would be nice but, seventy years ago, in Vimoutiers in Normandy, the French erected a statue of Marie Harel, the woman who symbolised camembert. In that action, the French elevated camembert to the status of a national symbol. It's time for us to do the same. (Eyeries, Beara ☎ 027-74079 milleens@eircom.net www.milleenscheese.com)

Cork West

Glandore

Gastro Pub

Glandore Inn

The best way to enjoy the Glandore Inn is to sit outside on a sunny day, overlooking the bay and enjoy their classic open sandwiches of crab, smoked salmon or prawns. Have a great holiday. (Glandore ☎ 028- 33468 – Open Lunch & Dinner)

Gastro Pub

Hayes' Bar

The character of Declan & Ada Hayes' bar comes from the piles of books that sit on all available space, the clever tongue and groove walls made from old wine cases, and the tea pots and old china cups that adorn the tables. The food is quirky and distinctive. A much-loved address. (Glandore ☎ 028-33214 www.hayesbar.ie – Open Lunch. No credit cards)

"A firm defence of quiet material pleasure is the only way to oppose the universal folly of Fast Life."

SLOW FOOD MANIFESTO, 1989

Preserves

Sonia's Inner Pickle

Sonia Bower's pickles are unlike anyone else's. Powerful and refulgent in flavour, they use roasted vegetables – aubergine and green pepper; roasted red pepper – and ally them with pine nuts, vinegar, shards of garlic and onion – to create the maximum flavour kapow! You have to borrow the young person's vocabulary to describe these fabulous foods: wicked! savage! sound! They are truly superb, to use the old guy's vocabulary, and they are actually a stand-alone food: lather them on some bread and open a good bottle of ale. (Glandore ☎ 086-313 1362)

Goleen

B&B

Fortview House

Violet and Richard Connell's farmhouse B&B is both a legendary B&B and a legendary farm, indeed a farm of demonstration standard. But then, doing things to demonstration standard level is what this couple are all about, and it explains the cult reputation of this lovely house, one of the stars of West Cork. (Gurtyowen, Toormore, Goleen ☎ 028-35324 fortviewhousegoleen@eircom.net www.fortviewhousegoleen.com)

Country House

Rock Cottage

"I think this place deserves an extra mention in any guide book on Ireland." That was the word from our most recent correspondent – writing from Brussels – about Barbara Klotzer's Rock Cottage, and it forms part of a consistent chain of praise this host and her house win from visitors to the Mizen peninsula. It's a smashing house, and it is a Georgian house, and not a cottage as you might imagine, and Ms Klotzer earns all the praise she receives thanks to tenacious hard work. (Barnatonicane, Schull ☎ 028-35538 rockcottage@eircom.net www.rockcottage.ie)

Gougane Barra

Hotel and Restaurant

Gougane Barra Hotel

Not many hotels can boast a theatre, but Katy and Neil Lucey's family hotel has one, and stages stupendously successful productions during the sumer season – you couldn't get a ticket for *The Tailor and Ansty* during 2005, and Mick Lally in John B Keane's *The Matchmaker* will be filling the room in 2007. But aside from this, Neil and Katy simply run a lovely, fashion-free hotel, with good comfort cooking from Katy – this girl is one of the Vaughans of Lahinch, so food is in the family genes – and lots of r'n'r for those who are here for walking holidays in this magical valley. A week in Gougane Barra, enjoying Bantry Bay mussels, and roast duck with parsnip crisps, and Ted Browne's Dingle Bay scampi: now that's just what we will need when we finally have this book written. (Gougane Barra, Macroom, ☎ 026-47069
gouganebarrahotel@eircom.net
www.gouganebarrahotel.com)

Cork West

Inishannon

Shortbread

Seymour's of Cork

A brand new product, and a very fine one at that, Seymour's shortbread biscuits are sweet, crumbly, delicate and delicious. We have found them so far only in URRU stores, but they aren't going to stop there, for these are amongst the best biscuits we have come across in recent times. Look out also for their new toffee biscuits, which are every bit as fine as the shortbread. (Russell Hill, Innishannon)

Kilbrittan

Restaurant

Casino House

"Ate in Casino House on five of our evenings, and found the atmosphere, food and service as good as we expected from your panegyric". Nice to get a letter from friends that lets you know your laudatory words about Michael and Kerrin Relja's restaurant are well-founded. But we do admire this beautifully designed restaurant, and Mr Relja's technique-led cooking can produce some very fine food indeed, in just the sort of space that creates some of those magic West Cork moments. (Coolmain Bay, Kilbrittain ☎ 023-49944 ✉ chouse@eircom.net – Open 7pm-9pm Mon-Sun, closed Wed; weekends only Nov-Dec. Sun lunch)

Guesthouse

The Glen

Diana and Guy Scott's house is one of the most stylish and artistic to be found in West Cork, and this couple have the energy to match their gracious manor house. Fantastic breakfasts, blissful comfort and, should the sun be shining and you get to have tea and lemonade on the lawn, you will never forget it. (Kilbrittain ☎ 023-49862 ✉ info@glencountryhouse.com 🖱 www.glencountryhouse.ie – Open Easter-Nov)

Restaurant

The Pink Elephant

Richard Milnes made quite a splash working in Neil Hegarty's Pink Elephant, earning comparison from food lovers with the quality of food at Good Things in Durrus, where Richard worked before moving east. Drawing on the same mantra of fresh local foods, he concocts a smoked mackerel pasty with dill cream and cucumber sauce, or warm duck salad, or lamb with pommes anna. Start with goat's cheese soufflé, then have grilled lobsters, finish with lemon tart, enjoy the (awesome!) view, and it's purest West Cork heaven. (Harbour View, Kilbrittain ☎ 023-49608 – Open 12.30pm-3pm, 6pm-9pm Mon-Sun)

Local Speciality
PLAICE

Kinsale

B&B

Blindgate House

Maeve Coakley's house looks plain from the outside, but inside is a design jewel, with public rooms and bedrooms a pure visual and tactile treat. Breakfasts are just as vividly pleasurable. (Blindgate, Kinsale ☎ 021-477 7858 ✉ info@blindgatehouse.com 🖱 www.blindgatehouse.com)

Restaurant

Crackpots

Carole Norman has been one of the great Kinsale culinary figures, having worked in The Bistro and other destinations before opening Crackpots almost a decade ago. The mix of ceramics and cooking is a happy combination, and their enlightened policy on feeding children is a joy. (Cork Street, Kinsale ☎ 021-477 2847 crackpts@iol.ie – Open 6.30pm-10pm Mon-Fri)

Café & B&B

Cucina

Cork West

A smart little café with smart, inexpensive rooms upstairs, Cucina is a true treat of a place, with a calm, sure style in both the modern cooking and in the way Ursula Roncken and her crew go about their business. (9 Market Street, Kinsale ☎ 021-470 0707 ursula@cucina.ie www.cucina.ie)

Restaurant & Fishmonger

Fishy Fishy Café

Martin and Marie Shanahan opened FFC – their second fish restaurant – one Friday in May 2006, having told no one that they were ready to do business. One hour later, the restaurant was full. By lunchtime the following day, the queue snaked out the gate and down the road. Why? How? Simple. Fishy Fishy is an archetype. As you drive down the hill into Kinsale, as you see the masts and the glint of water, your mind is hoping that you will find a simple, smart restaurant cooking fabulous, fresh fish. Here it is, superlative cooking and glorious style, great relaxed service, good value. That's your archetype, that's Fishy Fishy Café. (Crowley Quay, Kinsale ☎ 021-470 0415 – Open Day-time. No credit cards)

Restaurant & Fishmonger

Fishy Fishy Shop

The original FFC is today a lovely wet fish shop with a somewhat simpler menu than the new restaurant, but the chowders, fish and chips and daily specials are as pristine and singular as ever, and as a destination to buy fresh fish and cooked fish pies and crumbles it is second-to-none. (The Guardwell, Kinsale ☎ 021-477 4453 – Open Day-time. No credit cards)

Brewery

Kinsale Brewing Company

We wish they would tidy up the entrance to the Brewery and make it more presentable when you first walk in off the street, those lovely vats and all that glass should be gleaming!, but we can't quibble with the creaminess of the Kinsale stout and the freshness of their lager and wheat beer. You can also have a conducted tour of the brewery and a tasting, and the brews are available in many local pubs. (The Glen, Kinsale ☎ 021-470 2124 info@kinsalebrewing.com www.kinsalebrewing.com)

Farmers' Market

Kinsale Farmers' Market

Miles Cattell has been the driving force behind the popular KFM which started with a bang in early 2006 and which has been building up a steamy head of success ever since. A great array of producers bring a great array of good things every week, and it is interesting that this is one of the favourite markets for the County Cork stall-holders, thanks to a hungrily appreciative audience and a great location. (Short Quay, Kinsale, Tuesday mornings)

Restaurant

Man Friday

Philip Horgan's busy, characterful restaurant up on the hill of Scilly is all about having a good time, and the punchy, traditional menu delivers dishes that speed along the flow of conversation, craic and wine consumption that means you will do just that. And tomorrow? Never mind tomorrow! Oh, and do mind yourself on the archingly steep steps. (Scilly, Kinsale ☎ 021-477 2260 www.man-friday.net – Open 6.30pm-10.15pm)

Traiteur & Deli

Mange Tout

Three successful years down the line, and Guillaume Lequin has expanded the kitchen in his smart traiteur and deli, tucked into a corner of Boland's craft shop. Aside from the very fine cooked dishes – now smartly packaged with see-through covers – there are lots of other well-chosen things, from cheeses to breads to local honeys and good chocolates, all the better to fill up your basket. (Pearse Street, Kinsale ☎ 021-477 2161 www.bolandskinsale.com – Open 7.45am-6pm Mon-Sun)

Wine Bar

Max's Wine Bar

Max's is one of the great Kinsale stalwarts, and we hope the current renovations – being conducted on a grand scale – will preserve a very enjoyable, cosy, quirky little place in which to enjoy some tasty cooking– the boeuf bourguignonne we had in here last time was every bit as good as the service. (48 Main Street, Kinsale ☎ 021-477 2443)

B&B

Pier House

Cork West

Ann and Pat Hegarty's funky house is right, smack bang in the centre of town, but manages to be quiet and peaceful even when the town is overheating at weekends. Great breakfasts, and great hosts who will mark your card about everything you need to see and do. (Pier Road, Kinsale ☎ 021-477 4475 pierhouseaccom@eircom.net www.pierhousekinsale.com – Open all year)

Delicatessen

Quay Food Co

Donal and Laura Hayes run an excellent deli, with a lot of choice whole foods, in the centre of town, and we like the bohemian feel and appearance of the shop, as well as all the thoughtfully selected stock. (Market Quay, Kinsale ☎ 021-477 4000– Open 9am-6pm May-Sept, 9.30am-5.30pm winter)

Fishmonger

Ship To Shore

A petite fish shop with an iced selection of fresh fish and a small fridge of prepared fish specialities. The shop is owned by fisherman Johnny Walshe, which ensures a regular supply of superb fresh fish. (Market Square, Kinsale ☎ 021-477 7443)

Restaurant

Toddies @ The Kinsale Brewery

Pearse and Mary O'Sullivan made a smart move into the centre of town to the KB a couple of years back, and being in the bustle has helped the cooking of this fine chef to become both better known and better appreciated. Given the place he is in, fresh fish and shellfish are always amongst the best choices, cooked with modern imaginative twists, but even modern staples such as hake in beer batter with pea purée and hand-cut chips are vivid, fresh and hip, and he makes a demon pizza. (The Glen, Kinsale ☎ 021-477 7769 ⌖ www.toddies.ie – Open 6.30pm-10.30pm Tue-Sun, Mon-Sun high season. Closed Jan & Feb)

Wine Bar

● Vista Wine Bar

A slick new Miesian glass and metal building just by the pier houses the new Vista, which opens for breakfast, offers a good lunch menu, and then has an array of tapas dishes on offer from 6pm. Great views from upstairs, friendly and engaged staff and a promising new concept. (46 Main Street, Kinsale ☎ 087-233 9434)

Cork West

Rosscarbery

Free-range Pork & Sausages

● Caherbeg Free-Range Pork

With a superb new duo of black and white puddings complementing their range of Caherbeg and Rosscarbery sausages, bacons and hams, Willie and Avril Allshire's company is a totemic example of how to carve out an artisan industry in less than a decade. Their consistency hasn't faltered since those first sausages were made in November 2000, and each new addition to the range has been distinguished by the Caherbeg signatures of pure, subtle flavours and superb cooking characteristics. That brand new black puddding, by the way, won a gold medal at a boudin competition in France when it was less than three months on the market, an utterly incredible – and richly deserved – achievement. Beating the French at their own game: who would ever have believed it?(Caherbeg, Rosscarbery ☎ 023-48474 ✉ caher@caherbegfreerangepork.ie ⌖ www.caherbegfreerangepork.ie)

Restaurant

● O'Callaghan-Walshe

"Comfort cooking, I suppose, is where we're at, or what we hope to be about." So says Sean Kearney, one of the great West Cork hosts, indeed one of the great West Cork characters. With Tina at the stoves, this pair produce the very best West Cork fish cookery you can find, using only locally landed fish and shellfish. Grilled Dover sole. Turbot with lemon butter. John Dory with cider. O'C-W is fish cookery as you might find it in Galicia or the Ligurian coast: direct, idiosyncratic, confident, at times both sublime and unforgettable, which makes O'C-W unmissable. (The Square, Rosscarbery ☎ 023-48125 funfish@indigo – Open Dinner)

Restaurant

Steven's Bistro

A friendly bistro on the square with tasty friendly food and a welcoming, laid-back ambience. "Food for all the family", is what they say, and that is just what they deliver, with a pleasing eagerness and lack of pretension. (10 South Square, Rosscarbery ☎ 023-31950 – Open Mon-Sun)

Cork West

Schull

Guesthouse

Grove House

Katerina Runske's B&B is one of Schull's finest houses, an elegant villa that previously had guests such as George Bernard Shaw, J.B. Yeats and Edith Summerville. Today Grove is both B&B and restaurant, where Katerina and her Mum, Katherine, cook food with a vivid Swedish accent – you must try those Swedish meatballs. (Colla Road, Schull ☎ 028-28067 info@grovehouseschull.com www.grovehouseschull.com – Open 7pm-7pm Mon-Sun. Also open for light lunches outside when the weather is good)

Farmhouse Cheese

Gubbeen Farmhouse Cheese

There are two types of farmers in Ireland. The first group includes those who have little or no control over their destiny, their income and their farming future. The second group is those who control their destiny, control their income, and who have confidence in their farming future. If you want the archetype of the second group, then a visit to Tom and Giana Ferguson's Gubbeen Farm is essential. Gubbeen Farm turns commodity materials – milk, meat, smoke, crops – into luxury brand foods. Milk from their herd makes the acclaimed Gubbeen cheeses, a cheese which enjoys its own unique flora – Microbacterium gubbeenense. Whey is fed to pigs to make Gubbeen pork. Vegetable and salad leaves are planted, grown and sold locally by Clovisse Ferguson. All of this is controlled by the Fergusons, with most of the selling happening through farmers' markets. They enjoy autonomy. They enjoy control. The creativity and optimism their work engenders is evident in their foods – Gubbeen may be the chicest food brand in Ireland. (Gubbeen, Schull ☎ 028-28231 www.gubbeen.com)

Farmhouse Cheese

Gubbeen Smokehouse

Fingal Ferguson's smokehouse grew out of his job smoking Gubbeen cheese for his Mum. In just five years, the business has mushroomed in terms of the range of products created, and the spread of places where you can buy them. Mr Ferguson's signature is a light hand with the smoke, and an inherent sweetness in his products, whether the excellent breakfast sausages, the lovely smoked back bacon, or the Gubbeen salamis. New products are concocted consistently and with consistent excellence, and they are an epicure's dream. (Gubbeen, Schull ☎ 028-27824 smokehouse@eircom.net www.gubbeen.com)

Chocolates

Gwen's Chocolates

Gwen Lasserre is a most gifted chocolatier, a young man who got turned on to the great art by a local chocolate maker back in his native France. Those early lessons have stood M. Lasserre in fine stead, and we rate these as being amongst the best chocolates available anywhere in Ireland. (Main Street, Schull ☎ 086-3171369 gwenlasserre@hotmail.com – Open9am-1pm, 2.30pm-6pm Tue-Sat, 9am-1pm Sun and at the Schull Market)

Bar

Hackett's Bar

Hackett's is a lively bar, due in large measure to the extra-lively food that Trudy Etchells and her crew fire out every day. The soups are just the best – in truth, they are meals unto themselves – and the newest development in Hackett's is their decision to open for dinner at weekends. Cracking. (Main Street, Schull ☎ 028-28625 trudyetchells@eircom.net – Food served noon-3pm Mon-Sat, 7pm-9pm Fri & Sat)

Cork West

Charcutier

Krawczyk's West Cork Salamis

The next time you have a piece of a Franck Krawczyk meat product, perhaps the Dereenatra Dry, an oak-smoked air-dried sausage, or the Schull salami, or the superb pastrami or his classic Bolg Doire speck, consider what it is you are eating, and consider what Mr Krawczyk told Colman Andrews in *Saveur* magazine: " I tried to create something with a specific character of its own, something that defines the nature of West Cork – which is rural but cosmopolitan, very diverse in many ways, and probably the most forward-thinking place in Ireland".
So, where could be better than to fashion these extraordinary meat products, ancient Polish recipes which have come to be amongst the quintessential West Cork foods. It's not fanciful to suggest, as you eat them, that you can taste that history, and taste that West Cork thing. These aren't mere foods; they are cultural artefacts.
(The Barn, Dereenatra, Schull ☎ 028-28579
frankk@oceanfree.net)

Fishmonger

Normandy Ireland Exports Ltd

There is a fish shop attached to this seafood wholesaler at the edge of the pier in Schull Harbour. It opens seasonally and intermittently, but is a good place to buy fresh fish.
(The Pier, Schull ☎ 028-28599)

Fish Stalls

O'Driscoll's

The O'Driscoll brothers have no logos, no signage and no fliers to announce their stalls at any of the markets they attend in the Limerick Milk Market and throughout County Cork. So, how will you know who and where they are? By their queue shall ye know them. Wherever they sell, the boys have a long queue of punters looking to buy excellent fish – and probably to admire their dazzling fish filleting skills. Great fish, great service, and amazing value for money. (Schull ☎ 028-27569 olischull@hotmail.com)

Wholefood Shop

Roaring Water Wholefood Shop

This lovely wee shop on the main street is so packed with goods of every description that their organic veg is usually arrayed outside on the street, perched on a few boxes. Step inside and you may find the experiments of local wannabee cheese makers – it was a goat's milk cheese from Ballydehob the last time – and lots more splendid stuff. (47 Main Street, Schull ☎ 028-27834 – 9.30am-6pm Mon-Sat & Sun during the summer)

Farmers' Market

● Schull Market

The Sunday market at the car park on the road down to the harbour is one of the liveliest in Cork, and on a fine summer Sunday it's the perfect spot to head to for a shopping – and eating – expedition. (Pier Car Park, Sundays 10am-3pm)

Farmhouse Cheese

● West Cork Natural Cheese Company

Bill Hogan discovered, on a visit to a cheese making plant in southern Ontario, aged 10, that cheese making was what he wanted to do. This fact is proof that cheese making to this man is not merely occupation and profession, but actually amounts to a vocation. His cheeses, Gabriel and Desmond, made with Sean Ferry, are unique in Ireland, being super-hard thermophilic cheeses, piquant, complex, the mirror-image of the cheese maker himself. They are Mr Hogan and Mr Ferry's statement of food authenticity, and even though production has moved to the Newmarket Co-Op in recent times, that authenticity remains as direct and resonant as ever, and it is not merely culinary authenticity, for these superb cheeses speak of cultural and social authenticity in every bite. (Dereenatra, Schull ☎ 028-28593 bh@wcnc.ie www.wcnc.ie)

Deli Café

● West Cork Gourmet Store

The WCGS is not just a good place to take lunch and dinner – and breakfast and snacks during the day – in pretty Schull. It also acts as a setting for Slow Food events by the local convivium, so we have eaten everything in here from Philippino cooking to a vegetarian feast by Denis Cotter. They offer nice wines, nice simple cooking, and an easy-does-it ambience, which makes the Gourmet Store a treat at any time and every time. (East End, Schull ☎ 028-27613 – Open 9.30am-6pm Mon-Sat, 11am-4pm Sun with extended opening hours and evening openings during the summer, holidays, and for special evenings.)

Skibbereen

Fishmonger

Baltimore Fresh Fish

Alan Hassett was for many years a fisherman trawling the south coast on *Ocean Freedom*, his own boat. "I buy small quantities of fish every day, and get most of my fish from the day boats to ensure maximum freshness." Alan also operates a trailer on Baltimore pier during the summer. His fish preparation is exceptional, a skill he puts down to the fact that he loves to cook fish himself. (27 North Street, Skibbereen ☎ 028-40924)

Cork West

Organic Seeds

Brown Envelope Seeds

You seek the dazzlingly beautiful Painted Mountain corn? What about Dzeltenais Gigantis, a tomato from Latvia? Texel greens? Madeline McKeever is your girl, should you be searching for the real queer gear. Brown Envelope Seeds has almost 100 different types of seeds, from the strangest of stuff like Painted Mountain, to more common tomatoes, brassicas and salad leaves, all of organic standard. In her 2007 catalogue, Madeline writes: "Each seed embodies the miracle of life itself as well as the collective efforts of countless generations of farmers and growers. Handling them is a responsibility we take seriously. Growing them shows that you have faith in the future". Pure poetry. (Ardagh, Church Cross, Skibbereen ☎ 028-38184
madsmckeever@eircom.net
www.brownenvelopeseeds.com)

Dressed Crab

Crab & Co

Nichola Nesbitt makes the best dressed crab you can find, and a good dressed crab is a very fine thing to find indeed. She showed us all how she does it at a Slow Food evening in Good Things in Durrus, and what she also revealed is that this is a woman with dextrous skills and an epicurean attitude. She flavours the fish with English mustard and good mayonnaise, and presents it in the traditional fashion, back in its shell. It has become one of the don't-miss-it foods of the Skibb Saturday morning market. (Skibbereen Market, Saturdays ☎ 086-171 5484)

Supermarket

Field's

"Wouldn't the world be a better place if all supermarkets could be like this?" asked Caroline Workman and Myrtle Allen in their invaluable *Good Food in Cork* booklet. Well, it most certainly would, because Field's is actually the antithesis of the modern supermarket. It is owner-run. It sells local foods. It has skilled staff who understand their meat, their fish, their veg, their dairy products. It has a wonderful ambience, and it has a rather nice café which is the best place to enjoy their own sweet and savoury baking. It is an icon address, because unlike bland supermarkets it is heterogeneous, distinct, distinguished, and proud to be different. (26 Main Street, Skibbereen ☎ 028-21400 – Open 8am-7pm Mon-Tue, 8am-9pm Wed-Fri, 8am-6.30pm Sat, 9.30am-6pm Sun)

B&B

Glebe Shore

Una Maguire and Aveen Henry's B&B is a design jewel, a real West Cork hideaway that has sprung straight from the pages of a style guide, as well as from your deepest wishes. The style is great, the breakfasts are simply benchmark, a litany of great local foods. (Lisheen, Church Cross, Skibbereen ☎ 028-38590 stay@glebeshore.com www.glebeshore.com – Open all year)

Restaurant & Cookery Courses

Island Cottage

"Not just a meal; an experience. Part awkward dinner party, part great home-cooked repast (but home-cooked by a French-trained chef)." That's how Colman Andrews, in *Saveur* magazine's ground breaking March 2006 issue dedicated to Ireland, summed up the Island Cottage gig. Yes, you come to John and Ellmary's restaurant to eat, but the boat trip and the boreen hike and the companionship all manage to make it more than the sum of its parts. The strangeness of it all – a no-choice menu in a one room restaurant on an island – is pure West Cork, but the cooking is pure John Desmond, and is strikingly fine. (Heir Island, Skibbereen ☎ 028-38102 info@heirislandcottage.com www.islandcottage.com – Open Dinner Wed-Sat. No credit cards. Closed 15 Sept-15 June)

Restaurant

Kalbo's Bistro

Siobhan O'Callaghan's bistro is rock steady, rock solid, but their consistency isn't won at the expense of creativity, and Kalbo's is a kitchen distinguished by a constant striving to be better, to exceed their own expectations. This hunger makes for cooking that has freshness and verve, and which is always a sheer delight, as well as being excellent value. (48 North Street, Skibbereen ☎ 028-21515 – Open 11.30am-3.30pm, 6.30pm-9.30pm Mon-Sat, noon-2.30pm, 6.30pm-9.30pm Sun)

Cork West

Farmers' Market

Skibbereen Saturday Market

Alan and Valerie. Sally. Bob. Caroline. Cathy. Jean. Judy. Madeline. Myra and Karen. Paul. Fingal. Winnifred and Willie. What a bunch of larger-than-life characters the Skibb market collective are, and what a splendiferous market they concoct every Saturday, from salamis to gjetost, rare breeds to rare seeds, jewellery to quark. A demon event. (Fairfield, Skibbereen, Saturdays 10am-2pm)

Herb Preserves

West Cork Herb Farm

Rosarie O'Byrne is a West Cork food pioneer, producing a superb range of herb jellies and condiments and acting as a sage on the subjects of herbs and their efficacy as healing agents. (Church Cross, Skibbereen ☎ 028-38428)

Café

Zilli Café

They do good stuff in the little square-shaped room that is Zilli: squidgy fresh breads, nice lunchtime treats, good coffee to perk you up mid-morning or mid-afternoon. Doing the good thing, of course, means that the perennial problem in Zilli is actually getting a table. (26 North Street, Skibbereen ☎ 028 23515 – Open 9.30am-4.30pm Mon-Sat)

Timoleague

Café Bar

Dillon's Restaurant

Always one of the hippest West Cork addresses, Dillon's retains and maintains an energy, a signature style and a culinary creativity that keeps it ahead of the ever-competitive West Cork posse. They do good things such as vegetarian stifado, and classics like sirloin with a mustard cognac sauce, and roasted cod with a crab gratin and a basil butter sauce, unpretentious and tasty food in an ace space. (Mill Street, Timoleague ☎ 023-46390 – Open Lunch & Dinner from 6.30pm-9.30pm Thur-Sun)

Mella's Fudge

Fudge is a difficult product to master, with many fudge makers erring on the side of sweetness and, thereby, sickliness. Mella errs on the right side of sweetness, so her four fudges – vanilla, rum'n'raisin, chocolate, and walnut – are pure swooshes of buttery goodness and energy without a David Lynch-style sugar jag following through at the end. Beautiful fudges, beautifully made and packaged, and a real treat as a gift. For yourself. Because you're worth it. (Lettercollum, Timoleague ☎ 086-159 5949 mellasfudge@hotmail.com)

Cork West

Black & White Pudding

Staunton's

Staunton's brown pudding is one of the few Irish foods to enjoy PDO status, most recently joined in this small bunch by Connemara lamb. Locally sourced pigs make for a super-tasty, pleasingly liverish pudding. A black pudding and a white pudding are also produced. (Timoleague ☎ 023-46128)

Smokehouse

Ummera Smokehouse

Anthony Cresswell seems to pick up culinary awards as often as the rest of us have hot dinners. It's no surprise that his smoked foods should be so garlanded, for they have a delicacy, a subtlety, that shows the smoking process being used at its zenith. Anthony uses oak wood, and a sugar-salt brining for his salmon. But Ummera is especially interesting as a smokehouse that smokes more than salmon and superb eel: their smoked bacon is a unique product – sliced see-through thin, and with the most sublime aroma as it cooks, and their smoked chicken is a favourite resource of professional chefs, and a life saver for concocting a smashing starter for tonight's dinner. (Inchybridge, Timoleague ☎ 023-46644/087-2027227 info@ummera.com www.ummera.com)

County Donegal

Ardara

B&B

The Green Gate

Paul Chatenoud's spartan collection of cottages up the hill and behind the green gate just outside Ardara isn't to everyone's taste. Those used to contemporary standards of luxury will find everything here just a little too Spartan. But for others there is something profoundly holistic about staying here that can't be found anywhere else. Not for those who need power showers and deep-pile carpets and LCD screens, then, but if you seek something else you just might find it behind the green gate. (Ardvally, Ardara ☎ 075-954 1546 – Open all year. No credit cards)

Donegal

Café

The West End Café

Charlie and Philomena run a smashing operation at the West End. Great fried fish, great chips, hot mugs of tea, and whilst there are many more modern things on the menu, the smart choice is the smartly battered fish and the crisp and salty chips and a plate of mushy peas, please. Only wonderful. (Main Street, Ardara ☎ 074-954 1656 – Open 9.30am-10pm Mon-Sun)

Bridgend

Bar & Restaurant

Harry's Restaurant

Donal Doherty has been at the helm of Harry's for the past three years or so, though the family have been doing good things here for more than 15 years. Donal's speciality is the proper hanging of prime Donegal beef, dry-aging it for maximum impact, so if you seek all the good omega oils from pasture-grazed, dry-aged sirloin, then Harry's is your only destination. This is a very promising and ambitious venture, and another Donegal address that marries an owner's high level of skill and discrimination with a modest, charming place. (Bonemaine, Bridgend, Donegal ☎ 074-936 8544 – Open 12.15pm-9pm Mon-Sun. Closed 8pm Mon & Tue in winter)

Buncrana

Bar

● The Beach House Bar & Restaurant

Claire McGowan opened the Beach House restaurant in summer 2006, with Pascal Desmet at the stoves. The restaurant is located on the beach in Buncrana and enjoys spectacular views out across the water. This is a promising new venture for the town. (Swilly Road, Buncrana ☎ 074-936 1050 ✉ www.thebeachhouse.ie – Open noon-9pm Mon-Sun. Off season closed Monday, and open from 5.30pm during the week)

"There is practically no field of human eandeavour that does not relate to agriculture in some way. Seen from whatever perspective you choose, agriculture touches on every single aspect of human life."

RUDOLF STEINER, *AGRICULTURE, 1924*

Donegal

Burtonport

Wine Merchant

● Inis Wines

Alice and Liam Sweeney's wine company is one of the trio of distinguished wine merchants – the others being Tyrrell & Co and The Wicklow Wine Company – who together make up "The Wine Bunch", independent wine merchants with outstanding lists who exhibit their wines together. Inis bring in wines from Australia, France and, just recently, South Africa. "It is very important to us that we only sell wines we enjoy ourselves", they say, and the list reflects great care and application, and hard work. Great producers such as Sylvain Dussort from Burgundy and Domaine Lardy from Beaujolais are just two of an exciting portfolio of French winemakers, whilst the new Sumaridge Estate accounts for the South Africans and Classic McLaren, Sandalyn Wilderness and Setanta Wines account for the Aussies. These are serious, distinctive wines, so look out for them on good wine lists and in the best wine shops throughout the country. (Lackenagh, Burtonport ☎ 074-954 2940 ✉ www.iniswines.com)

Restaurant

● The Lobster Pot

A popular bar and seafood restaurant in Burtonport. (Burtonport ☎ 074-954 2012 ✉ lobsterpot@eircom.net – Open 10.30am-11.30pm Mon-Sun)

Culdaff

Restaurant and Bar

● McGrory's

McGrory's is a textbook example of how to run a successful hospitality business. When Anne, John and Neil McGrory took over the old family business in 1989, it was simply a 10-room guesthouse, and it was on the market. First off, they opened a café, then they tried bar food. At the same time the brothers used their expertise as musicians to develop the music side of the business, and seriously interesting music has always been an important part of the attraction at McGrory's. By 1999 they had their restaurant opened, and the rooms upstairs were gradually developed. Today they attract diners, tourists, music heads, weekenders, golfers, and huge numbers of folk from Northern Ireland who hop over from Derry. It's a fantastic mix of folk, and it animates this lovely place with great energy and vitality. This is a really special place, in a very special place. (Culdaff ☎ 074-937 9104 ✉ info@mcgrorys.ie 🖱 www.mcgrorys.ie – Open 6.30pm-9pm Tue-Thur, 6.30pm-9.30pm Fri & Sat, 1pm-3.30pm, 6pm-8.30pm Sun)

Donegal

Coffee Shop and Mini Bakery

● Aroma Coffee Shop

There is no more cult address in Irish food than Tom Dooley and Arturo de Alba's tiny eating space and bakery, Aroma. Part of the Donegal Craft Village, it seems the most unlikely place in which to find great food and sublime baking, and their own modest title of "coffee shop & mini bakery" gives little hint of the ambition at work. But no food lover ever uses the Donegal town by-pass. By-pass this level of cooking?! Are you nuts! So, start with the baking: superlative brown bread that would win any baking competition you cared to enter it for. The sweet stuff, such as their legendary Tunisian orange cake, is art on the plate. And then the food in the café: just try the pimentos rellenos, where roasted red peppers are stuffed with minced meat and served with sour cream, tomato sauce and basmati rice, and you will understand why people turn up here early to make sure they get a seat before service begins. One of the great Donegal destinations. (The Craft Village, Donegal Town ☎ 074-972 3222 – Open 9.30am-5.30pm Tue-Sat, 7 days in high season)

Farmers' Market

● Donegal Farmers' Market

Markets have had a fitful history throughout Donegal, but the market in The Diamond, held every 3rd Saturday, really seems to be taking off, and the mix of music and dancing that provides entertainment as you browse and buy is helping to create a new success story. (The Diamond, Donegal, 3rd Saturday 10am-2pm)

Donegal

Wholefood Shop

● Simple Simon Natural Foods

Andrew Cape has a pair of Simple Simons, with the excellent shop in The Diamond paired with another just off the Main Strip of Letterkenny. Ever since setting up his first stall at the Donegal Food Co-op back in 1989, this genial man has run an excellent operation, and here you will find superb baking from their own bakery, lots of the best local foods and a beatific calmness in both stores. The shop in Letterkenny also has a sweet little coffee shop with very nice things to eat. (The Diamond, Donegal ☎ 074-972 2687 ✉ simplesimon@eircom.net. Simple Simon Living Food, Oliver Plunkett Road, Letterkenny ☎ 074-912 2382 – Open 9am-6pm Mon-Wed, 9am-6.30pm Thur-Sat)

Dunfanaghy

Restaurant and Accommodation

● The Mill Restaurant

Derek and Susan Alcorn's restaurant with rooms is one of those Donegal addresses that defines the pinnacle of quality in its genre. The rooms are superb, the restaurant is superb, the staff are particularly superb and value for money is outstanding. We have said it before, but it bears repetition: if Mr Alcorn wasn't cooking at the farthest extremity of the country, he would be feted by the media as a genial, gifted, individual contemporary chef. But, he is too far from the madding media crowd, so he just gets on with it, cooking wonderful food for a devoted audience of regulars. In every respect and regard, The Mill is outstanding. (Figart, Dunfanaghy ☎ 074-913 6985 www.themillrestaurant.com – Open Easter-Halloween, Restaurant open 7pm-9pm Tue-Sun)

Dunkineely

Restaurant with Rooms

Castle Murray House

Marguerite Howley's restaurant-with-rooms is one of the original of the species, and it remains one of the best. As a romantic getaway it is hard to beat, with simple rooms, the most jaw-dropping location and views, and patient, polite staff who look after you extra well. As a place to eat, it offers delicious cooking at very, very keen prices, and the only problem here lies in not deciding to have what you had the last time: well, the char-grilled scallops with creamed leeks, and the turbot with saffron and Pernod, is always going to be hard to beat, though everything else on the menu promises to be just as real, simple, tasty and enjoyable. Only splendid. (Dunkineely ☎ 074-973 7022 www.castlemurray.com – Restaurant open 6.30pm-9.30pm Mon-Sat; 1.30pm-3.30pm, 6.30pm-8.30pm Sun)

Glenties

Biodynamic Grower

Thomas Becht

Thomas Becht covers a couple of hundred miles every Friday, whilst Lucy Becht racks up almost a hundred miles, as this dynamic couple deliver good things to the 100 customers who subscribe to their box delivery scheme. Their enterprise makes the heart sing: whilst other farmers seem bereft of hope, the Bechts farm bio-dynamically on 800 acres, run a terrific farm shop, have three rental flats in their farmhouse, and are a powerhouse pair whose farm is of demonstration standard. They also make wickedly good salamis and, if you are ever feeling low, just click onto their website and read their mission statement, a call to arms for the dignity of farming, and an inspirational agenda for modern agriculture. Brilliant. (Doorian, Glenties ☎ 074-955 1286 donegalorganic@hotmail.com www.donegalorganic.ie – Shop open 8.30am-8pm Mon-Sun)

Preserves

Filligan's Preserves

Philip and Sarah Moss's company has a simple, short, slogan: "Eat Art" . We couldn't put it better ourselves, for enjoying the relishes, mustards, preserves, pickles and jams of these artful artisans is nothing less than enjoying the art of cooking. Everything they make is distinguished by being distinguished: the jams fresh and fruity, the mustards piquant and aromatic, the relishes agrestic and tactile, the sauces deep and fulsome. For our money, Filligan's is one of the most distinguished food companies in the country, and their working methods, of producing in small batches in order to maximise the distinctiveness of each product, is the art of artisanship in action. (Tullyard, Glenties ☎ 074-955 1628 moss@filligans.com www.filligans.com)

Greencastle

Restaurant

Kealy's Seafood Bar

James Kealy's death, at an all-too-early age, robbed Donegal not just of one of its most distinguished cooks, but also of one of the county's most distinguished champions, a man who worked tirelessly to promote his region and its foods, and whose work show-cased that produce in the most direct and delicious fashion. Happily, Tricia Kealy is continuing to run the splendid seafood bar and is continuing to offer the seafood cookery that has made Kealy's so celebrated. (The Harbour, Greencastle ☎ 074-938 1010 – Open 12.30pm-2.45pm 7pm-9.30pm Tue-Sun)

Laghey

Restaurant and Accommodation

Coxtown Manor

In the last edition of this book we relayed a story about how a friend, at a loss for somewhere to eat and stay near Donegal town late one night, had stayed at Coxtown on our recommendation.

Next morning he called to say that the meal he had was the best he had enjoyed in Ireland in a decade.
This time, a friend, at a loss for somewhere to eat and stay near Donegal town late at night, managed to get a room in Coxtown following our recommendation. Next morning, he called to say that it was the best place he had ever stayed at anywhere in Ireland.
Blimey! How does Ed Dewael manage to acquire these accolades? Well, he is a most charming host, and he runs a beautiful, sort-of-left-field country house that has a unique character. And his crew produce some glorious food, including one of the best breakfasts in Ireland. And that's how he does it, and there is no little magic about it, to be honest. So, should you be at a loss for somewhere to eat and stay near to Donegal town, Coxtown is the choice. (Laghey ☎ 074-973 4574 ✉ coxtownmanor@oddpost.com 🖱 www.coxtownmanor.com – Open mid Feb-end October)

Donegal

Letterkenny

Butcher

● McGee's Butcher's

We knew Joe McGee back when he only had one wee butcher's shop, in County Monaghan. Now there are four stores, two in the North, and with the Letterkenny shop in the busy shopping centre pairing up with the original Monaghan store. In addition to being a sharp retailer with a sharp eye on what the market wants, Mr McGee has begun to produce his own beef from the farm at Gortnagran in County Tyrone. "Soft Rain, Slow Food" is their slogan, and that rain and good grass rears Angus-Hereford cross cattle which are hip-hung and dry-aged to maximise flavour. What does it all add up to? "That essential element of trust that every customer requires when they purchase meat today" says Joe. Too right. (Unit 29 Letterkenny SC, Port Rd, L'kenny ☎ 074-917 6567 ✉ mail@mcgeesfood.ie 🖱 www.mcgeesfood.com – Open 9am-6pm Mon-Wed, 9am-8pm Thur & Fri, 9am-7pm Sat, noon-6pm Sun)

Local Specialities

MALIN LAMB

HORN HEAD MACKEREL

GLEN BAY LOBSTER

Rathmullan

Restaurant

● An Bonnan Bui

Martin and Monica Kelly's little restaurant is a wee charmer. She cooks, he does front-of-house, and everything is carried out with patient charm and care. Mrs Kelly is Brazilian, and so the menu features some Brazilian dishes such as Moqueca de frutos do mar, or bolinho de bacalhau, as well as more mainstream modern European cooking. We like the simplicity and the Mom'n'Pop feel of the place, and it's a terrific asset to little Rathmullan. (Pier Road, Rathmullan ☎ 074-915 8453 bonnanbui@yahoo.ie www.anbonnanbui.com – Open 5.30pm-9.30pm Thur-Sun, 1pm-5pm Sun. Open lunch and dinner seven days during high season)

Country House

● Rathmullan House

Rathmullan is one of those houses, along with Ballymaloe and Ballyvolane and a small handful of others, that defines what we mean by the Irish country house experience. That is to say, it is professional, but charmingly domestic. The cooking is cutting-edge cuisine, but based on local foods from local producers. The style is efficient, yet it is still run by the Wheeler family. It's not inexpensive, and yet it offers superb value for money. It is contemporary in style, yet their membership of Slow Food shows that their values are ageless. In rationalising and synthesising all of these seemingly contradictory elements, Rathmullan emerges as a splendid sport of nature, a house pursuing its own furrow of distinguished hospitality, and great cooking, all done without any element of cliché, all done with originality. Well, so much for the theory, but what counts is the reality, and in this regard Rathmullan is sublimely comfortable, has the most charming staff, and the cooking is some of the best contemporary food in Ireland (Lough Swilly, Rathmullan ☎ 074-915 8188 info@rathmullanhouse.com www.rathmullanhouse.com – Open 7.30pm-8.45pm, 'till 9pm Fri-Sat, Mon-Sun. Mid-week and weekends only off season)

County Dublin

DUBLIN CENTRAL

Guesthouse

Aberdeen Lodge

Pat Halpin's pair of Ballsbridge houses – he also owns Merrion Hall on the Merrion Road – are, for our money, the best places to stay in Dublin. Both houses are characterised by the most attentive and motivated staff you will find working anywhere in town, by superb breakfasts, and by customers who stay here each and every time they visit town. (53-55 Park Avenue, Ballsbridge, D4 ☎ 01-283 8155 www.halpinsprivatehotels.com – Open all year. Also Merrion Hall, 54-56 Merrion Road, Ballsbridge, D4 ☎ 01-668 1426)

Dublin Central

Market

Airfield House

There are ambitious plans to extend the food offer at the late Letitia and Naomi Overend's famous house and garden, and to develop further the market and food education side of this splendidly altruistic endeavour. Four new Jersey cows have just been introduced to bolster their celebrated herd. (Upper Kilmacud Road, Dundrum, D14 ☎ 01-298 4301 info@airfield.ie www.airfield.ie)

Restaurant

Akasaka

High-quality sushi is the best choice in Akasaka, especially as you can watch the sushi chef at work, and this is a promising venture in food-bereft Castleknock. (Unit 1-2 Castleknock Village Centre, D15 ☎ 01-810 3564 – Open 12.30pm-11pm Sun-Thurs, 12.30pm-midnight Fri & Sat)

Ethnic Store

Al-Khyrat

Al Khyrat is great for fresh vegetables and eastern exotica, but look out especially for their Algerian Muhajab layered bread and also some very fine Algerian Baklava – the almond and honey concoction is as good as any we have tasted. (22 Upper Rathmines Road, D6 ☎ 01-496 3968 – Open 10.30am-8pm Mon-Sat)

Restaurant

Anderson's

The star of the Northside, Noel Delaney's super-hip café and deli has spawned a second outlet in Drumcondra, which specialises in crêpes, cooked in front of the diners. Mr Delaney has proven something simple: give people the good thing, and they will snap it up, whatever side of the river you are on. Northsiders have a lot to be grateful for, thanks to this man's inspired and original take on food and service, and thanks to the stylishness with which he creates rooms in which to eat and relax. Everything sold in here is chosen with ultimate care, and served with unpretentious assistance. (3 The Rise, Glasnevin, D9 ☎ 01-837 8394 info@andersons.ie www.andersons.ie – Open 9am-7pm Mon-Wed, 9am-9pm Thur-Sat, 10am-7.30pm Sun. Note: Wed hours can vary due to jazz night)

"I realised food was a matter of a civilised achivement. The fruit of civilisation." MYRTLE ALLEN

Restaurant

Anderson's Crêperie

Lip-smacking savoury buckwheat, and sweet wheat crêpes, are cooked at the counter in front of the diners and are allied to punchy savoury combinations – ham, brie and mushrooms; Raclette, peppers and mushrooms – and decadent sweet blow-outs – chocolate and banana; figs with Amaretto and ice cream. Open sandwiches, savoury platters and good coffees square the circle of goodness. (3 Carlingford Road, Drumcondra, D9 ☎ 01-830 5171 info@andersons.ie www.andersons.ie – Open 9am-7pm Mon-Wed, 9am-9pm Thur-Sat, 10am-7.30pm Sun)

Café and Bakery

Arnott's

Nancy Silverton, one of the goddesses of American contemporary cooking, flew to Ireland to open the La Brea café on the Middle Abbey St. side of Arnott's, but the café almost didn't need the sparkle dust of the great cook and baker who created the la Brea brand, such has been its success. The planned development of Arnott's, which will see it occupy almost the entire block behind the GPO, along with the creation of a new street right in the centre, will likely feature other new food destinations. (Henry St, D1 ☎ 01-805 0400 www.arnotts.ie)

Asian Supermarket

Asia Market

The original of all the Dublin ethnic stores remains one of the best, with an enormous range of produce from the wider world. Basically, if they don't have it, then it doesn't exist. So, if you search for the best Chinese vegetables in tip-top condition, fresh shiitake, and every known manner of rice, noodle, meat portion or frozen fish, it is all here. (18 Drury Street, D2 ☎ 01-677 9764 – Open 10am-7pm Mon-Sun)

Restaurant & Shop

Avoca

The Avoca chain is expanding, with the newest Rathcoole store being followed by another complex at the glorious Mount Usher gardens in Wicklow. This is a thoroughly good thing, for the Pratt family's stores are havens of culture, democratic good taste and, above all, of food that is blessed with thoroughly good tastes. Avoca, for us, is the supreme Irish luxury brand, and it improves the life of everyone who comes in contact with it. (Suffolk Street, D2 ☎ 01-672 6019 info@avoca.ie www.avoca.ie – Open 10am-5.30pm Mon-Sat, 11am-5pm Sun)

Dublin Central

Sushi Bar

AYA

Yoichi Hoashi's conveyor belt sushi bar is probably the favourite Dublin eating destination for the young McKennas, who hoover up rafts of plates as they career around on their chainbelt. Other Japanese restaurants may offer a more echt experience of eating, but none offers more fun and charm than this brilliant address. (49-52 Clarendon Street, D2 ☎ 01-677 1544 www.aya.ie – Open 12.30pm-10pm Mon-Fri, noon-11pm Sat, 1pm-9pm Sun)

Restaurant

Il Baccaro

Il Baccaro deserves a distinguished service medal, for heroic efforts in offering a good time to people who can't quite believe it is 2am already. Simple Italian-style cooking, strapping Italian wines, and the best elements of Temple Bar are what you will find here. (Meeting House Square, Temple Bar, D2 ☎ 01-671 4597 – Open 5.30pm-10.30pm Mon-Sun, noon-3pm Sat)

Restaurant

Balzac

Younger readers may not realise that Paul Flynn, luminary star of The Tannery restaurant, was, in some small way, going back to his roots when he worked on the reopening and re-christening of Balzac, the old La Stampa restaurant. When Mr Flynn returned to Ireland after years spent working with Nico Ladenis in London, he first ran the kitchen here. Today, he has redesigned the room and the menu, and he has gone back to his culinary roots with a fusion of traditional Irish dishes – onion and cider soup; crubeens and colcannon; roast rib of beef; hake with black pudding – abetted by the contemporary riffs that this gifted chef loves – pot au feu of pork; scallops with orange and almonds; butterhead lettuce with steamed lobster. Tannery-graduate Jay Collier is firing up the stoves, and Balzac's modest chutzpah is already stealing the metropolitan show. (35 Dawson Street, D2 ☎ 01-677 8611 info@balzac.ie www.balzac.ie – Open 12.30pm-2.30pm, 6pm-11pm Tue-Sun, 'till 10.30pm Sun)

Restaurant

Bang Café

Lorcan Gribbin oversees the food in Bang and in The Clarendon, and will also be masterminding the grub in the Stokes brothers' newest club on St. Stephen's Green, which is in development as we write. A County Laois man who cut his teeth in such luminary addresses as The Ivy and L'Escargot in London, Mr Gribbin is a professional to his fingertips, and he has a sublime style of savoury cooking that seems simple, only because it is so well executed. Creating that simplicity, through sheer hard work and attention to detail, makes Bang one of the best restaurants in the city. (11 Merrion Row, D2 ☎ 01-676 0898 www.bangrestaurant.com – Open 12.30pm-3pm Mon-Sat; 6pm-10.30pm Mon-Wed; 6pm-11pm Thu-Sat. Closed Sun)

Restaurant

Bar Italia

A large glass-fronted room that faces onto the river and the Millennium Bridge, Bar Italia has a foothold on both sides of the river, with the small day-time café in Essex Quay open during the day, whilst the northsider also opens for dinner. As part of the Dunne & Crescenzi empire, you can expect smartly-turned, simple cooking, and very efficient staff who exude charm. (26 Lower Ormond Quay, D2 ☎ 01-874 1000 www.baritalia.ie – Open 10.30am-11.30pm Mon-Thur, 10.30am-11pm Fri & Sat, 1pm-9pm Sun; Essex Quay, Temple Bar, D2 ☎ 01-679 5128 Open 8am-5pm Mon-Sat, 9.30am-5pm Sat)

Wine Merchant

Berry Bros & Rudd

The attractive, agelessly-stylish Dublin shop of the venerable London wine specialists has a mighty offering of fine wines, and their own label wines are solid, reliable bottles that offer good value for money. Builders and developers and others with lots of moolah should note that they keep the pricey stuff downstairs, temperature controlled. (4 Harry Street, D2 ☎ 01-677 3444 www.bbr.com – Open 9am-7pm Mon-Fri, 9am-6.30pm Sat, 10am-4pm Sun)

Shop & Wholesaler

The Best of Italy

B of I is both shop and wholesaler of Italian deli products, and it's a good spot to find high-quality Italian staples. (37 Dunville Avenue, Ranelagh, D6 ☎ 01-497 3411 – Open 9am-7pm Mon-Fri, 9am-6.30pm Sat, 10am-4pm Sun)

Café

Bianconi

A long, lean room on Merrion Road just past the church, Bianconi does some very nice food, and is a very good choice for a lazy, long, indulgent breakfast, in particular. (232 Merrion Road, Ballsbridge, D4 ☎ 01-219 6033 – Open 9am-10pm Mon-Fri, 9.30am-10pm Sat, 9.30am-9pm Sun)

Restaurant

Bijou

The handsome Bijou is both first-floor bistro and upstairs restaurant, with both menus offering classic, familiar contemporary dishes, which are consistently delivered, making this The Ivy of Dublin 6. (47 Highfield Road, Rathgar, D6 ☎ 01-496 1518 bijourestaurant@eircom.net www.bijourathgar.ie – Open noon-10.30pm Mon-Thur, noon-11pm Fri, 11.30pm-11pm Sat, 11.30pm-9.30pm Sun)

Local Speciality
DUBLIN CODDLE

Restaurant

Bistro One

Mark Shannon's restaurant is one of the quietly unsung stars of the southside, producing high-quality, imaginatively cooked menus for many years now, content to simply do the good thing without making a song and dance about it. The secret of their success lies in smart, adroit sourcing of foods, so there are lots of organically produced ingredients used by the kitchen to make bistro classics that punch well above their weight. (3 Brighton Road, Foxrock Village, D18 ☎ 01-289 7711 – Open noon-2.30pm, 6pm-10pm Tue-Sat)

Restaurant

Blazing Salads

The Fitzmaurice family will celebrate 25 years in business in 2007, having opened the original Blazing Salads back in the dark days of 1982, when wholefoods and dedicated vegetarian cooking was scarce on the ground. Since then, they have built their business organically and patiently, developing their bakery, developing their deli, writing their cookery book. *The Blazing Salads Cookbook*. Their breads are found in farmers' markets as well as from the Drury Street shop, and are organic and naturally leavened, using a mother that was created back in 2000. The deli is awesomely busy, packed with dedicated customers who want to mainline this healthful, dynamic and creative cuisine. (42 Drury Street, D2 ☎ 01-671 9552 www.blazingsalads.com – Open 9am-6pm Mon-Fri, 9am-5.30pm Sat)

Restaurant

Bleu Bistro Moderne

Eamonn O'Reilly's second restaurant – One Pico just around the corner is his flagship – works as a slick, hip room with good modern cooking, and as evidence of O'Reilly's ability to master almost any form of cuisine. The menus have an almost surreal mix of Italian classics, eastern seasonings and Irish staples – happily not on the one plate – but the kitchen pulls this magpie cuisine together, and it's a fun place to be. (Joshua House, Dawson Street, D2 ☎ 01-676 7015 www.bleu.ie – Open 9am-midnight Mon-Sat, noon-10pm Sun)

Restaurant

The Boathouse

The Dunne & Crescenzi crew are taking on the food offer at the pretty Boathouse, so expect disciplined and simple Italian cooking, and expect long, long queues to get a table during fine days and weekends at the Farmleigh markets. (Farmleigh House, Castleknock, D15 ☎ 01-815 5920 www.farmleigh.ie – Open seasonally, noon-5.30pm Thu-Sun)

Restaurant

Bóbós

The whackiest menu you ever did see heralds the burger revolution, so order up a Coke Float (yikes!), a selection of Jacob's biscuits (Kimberley, Mikado and Coconut Cream, someone you love...!) and a Diorai for you – chilli with more chilli, salsa, gherkin, sour cream, jalapeno, salad and relish – and a Mick for me – vindaloo sauce, jalapeno, sour cream and relish, and then some crisps in a bowl. Meat from Danny O'Toole, surrealism for free, and early glitches were ironed out quickly. All this, and Taylor Keith red lemonade! We are not worthy. (22 Wexford Street, D2 ☎ 01-400 5750 www.bobos.ie – Open 8.30am-11.30pm Mon-Fri, 1pm-11.30pm Sat & Sun)

Wine Merchant

Brechin Watchorn

"We are a wine shop", say Stuart Brechin and Gavin Watchorn. Well, indeed they are, but that simple statement is not just a statement of fact, but a statement of intent: their focus is on wine, and wine alone, and the sort of peripheral stuff that fills up so many shelves in so many wine shops is absent from the shelves of this super-stylish store. Both in Dunville Avenue, and in the new store on Terenure Road West, what comes across with BW is a vividly focused company with a firm grasp on the culture of sourcing and selling wine, right through the range of almost 800 bottles they offer.
(Dunville Avenue, Ranelagh, D6 ☎ 01-491 1763, Terenure Road West, D6W ☎ 01-490 9906 www.brechinwatchornwine.com – Open 11am-7pm Mon-Thur, 11am-8pm Fri-Sat, 1pm-7pm Sun)

Bakery

Bretzel Bakery

The ageless Bretzel has been re-energised in recent years,

thanks to the hard work and application of William Despard, who took over this traditional Jewish bakery – which dates back to 1870 – in the year 2000. Old favourites like banana and carrot cake and Holzfaller brod have been reintroduced, they work with Derek O'Brien of Kevin Street's bakery school to get new recipes right, and the evangelical zeal that seizes people on the subject of bread is trumpeting louder than ever at The Bretzel. "This is about real bread, healthy bread", says Mr Despard, Indeed it is, and a great Dublin star is in better shape than ever. (1a Lennox Street, Sth Circular Road, Portobello, D8 ☎ 01-475 2742 www.bretzel.ie – Open 8.30am-6pm Mon-Fri, closed 3pm Mon, 9am-5pm Sat, 9am-1pm Sun)

Restaurant

Browne's

The good citizens of Sandymount have such a proprietorial attitude towards Browne's that you can almost feel slightly uneasy if you are a country bumpkin who has lucked in here in search of a great sandwich, or a nice quiet dinner with your BYO bottle. The cooking is colourful, imaginative and creative, and we should expect a lot from this buzzy, up-for-it address. (Sandymount Green, D4 ☎ 01-269 7316 www.feedmenow.ie – Open 8am-5.30pm Mon-Sat, 6pm-10.30pm Tue-Sat, 9am-5.30pm Sun)

Dublin Central

Restaurant

Cafe Bar Deli

CBD is taking over the country, and not before time. Bourke and Foyle understand that their customers want to have a good time, have something nice to eat, and not spend a whole lot of moolah getting it. So, that's the service CBD provides, and which it will soon be bringing to both Sligo and Limerick. (12 South Great Georges Street, D2 ☎ 01-677 1646 georgesstreet@cafebardeli.ie www.cafebardeli.ie – Open 12.30pm-11pm Mon-Sat, 2pm-10pm Sun. Also 62 Ranelagh Village ☎ 01-496 1886 ranelagh@cafebardeli.ie – Open 12.30pm-11pm Mon-Sat, 12.30pm-10pm Sun. Also Bewley's Café, Grafton Street ☎ 01-672 7720 graftonstreet@cafebardeli.ie – Open noon-11pm Thu-Sat, noon-10pm Sun-Wed)

Restaurant & Cookery Classes

Café Fresh

Mary Farrell's restaurant is one of the staples of Powerscourt, and one of the staples of Dublin vegetarian cooking. Whilst there are some ageless standards such as sheperdess pie, the food veers strongly towards the classics of vegetarian cooking from the east and the Middle East, and flavours are resonant and true. (Top Floor, Powerscourt Townhouse Centre, D2 ☎ 01-671 9669 info@cafe-fresh.com www.cafe-fresh.com – Open 10am-5.30pm Mon-Sat, open from 9am on Sat)

Café

The Cake Café

Michelle Darmody's restaurant is so good, so funky, that it's the sort of place we get unsolicited emails about. "There is a really nice new cafe open in Dublin called The Cake Cafe. You should check it out. It is off the top of Camden Street down a lane called Pleasents Place." That's the kind of heat Ms Carmody's cooking generates, getting folk so excited that they can neither spell nor punctuate properly, and it's richly deserved. This girl can cook, and she can bake, and it's simple food done with class: cannellini beans with sausage on toasted bread is beans on toast, and here it is beans on toast for the Gods, whilst the savoury tarts wobble just so, just right. The cakes are fast becoming the stuff of legend, served on mismatched crockery, which seems somehow just right, just so domestic, just so hip. (62 Pleasant's Place, D8 ☎ 01-478 9394 www.thecakecafe.ie - 8.30am-5.30pm Mon-Fri, 9am-6pm Sat)

Restaurant

The Canal Bank Café

The slightly more up-market sister of Tribeca in Ranelagh, the CBC offers good modern cooking in a pretty room, and the staff are unfailingly and unflaggingly charming. (146 Upper Leeson Street, D4 ☎ 01-664 2135 www.tribeca.ie – Open 10am-11pm Mon-Fri, 11am-11pm Sat, Sun & bank hols)

Food Importer

Caribbean Enterprises

Jennylynd James's company imports many specialists food products from Trinidad and Tobago, Jamaica and Barbados, which are then sold at farmers' markets and through an expanding network of specialist shops. You will find them at markets from Ranelagh to Bray to Naas and beyond. (26 Dean Swift Road, Glasnevin, D11 ☎ 086-871 3480 www.CaribbeanIreland.com)

Bar

The Cellar Bar

Damian Corr, who runs the adjacent Cellar Restaurant, has masterminded the transformation of the food and wine offer in The Cellar Bar with stunning success. One of the city's leading sommeliers, Mr Corr offers 50 wines by the glass, and he allies the wines with properly prepared and presented food that arrives quickly, and is just what you felt like: bacon and cabbage; beef on rye with caramelised onions; salmon fishcakes; fillet steak with dauphinoise potatoes. All the dishes have recommended wines, so be prepared to lose an afternoon. And what does Mr Corr recommend with their fish'n'chips? Taittinger Brut, of course. But non vintage. Phew! (Merrion Hotel, Upper Merrion Street, D2 ☎ 01-603 0600 www.merrionhotel.com – Open noon-2.30pm, from 6pm Mon-Sun)

Restaurant

The Cellar Restaurant

Widely regarded as the best-kept secret in Dublin, The Cellar is distinguished by great service, great value, and great cooking from Ed Cooney. Put those three together and, we have discovered over the years, you have one of the favourite destinations for our Dublin-based Bridgestone editors, who are unanimous in their praise of this glam room, and the excellent cooking. (The Merrion Hotel, Upper Merrion Street, D2 ☎ 01-603 0600 www.merrionhotel.com – Open breakfast 7am-10.30am Mon-Sun, lunch 12.30pm-2pm Mon-Fri (no lunch Sat), brunch 12.30pm-2.30pm Sun, dinner 6pm-10pm Mon-Sun)

Whiskey Shop

The Celtic Whiskey Shop

Our devotion to Power's Gold Label – and the odd dropeen of Redbreast – is true and unwavering, for we believe Irish whiskeys to be the best. But, introduce us to some Bruchladdich, or maybe a dram of Lagavulin, and we quickly forget the Scots can't spell whiskey properly as we get caught up in that mix of "peat smoke and spirit" to quote the great writer Andrew Jefford. All of those great malts, indeed all the great whiskeys of the world from bourbon to Bunnahabhain, can be found in this special shop – along with a good selection of wines. If you seek

something rare and special, you will find it here. (27-28 Dawson Street, D2 ☎ 01-675 9744
info@celticwhiskeyshop.com
www.celticwhiskeyshop.com – Open 10.30am-8pm Mon-Sat, 12.30pm-6pm Sun & bank holidays)

Restaurant

Chameleon

Carol Walsh and Kevin O'Toole's Chameleon specialises in Rijst-tafel – the Dutch-Indonesian speciality of rice table, where a selection of dishes are served all together with rice and condiments. It's a great fun way to eat, whether you are two or twenty in number, and the three floors of the Chameleon – with its helpful staff and surreal Sinatra – is just the place to get the most out of an evening. The fish rijst-tafel is very fine, with fried fishcakes, haddock baked in banana leaf, and cumin-spiced squid rings offset by excellent Asian salad, wok-fried cabbage, noodles with bean sprouts and fried rice with shrimps. There is also an a la carte if you don't want the whole shebang. (1 Fownes Street, Temple Bar, D2 ☎ 01-671 0362 book@chameleonrestaurant.com
www.chameleonrestaurant.com – Open 5pm-10pm Tue-Thur, 5pm-11pm weekends)

Dublin Central

Restaurant

Chapter One

Ross Lewis and Martin Corbett are on top of the world, on top of their game, at the pinnacle of restaurant practice. They have garnered star status the hard way, by remaining true to their vision and practice of vernacular cooking. Yes, Chapter One food is slick, cheffy, modern. But it is also ageless, traditional and subtle, just like the restaurant itself. Standing outside the fashions of the age, it has taken them longer to get to the top than others, but that anti-style is now recognised as the true style of our times, and Chapter One is the Dublin restaurant of the new century. The cooking is a sublime meditation on great Irish ingredients – wild Wicklow game; Ketyle Fermanagh beef; organic Wicklow vegetables; East Cork goat's cheese – and Chapter One offers not just the perfect Dublin restaurant experience, but also one of the most profound, and enjoyable, Irish culinary experiences. (18-19 Parnell Square, D1 ☎ 01-873 2266
www.chapteronerestaurant.com – Open 12.30pm-2.30pm Tue-Fri; 6pm-10.30pm Tue-Sat)

Deli & Wine Shop

The Cheese Pantry

With a purpose-built cheese room, and excellent wines chosen by Cathal McHugh, Aidan and Karen McNeice's deli and wine shop is the destination baby-booming Drumcondra has been waiting for. The location is the old Youkstetter's pork shop, and with Ariosa coffee and charcuterie plates for the punters who want to grab something to eat in store, and lots of fine foods that reflect the passionate, food lovin' nature of the proprietors, the CP is the latest element of the northside's culinary renaissance. (104 Upper Drumcondra Road, Drumcondra, D9 ☎ 01-804 0729 ✉ aidan@thecheesepantry.com 🖱 www.thecheesepantry.com)

Restaurant

China House

China House is one of the original Parnell Street cheap'n'delicious ethnic eateries, though it began life on Moore Street, and it has been followed by lots of interesting restaurants whose cooking more than makes up for the fact that they don't have a budget for an interior designer. It's bare bones style, then, in the cute China House, but who is looking at the decor when the food is this good, and this inexpensive? Great chive dumplings, great pig's ears with scallions, great jellyfish skin with vinegar. Aaah, the real queer gear. Yum. (180 Parnell Street, D1 ☎ 01-873 3870 – Open 11am-midnight Mon-Sun)

Bar & Restaurant

Clarendon Bar & Restaurant

Bang restaurant wizard Lorcan Gribben oversees the food here, and the cooking is rock-steady delicious, bar food with real style, and with a total lack of bar food cliché. They do things right: the risottos are rich, calf's liver is melting, fries are crisp and salty, pies are wholesome, and service is svelte and polite. (32 Clarendon Street, D2 ☎ 01-679 2909 🖱 www.clarendon.ie – Open noon-11.30pm Mon-Thur, noon-2am Fri & Sat, noon-1am Sun)

Coffee Stall

Coffee Angel

Karl Purdy's magnificently engineered coffee cart can usually be seen in the vicinity of the Sean O'Casey bridge at the IFSC, though he moves to Dun Laoghaire pier at the weekends. Mr Purdy is a perfectionist, which means his coffee is amongst the most exactingly concocted you can buy in the city. Catch a blast from 7am in the mornings. (CHQ, D1 www.coffeeangel.com)

Fishmonger

Stevie Connolly's Seafood

This is a classic Dublin fish shop where the most popular fish sold is properly prepared ray, sold on the bone, and spanking fresh cod. (Unit 3, Finglas Main Shopping Centre, Finglas, D11 ☎ 086-387 1160 – Open 9am-6pm Tue-Fri, 9am-2pm Sat)

Restaurant

Cooke's

John Cooke's restaurants have always been somewhat cursed to have been "fashionable". Before Cooke's he made Polo One the hottest ticket in early 1990's Dublin, and for many years Cooke's itself was the hippest place in town. Such fashionability tends to mean that his inordinate skills as a cook are overlooked, but this guy is one of the very best chefs in town, whether he is making the best Caesar salad, or perfect dry-aged sirloin, or in his brilliant seafood fusions which he can accomplish better than anyone else. (14 South William Street, D2 ☎ 01-679 0536 cookes1@eircom.net www.cookesrestaurant.com – Open noon-4.30pm, 6pm-10pm Mon-Sat, noon-6pm Sun)

Dublin Central

Wine Merchant

The Corkscrew

The Corkscrew is a minuscule shop, but it is jam-packed with good bottles and essential wine paraphernalia. (4 Chatham Street, D2 ☎ 01-674 5731 – Open 10.30am-7pm Mon-Sat, 10.30am-8pm Thur, 12.30pm-5.30pm Sun)

Bakery

The Corner Bakery

Cara Lloyd and David Brown ran The Big Cheese Company in the centre of town before decamping out to the wilds of Terenure to open this darling little bakery, the sort of hands-on, handmade, her'n'him bakery that should be on the corner of every one of Dublin's villages. Folk come from miles around to buy challah – on Friday – poppy seed stick; New York cheesecake; Black Forest gateau (!) and, in particular, their superb bagels which are made and boiled in house. Ms Lloyd studied gateaux and tart making in Paris before they opened, whilst Mr Brown takes care of most of the bread making, and the inherent wholesome goodness of the breads and cakes is complemented by a polish that is winningly professional. More, please. (17 Terenure Road North, D6W ☎ 01-490 6210 – Open 8am-5.30pm Mon-Sat, 9am-1pm Sun)

"Let the fish do the talking. Don't smother it, enhance it."

PETER CAVISTON

Restaurant

Cornucopia

Deirdre McCafferty's original-of-the-species vegetarian restaurant weathers the ages with unflappable ease, recently expanding by taking in the next door shop, and working on a cookery book of their recipes. Their signature has always been the same: honest food, healthy food, exceptional value, an anti-fashion stance that has stood the test of time. It's left field style has probably robbed Cornucopia of the acclaim it richly deserves, but the acclaim of their customers over more than 20 years is all they need. (19 Wicklow Street, D2 ☎ 01-677 7583 cornucopia@eircom.net – Open 8.30am-8pm Mon-Sat (open till 9pm Thur), noon-7pm Sun)

Restaurant

La Corte del Caffè

La Corte is a collaboration between David Izzo and Stefano Crescenzi of the Dunne & Crescenzi empire. Mr Izzo began selling coffee from a stall on Baggot Street, and graduated to a deli on Chatham Street, but since the pair teamed up in 1999 they have been unstoppable. Their success is built, quite simply, on making fabulous coffees, and then taking that application and attention to detail and applying it to everything they do, such as the very fine fish cookery in La Corte in Powerscourt. The cafés may all be slightly different, but they are unified by rigorous quality control, and really ace staff. (Epicurean Food Hall, 13 Lower Liffey Street, D1 ☎ 01-873 4200 www.lacortedelcaffee.ie – Open 8am-6pm Mon-Sat, Thurs 'till 7pm, 11am-5.30pm Sun. Also IFSC, Custom House Square, D1 ☎ 01-672 1929 – Open 7.30am-7pm Mon-Fri; Powerscourt Shopping Centre, South William Street, D2 ☎ 01-633 4477 – Open 10am-7pm Mon-Fri, 'till 7pm Thurs, 10am-6pm Sat)

Restaurant

Dax

"Good service, good value and good food" was how Elizabeth Field of the Bridgestone parish summed up a lunch in Olivier Meisonnave's excellent Dax. What was so good? Pan-fried pollock couldn't have been better; risotto of peas and mint was spot on, there was an excellent seasonal salad and a good seasonal soup, and a perfect vanilla crème brûlée and a superb lemon and lime tart. The wines, of course, are superb, as one would expect from such an accomplished sommelier (23 Upper Pembroke Street, D2 ☎ 01-676 1494 info@dax.ie www.dax.ie – Open 12.30pm-2.30pm Tue-Fri, 6pm-11pm Tue-Sat)

Delicatessen

Delizia Italian Delicatessen

Mina Fusco's Delizia is a paninoteca, a hot sandwich shop that also offers very good salads and drinks, and an excellent take-away menu of cooked foods, alongside superb Italian foods and wines crammed onto their shelves. Do note their very fine hampers: if you want to knock someone's socks off with a gift, then this is the way to do it. (4 The Mart, Leopardstown Road, D18 ☎ 01-207 0408 delizia@eircom.net – Open 9am-6.30pm Mon-Fri 10am-6pm Sat)

Dublin Central

Shop and Restaurant

Donnybrook Fair

Joe Doyle's ground-breaking store and restaurant predated the current U.S. trend of food halls also offering good food in dedicated eating spaces. DF itself is a superb shop, the sort of space that earns the epithet "sexy", because that is just what it is – swish, hip, beautifully arranged, ergonomically pleasing, a space that is a genuine pleasure to be in, even before you buy any of their wonderful foods. Upstairs, the DF café is open from breakfast through to dinner, and whilst it is popular with the well-heeled locals, it could have a more distinctive vibe to its food, which works a conventional riff on modern European food. (91 Morehampton Road, Donnybrook, D4 ☎ 01-668 3556 info@donnybrookfair.ie www.donnybrookfair.ie – Shop open 7.30am-10pm Mon-Sat, 9am-10pm Sun. Restaurant open 7.30am-10pm Mon-Thur, 7.30am-10.30pm Fri-Sat, 9am-10pm Sun)

Traiteur

Douglas Food Co

The DFC has always been a truly classy deli, right from the early days in the 90's when it was a pioneering traiteur in Dublin 4. There are many more competitors today, but it remains a tiny oasis of good food and wines to take away, and they also make superb sandwiches and rolls at lunchtime. (53 Main Street, Donnybrook, D4 ☎ 01-269 4066 grainne@thedouglasfoodcompany.ie – Open 10am-6.30pm Mon-Fri, 9.30am-6pm Sat)

Butcher

J Downey & Son

John and Mark Downey are amongst the most high-profile butchers in Dublin, indeed in Ireland. There is the real aura of creative charcuterie from this crew, who revel in transforming butchery staples into boutique charcuterie products. They have been winning awards for products from sausages to spiced beef, for more than twenty years, yet they remain as hungry as ever for new challenges. If you seek anything exotic in the world of meat, game and poultry, then these are the guys to head to. (27 Terenure Rd East, D6W ☎ 01-490 9239 www.organicfoodsireland.com – Open 8.30am-5.30pm Mon-Sat)

Co-Op and Market

Dublin Food Co-Op

In 2008, The Dublin Food Co-Op will celebrate 25 years of business, and can we suggest that the party should be a city-wide celebration for this is one of the jewels of good food in the city. Where else would you get "Scratch-it, Cluck and Go" eggs? Where else can you buy a dish of palak aloo to break your fast as you shop? What other market has Wicklow vegetables so bountiful that they make you smile? From organic wines brought by Vendemia of Kilkenny to food from the Sonairte ecology centre, to the breads of George Heise of Slane, and the outrageously fine produce of Penny and Udo Lange and Norman and Deirdre Kenny, the DFC is a dream. But not just a dream, for it is also an example of radical food politics in action: this is Dublin's Terre Madre, for it is global, local, specific and international, all in one glorious jamboree of producers, products and people. (St Andrew's Centre, 114-116 Pearse Street, D2 ☎ 01-873 0451 www.dublinfoodcoop.com – Open 9.30am-4pm Sat)

Farmers' Market

Dundrum Farmers' Market

A brand new Coco Market organised by Jackie Spillane, so expect quality producers and foods on Fashion Avenue. (Fashion Avenue, Dundrum, Sunday, noon-4pm)

Restaurant

Dunne & Crescenzi

It's the ultimate way of proving your food loving credentials: hands up all those who travelled out to Sutton to visit the little shop and post office where Eileen and Stefano Crescenzi first began to import Italian foods, back in 1995? We drove out, and wrote a story about this enigmatic couple for the *Irish Times*, but to tell the truth, there was little evidence back then that this couple would become the most powerful, influential and dynamic food operation since Avoca. How did they do it? Hard work, of course, but above all they have the gift of good taste, and they respect the merits of simplicity, in an almost aristocratic way. The D&C shops and cafés are superb food destinations: "As dining experiences go, it was just lovely!" a friend remarked after eating here late one night, "Buzzing and just incredibly down to earth. All good!!" All good. Two exclamation marks. That's D&C, all right. (14 South Frederick St, D2 ☎ 01-677 3815 – Open 10am-6pm Mon, 10am-11pm Tue-Sat, noon-6pm Sun; Also 16 South Frederick Street, D2 ☎ 01-675 9892 – Open 8.30am-11pm Mon-Sat, noon-6pm Sun; Also 11 Seafort Avenue, Sandymount D4 ☎ 01-667 3252 – Open 10am-6pm Mon, 10am-11pm Tue-Sat, noon-11pm Sun
www.dunneandcrescenzi.com)

Dublin Central

Local Specialities

"BRITZ" (Brill & Turbot)
"NOWD" (Gurnard)
"TONGUES, SLIPS, SNOWSHOES & BLANKETS" (different sizes of Sole)
"WITCHES" (White Sole)
"MEGRUMS" (Lemon Sole)
"BLOSSOM" (Pollock or Coley)
"RUCK" (Ray)
"YELLOW FISH" (Smoked Cod)

Restaurant

L'Ecrivain

Derry and Sallyanne Clarke are the modern Irish restaurant couple par excellence. Together, they run the most successful restaurant in the city, but it's not just astoundingly successful, it is also one of the best-loved places to eat in the capital. A lot of that affection is not simply due to the Clarkes' generosity and hospitality, but also to Mr Clarke's singular cooking. As a chef, he seems to see dishes differently to anyone else: a dish like carpaccio of scallop and Woodcock smoked salmon with whiskey yogurt and sweet mustard dressing, for example, or seared loin of rabbit stuffed with Clonakilty black pudding, smoked sausage cassoulet and ceps dressing – are typical of a culinary approach that is profoundly original, that spins off exciting riffs on artisan products with zealous creativity. Put that madcap originality alongside one of the best restaurant crews in the entire country and you have one mighty culinary narcotic. (109 Lower Baggot Street, D2
☎ 01-661 1919 enquiries@lecrivain.com
www.lecrivain.com – Open 12.30pm-2pm Mon-Fri; 7pm-10.30pm Mon-Sat)

Restaurant

Eden

Jay Bourke and Eoin Foyle's restaurant has celebrated 10 years in business, with everything firing ahead under the control of chef Michael Durkin. Eleanor Walsh masterminded the template of dishes that saw Eden hit the ground running – the famous smokies; roast kassler with apple mash; braised lamb shank with lemon barley – and the impressive consistency of this kitchen, and its respect for ingredients, has kept it ahead of the game at every stage. Ms Walsh now heads up the Eden kitchen at Bellinter House in Meath, whilst also keeping an eye on Mackerel, the Market Bar, and CafeBarDeli.
(Meeting House Square, Temple Bar, D2
☎ 01-670 5372 eden@edenrestaurant.ie
www.edenrestaurant.ie – Open 12.30pm-3pm Mon-Fri; noon-3pm Sat & Sun; 6pm-10.30pm Mon-Sun)

Restaurant

Ellen's Tea Room

Ellen's Tea Room is the café of the smart Seagreen store – sorry, it's a "lifestyle emporium", pardon us – in

Monkstown, where you can lavish several thousand euro on a sofa, or just browse and cast away a few euro on something nice to eat in Ellen's. It's simple food – chicken fajita; Mexican bean soup; quiche of the day; pear and almond tart – and the room is very pretty. (11a-12a Monkstown Crescent, Monkstown, Co Dublin ☎ 01-202 0130 www.seagreen.ie – Open Mon-Sat 9am-6pm, 'till 8pm Thu, noon-6pm Sun)

Wine Bar

Ely Wine Bar

Who would have thought that Erik and Michelle Robson could have adapted and expanded their Ely concept so swiftly and successfully from this modest two-floor wine bar and restaurant? Ely has grown to number 3 benchmark addresses, but there is actually no mystery as to how they have done it. First, the Robsons are pure blueblood food lovers, coming from a farming and restauranteuring family. Secondly, like Avoca and Sheridans and Ballymaloe and Dunne & Crescenzi, they get and motivate the very best staff, which makes passing on the baton easy. Finally, they know how to choose, they know the best wines, and the most suitable, simple food. It's a narcotic concoction. (22 Ely Place, D2 ☎ 01-676 8986 elywine@eircom.net www.elywinebar.ie – Open noon-3pm, 6pm-10pm Mon-Fri, 1pm-11pm Sat. Closed Sun)

Dublin Central

Restaurant

Ely CHQ

CHQ is a big, tall, stylish, glass-fronted room just at the new bridge, the antithesis of the cubby-hole, clubby room of the original. The punters are as slick as the room, the mixture of solid food and sensational wines seems heaven sent to Dublin's finance colony. (IFSC, D1 ☎ 01-672 0010 elychq@eircom.net www.elywinebar.ie – Open noon-3pm, 6pm-10pm Mon-Fri, 1pm-11pm Sat. Closed Sun)

Restaurant

Ely HQ

The third Ely repeats the rock-solid formula, creating another destination address in Dublin's newest waterside quarter. (Hanover Quay, Docklands, D2 ☎ 01-633 9986 www.elywinebar.ie – Open noon-10.30pm Mon-Sat, Sunday opening starts summer '07)

Restaurant

Enoteca delle Langhe

Builder, football fanatic, radical critic of contemporary Dublin commercial culture, and Italophile, Mick Wallace has constructed an entire corner of Italy on the northside of the Liffey, for along with his Enoteca, there is the new La Taverno di Bacco, a café, Café Cagliostro, an Italian deli, La Bottega, and a branch of Bar Italia. The Enoteca concentrates on platters of cheese and cold meats to pair with wines, whilst La Taverna has more contemporary Italian cooking, and both have interesting wines which Mr Wallace sources directly from Italy. (Blooms Lane, opp. Millennium Bridge, D1 ☎ 01-888 0834 – Open 12.30pm-11pm Mon-Sat, La Taverna ☎ 01-873 0040)

Wine Merchant

Enowine

Yvonne and James Connolly's Enowine has grown from a store in Monkstown to a large wine shop with a wine bar-restaurant upstairs in the IFSC. Their winning formula is simple: you can taste 88 different wines in a tasting measure before you commit yourself to buy a bottle, thanks to machinery called the Enomatic, which pours you out a shot from a roster of wines. You buy a card in advance, and pay a small sum for a taste out of your card's credit. In the restaurant, you can also taste and buy by the glass from a range of 32 wines. Enowine are working both sides of the street, with inexpensive wines from South-West France alongside wallet-busting trophy bottles but Yvonne Connolly recognises that "most people shop through comfort shopping", and the Eno system does just that. (Custom House Square, IFSC, D1 ☎ 01-636 0616 info@enowine.ie www.enowine.ie – Open 11am-8pm Mon-Fri, 10.30am-6pm Sat; Also at 23 The Crescent, Monkstown, Co Dublin ☎ 01-230 3500 – Open 11am-9pm Mon-Sat, 12.30pm-8pm Sun)

Dublin Central

Food Mall

Epicurean Food Mall

From Burdock's to Itsabagel, from Mamma Mia to bangers and mash, The Epicurean has the cooking of the world compressed into one food hall. There is also Turkish food, Thai cooking, Japanese, French and much more at the myriad food addresses, and the atmosphere is always slightly giddy and, like, fun. (Middle Abbey St, D1 Open 10am-6pm Mon-Sat)

Restaurant

Expresso Bar

Ann Marie Nohl's Expresso is a charming room, on a particularly charming leafy road, and they cook and serve the sort of food that one simpy can't tire of eating: chicken wings with Louisiana hot sauce; beef burger and chunky chips; salmon fish cakes; cod with lemon herb butter. Everything is confident and understated, quietly feminine, and very efficient. No wonder it's so popular with smart locals. (1 St Mary's Road, Ballsbridge, D4 ☎ 01-660 0585 – Open 7.30am-9.30pm Mon-Fri, 9am-9.30pm Sat, 10am-5pm Sun)

Restaurant & Shop

Fallon & Byrne

Dublin life can be summarised as: BF&B, and AF&B. Before Fallon & Byrne. After Fallon & Byrne. And AF&B is so much better. This colossal venture – basement wine shop, ground floor food emporium and eating bar, first floor brasserie restaurant, and there is even a top floor for functions and whatnots – achieved what various Government departments have talked about and talked about for years but never managed to achieve: a food showcase for brilliant foods, both from Ireland and abroad, in a gorgeous environment. Fiona McHugh and her team did what others believed to be impossible, and the fact that they got so much right from the outset is miraculous. We love the store, the wine shop, the brilliant staff – especially the guys behind the butcher's stall – and we love the restaurant. Brilliant. (Exchequer Building, 11-17 Exchequer Street, Dublin 2 ☎ 01-472 1010 feedback@fallonandbyrne.com www.fallonandbyrne.com – 12.30pm-2.30pm (lunch), 2.30pm-4pm (light late lunch) Mon-Fri, noon-3pm Sat & Sun, 6pm-10pm Sun-Wed, 6pm-10.30pm Thu, 6pm-11pm Fri & Sat)

Farmers' Market

Farmleigh House

The farmers' markets which they host at the beautiful Farmleigh in the Phoenix Park quickly became the stuff of legend amongst producers, who loved the hip crowds who seemed hell-bent on having a great time and spending lots of money whilst they were at it. The audience they attract here is really something special, and their eagerness transforms the events at the house into happy festivals. Don't miss the markets and the associated food events they hold during the summer and winter seasons, and be prepared to queue for the Boathouse Café. (Phoenix Park, D7 ☎ 01-815 5900 www.farmleigh.ie)

Wine Importer

● Febvre & Company Ltd

Anthony and Gregory Alkin's wine company is a prominent supporter of the Slow Food movement, a practical participation which shows the modus operandi of this fine wine company – they look for winemakers who do things in the time-trusted way, and who bring the broader culture of wine in all its magnificence to every bottle they produce. (Burton Hall Road, Sandyford Industrial Estate, Sandyford, D18 ☎ 01-2959030 info@febvre.ie www.febvre.ie)

Restaurant

● Five South Anne Street

A new restaurant opened by the entrepreneur Emmet O'Neill, who also owns the Bocca Italian restaurant two doors up – and who also owns the Smiles dental spa in the middle of Bocca and Five. The room is drop dead gorgeous, and chef Cathy Fingleton is busy working out her signature dishes, so this is one to watch. (5 Anne Street South, D2 ☎ 01- 672 8555 www.five.ie – Open 7am-11pm Mon-Fri, 10am-11pm Sat & Sun)

Dublin Central

Shop & Traiteur

● The Food Room

You should see the queue here at lunchtimes for the fine sandwiches which the FR fires out from behind their deli counter: it's humungous. The shop also sells lots of interesting things, so don't be put off by the appearance and entrance, which looks a little like a standard Spar. (46 Clontarf Road, D3 ☎ 01- 833 2258)

Patisserie

● Fothergill's

Fothergill's has been making the citizens of Upper Rathmines happy ever since it opened in 1984. Everything has changed in this neighbourhood since then, but nothing has changed in Fothergills. They work according to the mantra of John

Fothergill, a famed restaurateur of the 1920's, "that only the best is good enough for our customers". Fothergill's the shop puts into practice what Fothergill the epicurean preached, concocting beautiful cakes and desserts, making wonderful salads, selling excellent food and wines, and serving them with a friendly style that is simply enchanting. (141 Rathmines Rd Upr, D6 ☎ 01-496 2511 – Open 9am-7pm Mon-Fri, 9am-6pm Sat)

Shop

Roy Fox Gourmet Foods

One of the key Donnybrook addresses for fresh foods sold with a smile, Roy Fox is especially great fun at weekends when local food lovers turn up to hunt down the many specialities the shop sells. (49a Main Street, Donnybrook, D4 ☎ 01-269 2892 sales@royfox.ie – Open 9am-7pm Mon-Sat, 11am-6pm Sun)

Restaurant

Frank's Bar & Restaurant

Dublin Central

Liz Mee and John Hayes' restaurant is tucked in under a railway tunnel on the cobblestoned Grand Canal Quay, and whilst this area has exploded in terms of development and population over the last two years, Frank's was here first, sending out solid-server savoury food with impressive consistency. Their signature dishes are hard to resist when ordering: potted shrimp with pain Poilane; crispy duck salad with watercress; lemon and thyme chicken with mash; burger with cheddar and bacon; rice pudding with prunes and Armagnac. Some folk worry about relatively high prices for relatively simple cooking in Frank's, but this is handmade food, and its piquancy and distinctiveness is worth the money. (The Malting Tower, Grand Canal Quay, D2 ☎ 01-662 5870 www.franksbarandrestaurant.com – Open 11.30am-10m Mon-Sun)

"May suitable doses of guaranteed sensual pleasure and slow, long-lasting enjoyment preserve us from the contagion of the multitude who mistake frenzy for efficiency."

SLOW FOOD MANIFESTO, 1989

Restaurant

The French Paradox

Not a lot of cooking gets done in this hip restaurant and wine shop, but a lot of really good food makes its way out to happy customers. The FP assembles plates, rather than originating them, but their discrimination in choosing great ingredients means you simply ask for more. This is a great place, with great wines, and we have always had a wonderful time eating and drinking here. (53 Shelbourne Road, Ballsbridge, D4 ☎ 01-660 4068 wineshop@thefrenchparadox.com www.thefrenchparadox.com – Open noon-3pm, 6pm-midnight Mon-Fri, noon-midnight Sat. Amuses gueules served from 3pm-7pm)

Restaurant

Les Freres Jacques

Ravioli of snails; confit of duck; lamb cutlets with a Provençal crust; foie gras with Agen prunes; apple tartlet with crème Anglaise. They hardly make 'em like this anymore, so thank heavens for the venerable Les Freres Jacques and its quintessential cuisine bourgeois, which has been feeding food-loving Dubliners for nigh on thirty years, and has been doing it well for all that time. Sweet. (74 Dame Street, D2 ☎ 01-679 4555 info@lesfreresjacques.com www.lesfreresjacques.com – Open 12.30pm-2.30pm, 7.30pm-10.30pm Mon-Fri, 7.15pm-11pm Sat)

Restaurant

Furama

Furama has always been one of the best Chinese restaurants in Dublin, and whilst its style of high class sheen and high prices has been assailed by the new generation of ethnic eateries on Moore Street and Parnell Street, it continues to serve and satisfy the folk of Donnybrook very well indeed. (Ground Floor, Eirpage House, Donnybrook Main Road, D4 ☎ 01-283 0522 www.furama.ie – Open 12.30pm-2pm Mon-Fri, 6pm-11.30pm Mon-Sat)

Supermarket

Fresh The Good Food Market

It can't have been easy getting the Fresh stores right. How can you put a quotidian pack of bangers alongside Jane Russell's superior sausages? How can Glenilen dairy co-exist with Dairygold? The answer, perhaps surprisingly, is that you can put the two together, and there is simply no tension – peaceful co-existence in the culinary world. In fact, the mix concocted by owners Simon Kelly, David Kelly and Noel Smith has worked so well that Fresh has catapulted from the original Smithfield store into a rapidly expanding chain, with two new stores already operating. We like the fact that there are great staples – Bretzel bread, La Brea bread, organic veg, good butter – alongside the luxury stuff, meaning that these really are supermarkets for everyone, from food lovers, to folk who just want a sandwich at lunch or some food for their dinner. Very, very smart, and can we have more, please? (Smithfield Village, Unit 5, Block F, Smithfield, D7 ☎ 01-485 0271; Also Unit 3B, 4 Grand Canal Square, D2 ☎ 01-671 8004; Also Unit 5 Northern Cross, Malahide Road, D17 ☎ 01-848 9280)

Patisserie

The Gallic Kitchen

"Sarah Webb is, quite simply, an excellent cook". We wrote that back in 1989 in the first ever *Irish Food Guide*. All these years later, nothing has changed. Sarah Webb is a brilliant cook, making superb pastry-based products, from the best sausage rolls to the best pies and quiches you can buy. Today she heads up a crew that is one of the major players in the Dublin food culture, thanks to their presence at many farmers' markets, all the way from Temple Bar to Athy. The Gallic Kitchen shop on Thomas Street is as humungously busy as ever, and there is also a catering wing. In all the years that we have been buying GK food, we have never, ever had anything that was less than delicious, so Ms Webb is not just an excellent cook, she is a most disciplined and dedicated cook, and for us she is one of the most important people in the city's food culture. (49 Francis Street, D8 ☎ 01-454 4912, www.gallickitchen.com, galkit.iol.ie – Open 9am-5pm Mon-Fri, 9am-4.30pm Sat)

Shop

Get Fresh

Leslie Williams of the *Bridgestone* parish can sum up the special nature of Niall Dermody and Colm Eadie's shop in one line: "There is no fine food product I have ever looked for that they do not sell". The shop is a carnival of good things, with up to 40 different olive oils, for example, typifying their search for genuine variety and choice. But perhaps their real star is the superb selection of fresh vegetables and herbs, a selection that really can't be matched by anywhere else in the city. GF is virtually a one-stop shop for food lovers: don't miss it! (Unit 6, Rosemount S.C., Ballyroan, Rathfarnham, D14 ☎ 01-493 7148 ✉ getfresh5@msn.com – Open 9am-6pm Mon-Sat)

Arcade

● The George's Street Arcade Complex

The Arcade has been one of the quiet success stories of Dublin's recent food history. From Lara Lu Foods to Honest to Goodness to stalwarts like Simon's Place and the Green Olive Company and M&D Coffee, this Victorian arcade is packed with good things, a marvellous little souk in the heart of the city. And, dare we say it, but visitors to the city should not miss this iconoclastic warren of good food, and funky, left-field shops. (George's St Arcade, George's Street, D2 🖱 www.georgesstreetarcade.ie – Open 9am-6.30pm Mon-Sat, 'till 8pm Thu, 10am-6pm Sun)

Café

● The Good Food Kitchen

The daily "roast in the roll" is the signature of the GFK, served with Bretzel bread from Rathmines, and it makes this a valuable lunchtime address in an area that is still under-served by good places to eat. Carrot cake is also good, but make sure to get there early at lunchtimes to maximise your choice. (16 Gordon Street, Ringsend, D6 ☎ 01-668 4514 ✉ goodfood@eircom.net – Open 8am-4pm Mon-Fri)

Restaurant

● Good World Chinese Restaurant

Weekend dim sum is the main attraction in the Good World, and they prepare and present it very well indeed. (18 South Great Georges Street, D2 ☎ 01-677 5373 – Open 12.30pm-2.30pm Mon-Sun)

Restaurant

● Gruel

Gruel was the pioneer of the Dublin grungy restaurant, soon followed by L'Gueuleton and a host of Parnell Street ethnics, places where decor is bottom dollar and food quality is top dollar. Billy Scurry and his crew can take you all the way through the day from breakfast – "gruel awakening", ho, ho – of organic bacon sandwich or mini quiche, via good lunches, then their classic dinner dishes such as bangers and mash or braised lamb shank. For many Dubs, however, Gruel is the ultimate weekend brunch spot, which means it gets mighty, mighty crowded. (67 Dame Street, D2 ☎ 01-670 7119 – Open 9am-11.30am breakfast, 11.30am-4pm lunch, 5pm-10pm dinner)

Restaurant

● L'Gueuleton

Chef Troy Maguire has moved on from Declan O'Regan's pioneering L'Gueuleton, but this powerhouse restaurant is such a sound concept that its success is assured. The cooking and the running of the restaurant follows a simple rule – only do what you are good at – and it distils this mantra down to a mighty potion, and adds in a mass of moody atmospherics for everyone to soak up. Oysters Rockefeller; Nicoise salad; rib eye with bearnaise; pork belly with cider-braised cabbage: it's all no-nonsense food in a splendidly no-nonsense place. (1 Fade Street, D2 ☎ 01-675 3708 – Open 12.30pm-3pm, 6pm-10pm Mon-Sat)

Restaurant

● Restaurant Patrick Guilbaud

Writing about the movies of the late Krzysztof Kieslowski, the great David Thomson writes that, for him, going to see one of the Polish director's movies "requires a steeling, as if I were going into torture or church. Those films seem to think they're perfect, and I want to scream". So it is with us and RPG, a restaurant many others consider to be not just the finest in Dublin, but the finest in the entire country. They are happy, and we want to scream. Thank heavens the culinary arts are such a broad church. (The Merrion Hotel, Upper Merrion Street, D2 ☎ 01-676 4192 www.merrionhotel.com – Open 12.30pm-2pm, 7.30pm-10.15pm Tue-Sat)

Delicatessen

● Haddington Delicatessen

Rachel Keane's deli won an audience in double-quick time, and today it continues to thrive as a beacon of select good taste. That selection of good tasting things, whether it is what she sells or what she cooks, marks the Haddington out as a class act, and there isn't a standardised or quotidian thing offered here, which explains the long queues at lunchtime. (54 Haddington Road, D4 ☎ 01-667 6685 www.haddingtondeli.ie – Open 7.30am-4.30pm Mon-Fri, 9.30am-4.30pm Sat)

Restaurant & Delicatessen

Harvey Nichols

Robery Haughton's cooking in the First Floor restaurant has put Harvey Nick's up near the top of the pile in modern Dublin eating, and the swish post-punk, Bridget Riley-style room is just the place in which to enjoy hip, confident cooking. There is also a very funky bar, and the Ground Floor café, but it's the food in the First Floor that is the wow! bit. Mr Haughton makes even modern staples such as glazed belly of pork sing with flavour, and his style makes everything unctuously rich, and yet somehow understated and correct. Exciting cooking. (Dundrum Town Centre, Sandyford Road, D16 ☎ 01- 291 0488 www.harveynichols.com – Open noon-3pm, 6pm-10pm Mon-Fri (till 10.30pm Fri), 12.30pm-3.30pm, 6pm-10.30pm Sat, 12.30pm-4pm Sun

Fish Shop & Restaurant

Hemmingway's

An ultra-smart fish shop which also serves tapas plates and wines to the folk who get one of its 14 seats, Hemmingway's is a northside cult address. "A fish shop gone wild" is what Brian Creedon calls his hip shop and eaterie, and that's just what this fish traiteur is. Great if you just want wet fish, brilliant if you don't want to cook at all, when the take-away chowders, terrines and other seafood dishes will hit the spot, ideal if you want a glass of good wine and a piece of fish cooked for you. This is a new model fish business. (Vernon Avenue, Clontarf, D3 ☎ 01-833 3338 – Open 1pm-8pm Mon, 11am-8pm Tue-Thur, 11am-9pm Fri-Sat)

Restaurant

Hole in the Wall

Martin McCaffrey's famous pub has a brand new wine shop, with over 600 bottles on the shelves, in the centre of this meandering, comfy pub, and you can buy a bottle and take it into either the pub or into the restaurant, where there is some serious cooking taking place, thanks to chef Damien Grey. This is cheffy work: oxtail tartlet; scallops with piperade; oysters tempura; fillet of beef with chorizo hash brown, tarte tatin, but it's well accomplished and value is keen. Do note that Sunday lunch is strictly first-come, first-served. (Blackhorse Avenue, D7 ☎ 01-838 9491 – Restaurant open 6pm-10pm Mon-Sat, noon-7pm Sun. Bar food noon-10pm Mon-Fri, noon-7pm Sat)

Café

● Honest to Goodness

One of the George's Street Arcade specials, HTG lets Darragh Birkett and Martin Ansbro get all funky with their fine, freshly baked breads, producing everything from proper breakfasts to popular sandwiches and panini at lunch, along with good soups and salads. Their space is really funky and fun. (Open 9am-6pm, Sun noon-4pm, ☎ 01 6337727 www.georgesstreetarcade.ie)

Restaurant

● Hô Sen

Lovely Vietnamese cooking, in one of the few Temple Bar restaurants that deserves distinction for its culinary skills. Tim Costigan and Tuan Nguyen's restaurant is compact, charming, and attracts the hippest crowd of young women you will find in one room in Dublin. The girls love the cleanness and crispiness of pancakes with pork and shrimp; rice paper rolls, snapper in fish broth and some very fine tofu cookery. And so do we. (6 Cope St, Temple Bar, D2 ☎ 01-671 8181 – Open 12.30pm-2.30pm Thur-Sun, 'till 3pm Sun, 5pm-10.30pm Tue-Sun, 'till 9pm Sun)

Dublin Central

Farmers' Market

● IFSC Farmers' Market

Jackie Spillane's CoCo Market feeds the bankers at lunchtime every Wednesday, and gives them lots of good things to bring home for their dinner from a typically fastidious array of producers. (Mayor Square, IFSC. Wed 10.30am-4pm)

Pizzeria

● Il Fornaio

A well-kept secret until two years ago, when it opened a branch in the IFSC in the financial quarter, Il Fornaio has always done good pastas and pizzas, and contented itself with doing them right, just the way an Italian restaurant in Italy would. The pizzas are classic and crisply crunchy, the pastas are ace, again sticking to classic dishes and making sure they are true and precise. The coffee, of course, is also excellent. (55 Kilbarrack Road, Raheny, D15 ☎ 01-832 0277 info@ilfornaio.ie www.ilfornaio.ie – Open 8.30am-10pm Mon-Thu, 8.30am-11pm Fri, 10am-11pm Sat, 10am-10pm Sun. Also at 1b Valencia House, Custom House Square, D1 ☎ 01-672 1852)

Restaurant

Il Posto

Head chef Sean Drugan has been working hard in Il Posto over the last couple of years, sourcing interesting foods, creating interesting menus, and the interest and energy of this crew shines through in some interesting Italian-style cooking to which Mr Drugan brings lots of imagination. (10 St Stephen's Green, D2 ☎ 01-679 4769 www.ilpostorestaurant.com – Open noon-2pm Mon-Fri, noon-2.30pm Sat, from 5.30pm Mon-Sun)

Restaurant

Imperial Chinese Restaurant

One of the most senior of Dublin's ethnic restaurants, The Imperial still offers good conventional Chinese food, and some excellent dim sum at weekends. (12a Wicklow Street, D2 ☎ 01-677 2580 – Open noon-11pm Mon-Sun)

Bagel Bar

Itsabagel

The Kemp sisters' Itsabagel empire has extended to four branches, and the hungry lunchtime hordes from the city centre to Sandyford can't be wrong. These girls know how to make high-quality, high-octane filled bagels, and they know how to do it day in, day out. We are impressed. (Epicurean Food Hall, Lwr Liffey Street, D1 ☎ 01-874 0486; Fitzwilliam Lane, laneway Adjacent to the Merrion Hotel, D2 ☎ 01-644 9941; Unit 56a Blackthorn Road, Sandyford Industrial Estate, Sandyford, D18 ☎ 01-293 5994; The Pavilion, Royal Marine Road, Dun Laoghaire, Co Dublin ☎ 01-236 0644 www.itsabagel.com)

Restaurant

Itsa4

Okay, so you don't want anyone to tell you that you should go to a restaurant and have smoked salmon followed by steak. But that's what we are going to say about this über-hip Kemp sisters' address. Terry Butterly smokes the fish up in Louth, Maurice Kettyle rears the Angus beef up in Fermanagh, and put them together and it is a wow! of a dinner, which in a perfect world would be followed by a slice of Black Forest gateau. A great destination, with great food for everyone. (6A Sandymount Green, D4 ☎ 01-219 4676 www.itsabagel.com – noon-4pm Mon-Fri, 11am-4pm Sat-Sun, 6pm-10pm Mon-Sat, 5pm-9pm Sun)

Restaurant & Take-away

Jack's Restaurant

Jack and his wife, Na Na, run both a restaurant and a take-away, with the food drawing on the northern style of cooking from Liaoning province, close to Korea, which explains why the restaurant has Korean barbecue plates on the tables, and why there are dishes such as lamb kebabs with cumin alongside the queer gear such as beef tendons and pig's tongue hotpot. (140 Parnell Street, D1 ☎ 086-154 3434 – Open 5.30pm-midnight Mon-Sun)

Restaurant

Jacob's Ladder

Adrian Roche is the most undersung chef in Dublin, a man whose super-skilful cooking, and whose innovative menus, don't get half the attention they deserve. He is a very quiet, dedicated man, not at all interested in self-promotion, but his cooking should be tasted, not least because he enjoys experimenting with some wild transfusions of flavour in his dishes, like putting rosemary in a banana butterscotch pudding, or poaching pears in coffee. (4-5 Nassau Street, D2 ☎ 01-670 3865 www.jacobsladder.ie – Open 12.30pm-2.30pm Tue-Sat, 6pm-10pm Tue-Fri, 7pm-10pm Sat)

Restaurant

Jade Chinese Restaurant

Xiao Wei Guo's Jade Restaurant specialises in Chinese hot pot, making all stocks from scratch to achieve the necessary purity and delicacy of balance in the various dishes. The result of such care is a hotpot regarded by the Chinese community as probably the best in town. (Little Mary St, D7 01-887 4468 – Open noon-11pm Mon-Sun)

Café

KC Peaches

Soups, sarnies, salads and a shop: KC Peaches is all set to conquer the droves soon to be living and working in the Grand Canal Basin zone. Katie Cantwell figured Dublin needed a US-style eaterie with gourmet sandwiches and serious breads and cookies with lots of good things from their own bakery, and was she ever right. This is a dynamic organisation: be prepared to let them enter your life. (Unit 10A Trinity Enterprise Centre, Pearce Street, D2 ☎ 01-677 0333 www.kcpeaches.com – Open 8am-8pm Mon-Fri, 9am-5pm Sat, 11am-4pm Sun)

Restaurant

Kinara

Everyone's favourite Northside Indian restaurant, Kinara has built a formidable reputation thanks to stepping away from the ersatz cooking most Indian restaurants offer, and by delivering Indian and Pakistani specialities that enjoy authenticity. They also use organic chicken, lamb and beef, and the tandoori cooking is very fine. Keema aloo with paratha bread, please, some dal Kinara and beef lobia, and we are suddenly back in those happy days of the back pack and the shalwar kameez and the Karakoram Highway. (318 Clontarf Road, D3 ☎ 01-833 6759 info@kinara.ie www.kinara.ie – Open 12.30pm-3pm Thur, Fri & Sun, 5.30pm-11pm Mon-Thur, 6pm-11pm Fri-Sun)

Fishmonger

Kish Fish

Tadgh O'Meara's superb fish shop is one of the outstanding fish stores in the country, and was the deserved winner of the first IASC Retailer of the Year award in 2006. Queue up alongside the legal eagles and the Smithfield arrivistes to get your hands on superb fish and shellfish, still twitching with freshness. With all those financial heavy-hitters around, you will need to be there early if you want to get the pricey prime fillets. Superb, knowledgeable service from Tadgh and his team completes a picture of piscine perfection. (40/42 Bow Street, Smithfield, D7 ☎ 01-872 8211 – Open 9am-4.30pm Tues-Sat)

Dublin Central

Butcher's Stall

J & V's Rahara Farm Meats

Famed for their beef, in particular the rib eye which is their most popular cut, John and Valerie's meat selection also encompasses pork, poultry and lamb, and they do a humungous trade selling cooked burgers which are wickedly delicious. We bought some J&V pork for a friend who, as soon as she had cooked and eaten it, rang up to ask exactly where we had gotten it? it was so good! and she promptly got herself to Temple Bar market, though John and Valerie also sell at Leopardstown. Their sausages are also extremely good, and this is superb meat which really has to be tasted. They also do fab burgers: get one straight from the grill on Saturday at the market. (Rahara, Co Roscommon. – Available from Leopardstown Market, Fri, and Meeting House Square Market, Temple Bar Sat).

Kitchen Equipment

Kitchen Complements

There is nothing mechanical sold in Ann McNamee's shop, just beautiful tools and implements that will make you a much better cook and baker than you are at present. A vital address for food lovers. (Chatham Street, D2, ☎ 01-677 0734 www.kitchencomplements.ie – Open 10am-6pm Mon-Sat, 10am-7pm Thur)

Restaurant & Take-away

Konkan

The secret of Konkan is to make sure to order the southern Indian dishes the restaurant specialises in, which concentrate on fish dishes cooked with coconut. So go for the Mangalori fish and crab gassi, the prawns with mango, the Jardaloo boti from Bombay, and the chicken Chettinad. This is lovely Indian cooking, and do note that their take-away is also excellent. (46 Upper Clanbrassil Street, D8 ☎ 01-473-8252 info@konkan.ie www.konkan.ie – Open 5.30pm-11.30pm Mon-Sun)

Dublin Central

Soups, Sauces & Relishes

Laragh Stuart Foods

Laragh Stuart's soups, sauces, spreads and relishes have been colonising quality food stores throughout the country for the last few years, and Ms Stuart has the ability to bring a sense of the true culture of the Mediterranean cuisines she purloins to everything she cooks. (Spade Centre North King Street D7 ☎ 01-617 4827)

Food Stall

Lara Lu

At Lu Thornley's Lara Lu stall you can get Valrhona chocolate shots, perfect Thai chicken curry to take away, fantastically funky sandwiches that make the best use of Laragh Stuart relishes and hot savoury pies. This is a real culinary hotspot. (Stall 1A, Market Arcade, South Great George's Street, D2 ☎ 087-990 8003 luthornely@gmail.com www.laralufoods.com)

Delicatessen

Liston's

Karen Liston's deli is only brilliant. Carefully stocked shelves. Carefully cooked foods. Carefully selected wines. Funky staff who have always demonstrated the boss's attitude to service: "I say to the people that work in the shop that this isn't somewhere you just take the change and put it in the till". That attitude has made Liston's a star neighbourhood store, and a must-have destination for great food, from the morning's first cup of coffee to those delicious lunchtime sandwiches and on through into the excellent dinner dishes they offer: chicken and broccoli gratin; pork carbonnade; mahogany beef stew; Hungarian goulash. Excellent. (25 Camden Street, D2 ☎ 01-405 4779 ✉ listonsfood@eircom.net – Open 10am-6.30pm Mon-Fri, 10am-6pm Sat)

Restaurant

The Lobster Pot

Tommy and John and all the Lobster Pot crew have been doing good fish and shellfish cookery for years, and serving this good food with good wines, and it ain't broke and they sure ain't gonna fix it. Charming, fashion-free, so let's have sole bonne femme and coquilles St Jacques and some Chablis and off we go. (9 Ballsbridge Tce, Ballsbridge, D4 ☎ 01-668 0025 www.thelobsterpot.ie – Open 12.30pm-2.30pm Mon-Fri, 6.30pm-10.30pm Mon-Sat)

Restaurant

Locks

It's all change at Locks, as hip young chef Troy Maguire takes up the kitchen reins and Kelvin Rynhart and Teresa Carr take over the room. This trio have backgrounds in some of the best Dublin restaurants, so expect exciting cooking and a radical approach to artisan ingredients from Mr Maguire. (1 Windsor Tce, Portobello, D8 ☎ 01-454 3391 – Open Lunch & Dinner)

Wine Shop

Louis Albrouze

A spiffingly handsome wine shop in the bourgeois belt, Louis Albrouze concentrates on directly imported wines from lesser-known French producers and from small co-operatives, as well as a number of other producers in Italy and Spain. We liked the Domaine Barbanot Cotes du Rhone, and the Cave de Saint Etienne de Fontbellon chardonnay is a beauty, so this gorgeous shop is worth a hour of any wine lover's time. (127 Upper Leeson Street, D4 ☎ 01-667 4455 ✉ leesonstreet@louisalbrouze.com www.louisalbrouze.com – Open 10.30am-9.30pm Mon-Sat, noon-7pm Sun)

Restaurant

Mackerel

Fresh fish cooked in the centre of town, that's the Mackerel USP. With a busy CafeBarDeli down in the main room of the beautiful Bewley's building, the upstairs has been given over to a simple room with good fresh fish cooked with simplicity and imagination. Resurrecting and renovating Bewley's has been one of the most important acts carried out by the Bourke & Foyle partnership, and installing Mackerel was some sort of stroke of genius. Do try the rare arctic char from Lough Talt in County Sligo. (Bewley's Building, Grafton Street, Dublin 2 ☎ 01-672 7719 info@mackerel.ie www.mackerel.ie – Open noon-4pm, 5pm-10pm Mon-Sun. Closed bank holidays)

Shop and Café

La Maison des Gourmets

A bakery with a very popular small dining room upstairs that serves excellent tartines and savouries from a short, very sharp menu of French specialities. (15 Castle Market, D2 ☎ 01-672 7258 – Open 9am-5.30pm Mon-Sat)

Dublin Central

Tapas Bar

The Market Bar

A tapas menu in this big, busy bar in the George's Street complex has been a hit ever since they first opened their doors, and an impressive consistency – and an impressive simplicity – has kept everything running smoothly. Gets mighty busy after work. (Fade Street, D2 ☎ 01-613 9094 info@marketbar.ie www.marketbar.ie – Open noon-9.30pm Mon-Sat, 3pm-9pm Sun)

Cheese Shop

Matthew's Cheese Cellar

Annie McEvoy oversees this basement cheese store, and she minds her beautiful Irish and European cheeses as if they were wee babbies, so you can expect glorious cheeses in perfect condition. Do note that at lunchtime Annie also offers a salad, cold meats and cheese box to take away, a splendidly alternative lunch. A really fine shop, blessed with great service and sage advice. (17 Upper Baggot Street, D2 ☎ 01-668 5275
annie@matthewscheesecellar.com
www.matthewscheesecellar.com – Open Mon-Sat 10am-6pm)

Off Licence

McHugh's Off Licence

Cathal McHugh's two shops are superb examples of the independent wine shop and off licence in action, and they have deservedly garnered many awards over the years, recognising not just a superb range of wines, beers and spirits, but superbly motivated staff who get a gig kick out of selling those ace drinks. Beer lovers in particular should note that McHughs stock almost 120 different beers, but that is simply typical of a level of service that is nothing less than definitive. (57 Kilbarrack Road, D5 ☎ 01-839 4692, 25e Malahide Road, Artane, D5 ☎ 01-831 1867)

Restaurant

The Mermaid Café

"A distinctive cuisine" was how the food writer Paul Levy pithily summed up The Mermaid Café, for readers of the *Wall Street Journal*, a few years back. So it is. Ben Gorman and Mark Harrell's restaurant is one of that small but select group of Irish restaurants – Café Paradiso; Truffles; Good Things; Shanks; The Tannery – that have no obvious antecedents, and no obvious points of comparison to their colleagues in the restaurant game. Mr Gorman sees things differently from other cooks, his approach is oblique, bookish, intellectual. Right from our first meal back in 1996, we noted in a scribble on the back of the menu that "this food has its roots in travel and enjoyment, in exploring flavours – it's almost as if they cook for themselves". That is as true today as it was in 1996, and it explains why The Mermaid is such a star. Sunday brunch is one of the great metropolitan rites of passage for new arrivals to the city. (69/70 Dame Street, Temple Bar, D2 ☎ 01-670 8236 www.mermaid.ie – Open 12.30pm-2.30pm, 6pm-11pm Mon-Sat; noon-3.30pm Sun brunch; 6pm-9pm Sun)

Afternoon Tea

The Merrion Hotel

The Merrion Hotel serves the best afternoon tea you can enjoy in the city. It is expensive – extremely expensive – it is preposterously indulgent, and it is only, totally, brilliant. Try to get your children to pay for it. They owe you. (The Merrion Hotel, Upper Merrion Street, D2 ☎ 01-603 0600 www.merrionhotel.com – Snacks and afternoon tea served 7.30am-2.30pm, 3pm-6pm Mon-Sun)

Dublin Central

Restaurant

Mint

Dylan McGrath is the hottest chef in town as we write in 2007, and it's become commonplace to hear people talking of "3-star cooking" coming from this man and his kitchen. McGrath's menus read straight-ahead, but what comes out from the kitchen is, quite simply, beyond expectation, fusing elements of molecular cookery technique – froths, foams and so on – with rock-solid disciplined classical practices. The results are spectacular, and it is as if McGrath can somehow manage to take the lessons of the great chefs he has worked with – Paul Rankin, Aidan McGrath, Tom Aikens, Conrad Gallagher, John Burton-Race – and to synthesise these influences into a new cuisine. You would need a book to describe the food, so experiencing it yourself is the only option. Expect to be blown away. (47 Ranelagh Village, D6 ☎ 01-497 8655 info@mintrestaurant.ie www.mintrestaurant.ie – Open 6.30pm-10.30pm Tue-Sat; 12.30pm-2.30pm Tue-Fri)

Dublin Central

Wine Merchant

Mitchell & Son

Mitchell's is simply a top-notch firm. Wines are selected with top-notch discrimination and certitude. Wines are sold in top-notch shops which back up the selection with top-notch advice and service. The net result of these stellar standards is that lots of folk simply take them for granted, but you should not make that mistake: Mitchell's are one of the enduring stars of the Dublin culture of food and wine, and should be celebrated as such. (Kildare Street, D2 ☎ 01-676 0766. Also at Glasthule, Co. Dublin ☎ 01-230 2301 glasthule@mitchellandson.com www.mitchellandson.com – Open 9.30am-7pm Mon-Thur, 9.30am-10pm Fri, 10am-7pm Sat)

Restaurant

Monty's of Kathmandu

Shiva Gautam's restaurant has lovely food, but a somewhat less-than-lovely room. No matter: we have always had truly terrific Nepalese cooking in here, their tandoori specialities are spectacularly fine, and the authenticity of the food is a vital element amidst the ersatz offerings in Temple Bar. (28 Eustace Street, Temple Bar, D2 ☎ 01-670 4911 shiva@tinet.ie www.montys.ie – Open noon-2pm, 6pm-11.30pm Mon-Sat; 6pm-10.30pm Sun)

Hotel, Restaurant and Cafe Bar

The Morrison

The rooms in The Morrison remain amongst our favourites in the city, but the Halo restaurant has yet to re-establish a signature of its own, following the departure of Jean-Michel Poulot to his own restaurant in Donnybrook. (The Morrison Hotel, Ormond Quay, D1 ☎ 01-887 2421 www.morrisonhotel.ie)

Shop

Morton's

Everyone loves Morton's. What's to love? The most terrific selection of quality Irish foods, for a start, collected together and sold in a shop that manages to feel like a family store, a village family store, which is another of its major attractions. Despite that ambience, Morton's is in reality a blue-chip address, and one that genuinely has virtually everything you could possibly need to eat well and, thereby, to live well. Only brilliant. (15-17 Dunville Avenue, Ranelagh, D6 ☎ 01-497 1913 info@mortons.ie www.mortons.ie – Open 8am-8pm Mon-Fri, 8am-6.30pm Sat, 11am-4pm Sun)

Fish & Game

Thomas Mulloy

Tommy and Ross Mulloy's shop is a long-established, unchanging, traditional city-centre shop, where the specialisation in excellent prime fish and shellfish is matched equally by an expertise in seasonal game birds. (12 Lower Baggot Street, D2 ☎ 01-661 1221 – Open 9am-5pm Mon, 9am-6pm Tue-Fri, 9am-4pm Sat)

Wine Merchant

Nectar Wines

John McGrath and Carl Byrne's choice wine company imports some excellent wines, from France, Australia and Tuscany, and bands together with other emerging wine importers – Tom Dunphy's Table View Wines who import from South Africa (☎ 01-285 2322), Paul Stafford's Stafford Wines, who import from Argentina, Chile, Sicily and Sardinia (☎ 01-621 1300), and Grace Campbell Wines run by Kevin O'Hara who import from Portugal (☎ 01-494 1203) – under the Independents Day flag. These guys are passionate about their wines, and represent exciting new winemakers. (3 Sandyford Village, D18, ☎ 01-294 4067 sales@nectarwines.com)

Restaurant

New Han Yung BBQ Restaurant

New Han Yung BBQ Restaurant is Korean and serves Korean sushi, and Korean vodka, and things like bimibap and beef bulgogi. You light your table-top grill, then you grill your chosen meat on the table burner and wrap it in lettuce and dip it in spicy sauces, and knock back some vodka. All the while girls in great outfits flirt with dudes in white leather suits, whilst families with babies pretend to ignore the flirting. Mamma mia! Is this Dublin? Indeed it is. As the young people would say: wicked, man! (103 Parnell Street, D1 ☎ 01-873 3849 – Open 11am-late Mon-Sun)

Shop

New Millennium Chinese Restaurant

Is this the place where you get the best dim sum in Dublin? Many food lovers believe it is, the same folk who believe that the New Millennium also makes the best roast duck noodle soup you can get your hands on. So, it's late Sunday morning, and bring it on: crispy squid and spicy tripe come first, then steamed char siu puffs, then squid cakes with chili sauce, then deep-fried bean curd, then Shanghai dumplings followed by spring onion Cheung Fun, with lotus seed buns for pudding, Magnificent food, fantastic prices, and a real Dublin treasure. (51 South King Street, Dublin 2 ☎ 01-635 1525 Open – noon-3am Mon-Sun)

Shop

Nolan's

Clontarf's star supermarket is to the Northside what Morton's is to the southside. The best foods, the best ambience, the best service, the best shop. (49 Vernon Avenue, Clontarf, D3 ☎ 01-833 8361 – Open 9am-7pm Mon-Wed, 9am-9pm Sat, 11am-4pm Sun)

Restaurant

Nonna Valentina

At the same time as establishing one of the most dynamic food companies in Dublin under the Dunne & Crescenzi, La Corte, Bar Italia and L'Officina brands, Stefan Crescenzi has gone right back to his roots. Nonna Valentina is dedicated to cucina casalinga – Italian home cooking – and, if it doesn't seem a contradiction in terms for such simple food, the results are spectacular. Mr Crescenzi uses the

Italian term "curato" to describe his food, meaning dishes that are properly nurtured, sourced and cooked, and curato is what you get from the cuisine inspired by his granny: carpaccio of swordfish, or bresaola with Parmesan; gnocchetti with scampi tails and artichokes; panzerotti with pheasant ragu; venison with juniper and potato purée; beef fillet with barbera. This food walks a tightrope in its simplicity, but Mr Crescenzi is quite a talent on the high wire. (1-2 Portobello Road, D8 ☎ 01-454 9866 www.dunneandcrescenzi.com – Open noon-11pm Mon-Sat)

Café

Nude

Nude has expanded to three city centre restaurants, and there is also a franchise out at Dublin airport which manages to give some respite to the indifferent quality of food offered to air passengers. Norman Hewson's stores were the first to offer fresh, high-quality, high energy, healthful foods and drinks, and the formula remains as crisp and attractive today as ever. (21 Suffolk Street, D2 ☎ 01-672 5577 – Open 7.30am-10pm Mon-Sun; Also 38 Upr Baggot St ☎ 01-668 0551 – Open 7.30am-5pm Mon-Fri; Also George's Quay ☎ 01-677 4661 – Open 7.30am-5pm Mon-Fri)

Wine Merchant

O'Brien's Wines

O'Brien's has become something of a monolith in Irish wine retailing, with loads of new stores opening up all over the country as the group has expanded to more than 20 shops. The shops have enthusiastic staff and an excellent range of popular wines as well as choice superstars from all over the globe, and they offer a most valuable alternative to the bland wine retailing of the supermarkets. (30 Donnybrook Road, D4 ☎ 01-269 3310 sales@obrienswine.ie www.obrienswine.ie – Open 10am-11pm Mon-Sat, 12.30pm-11pm Sun)

Restaurant

O'Connell's

People tend to take for granted the innovations which Tom O'Connell has consistently and winningly introduced to this big, luxurious brasserie ever since it first opened eight years ago. They don't seem to notice that the winning formula is always being tweaked and sharpened. Most recently, Mr O'Connell has grouped the menu in a style that is similar to modern American menus: salads; soups; seafood; pasta, pizza and vegetarian; bakes, roasts and grills; fish; little desserts. This is a radical restructuring, and shows a restaurateur who is consistently ahead of his time, consistently setting a new agenda for happy eating. We regard O'Connell's as the most democratic restaurant in Dublin, and one of the finest restaurants in Dublin, a place where the cooking is as intellectually creative as the owner. (Merrion Road, Ballsbridge, D4 ☎ 01-647 3304 info@oconnellsballsbridge.com www.oconnellsballsbridge.com – Open 7am-10.30am, noon-2.30pm, 2.30pm-6pm (afternoon menu, table service), 5.30pm-10pm Mon-Sat. 8am-11am, 12.45pm-3.30pm, 5.30pm-9.30pm Sun)

Restaurant

L'Officina

Dublin Central

The newest incarnation of the Dunne & Crescenzi empire has a branch in the vast Dundrum centre, and another branch in Kildare town. As always with D&C, simplicity is achieved through meticulously careful sourcing of ingredients, which are then left well alone to speak for themselves. The trademark platters are perfect for daytime sharing, in the evenings the meat and fish cookery is slightly more involved but is always as pure and simple as they can make it. (Dundrum Town Centre, D14 ☎ 01-216 6764 www.dunneandcrescenzi.com – Open 10.30am-10pm Mon-Wed, 10.30am-10.30pm Thu, 10.30am-11pm Fri & Sat, noon-10pm Sun)

"I wish I could just sit people down and give them something to eat; then I know they would understand."

ALICE WATERS

Market Stall

Olive Green

One of the cult addresses of the cult George's Arcade food collective, Olive Green is home to seeds, grains, pulses, staples, olives, all the ingredients you need to cook Mediterranean cooking. So, if you have been given a copy of Claudia Roden's *Arabesque*, or Diana Henry's classic *Crazy Water, Pickled Lemons,* you need only come here to get every single thing you need. Easy. (Stall 17, Market Arcade, South Great Georges Street, D2 www.georgesstreetarcade.ie)

Preserves

Olvi Oils

Miriam Griffith's flavoured oils and sauces are very fine indeed, especially an excellent basil pesto that makes lunchtime pasta dishes into a speedy, simple treat, and good sweet sauces that make dessert simple. You will find them in good delis in and around Dublin and as far south as Urru in Bandon and Mallow. (Unit B21, KCR Ind. Est, D 12 ☎ 01-490 6728)

Restaurant

One Pico

Eamonn O'Reilly's flagship restaurant has been putting out some impressive cooking in recent times, and Mr O'Reilly is fortunate to have one of the city's most gorgeous rooms in which to entertain. The more experimental style which led to inconsistencies in the past has been jettisoned in favour of a classic, modern style of European cooking – terrine of foie gras with duck rillette; warm asparagus with deep-fried egg; roast cod with pistou broth; cep risotto; belly pork with cassoulet of white beans. Set menus offer very good value for money. (5-6 Molesworth Place, D2 ☎ 01-676 0300 www.onepico.com – Open 12.30pm-2.30pm, 6pm-10.30pm Mon-Sat. Closed bank hols & first two weeks in Aug, Christmas)

Restaurant

101 Talbot

Some people don't get it with 101. They don't get the simplicity, they think the food should be posher. What these people also don't get is the fact that 101 is one of the most original and most pioneering of Dublin's restaurants. They forget – if they ever knew – what it was like to open and run a restaurant in the 1980's on a street like Talbot Street, when Talbot Street was the mean streets of the capital. But we remember, and that is why we respect what Pascal and Margaret do, and why we respect what they have done in 101. We also love the food, of course, and Pascal is the wittiest front of house in the city. (101 Talbot Street, D1 ☎ 01-874 5011 www.101talbot.com – Open 5pm-11pm Tue-Sat)

Butcher

Danny O'Toole

Not all of the meat that Danny O'Toole sells is certified organic, but he remains the butcher most identified in the public eye with sourcing and selling meat of organic symbol standard. The organic label, however, does mean that people can tend to overlook the super-skilful charcuterie that you will find in the O'Toole shops in Terenure and Glasthule, and it is that combination of skill and sourcing that makes these shops special places.
(138 Terenure Road Nth, D6W ☎ 01-490 5457
✉ otoolebutcher@eircom.net – Open 9.30am-6pm Mon-Sat)

Deli & Bakery

Panem

Ann Murphy's bakery and deli is a beauty, their fresh focaccias, sweet bakes and daily soups offering a real treat. Everything in Panem is made not just with superb ingredients, but also with nous and discrimination, which explains why Panem has such a dedicated audience, and why it is so jam-packed in here for most of the day. (21 Lwr Ormond Quay, D1 ☎ 01-872 8510 – Open 8am-6pm Mon-Fri, 9am-6pm Sat, 10am-4.30pm Sun)

Dublin Central

Restaurant

Pearl Brasserie

Sebastian Masi and Kirsten Batt have made the Pearl into a real success story ever since taking over this basement restaurant at the top of Merrion Street. Mr Masi's menus simply offer fail-safe choices – chicory salad with Cashel Blue; duck foie gras with brioche; chicken supreme with tarragon; sirloin with gratin dauphinoise – and the polish of the execution and good service explains their success. (20 Merrion St Upr, D2 ☎ 01-661 3572
✉ info@pearl-brasserie.com 🖱 www.pearl-brasserie.com – Open Open noon-2.30pm Tue-Fri, 6pm-10.30pm Mon-Sun. Closed bank holidays)

Restaurant

Peploe's

The room is a beauty, the location on St Stephen's Green is a winner, and being able to eat something at almost any time of day makes Peploe's a great asset. But we would love to see the food making a greater signature statement in Peploe's, because the ambience and the glamorous surroundings are worth a more distinctive, Dublinesque offer. Mind you, everyone else is as happy as Larry with the way things are in here. (16 St Stephen's Green, D2 ☎ 01-676 3144 info@peploes.com www.peploes.com – Open noon-midnight Mon-Sun)

Restaurant

Poppadom

The original of the up-market Indian restaurant, Poppadom continues to do a fine job serving elegantly concocted Indian food in a comfortable room with extremely good service. (91a Rathgar Road, D6 ☎ 01-490 2383 – Open 6pm-midnight Mon-Sun)

Brewery

Porterhouse Brewing Co.

We love the Porterhouse brews, and their success in expanding into other branches is a source of pleasure, but underlines the fact that other craft brewers just can't seem to operate with the same commercial efficiency as the Porterhouse team. Ireland should be awash with craft breweries, but in Dublin there is only Messrs Maguire, at O'Connell Street bridge, and the Porterhouse. No matter: serve us a pint of oyster stout, or even a glass of chocolate stout – really – and we are as happy as sandboys.There are now five Porterhouses, including a branch in Covent Garden in London, and no visitor to the city of Guinness should miss these brews, which reveal modern Guinness to be a pale shadow of its former magnificence. (Parliament Street, D2 ☎ 01-679 8847 www.porterhousebrewco.com.)

Tapas Bar & Restaurant

The Port House

Bono would find it way, way too dark in here if he kept his shades on, but apart from the gloominess the Port House has been a wowee! hit ever since this little tapas bar in a basement opened its doors. The paella is ace, the calamari is fab, the patatas bravas are yum, the chorizo in red wine is everyone's favourite, and just to show their Basque side they also do some good pintxos. The puddings are almost the star of the show, especially anything to do with chocolate. No reservations, so be prepared to wait, with a glass of good fino. (64a South William Street, D2 ☎ 01-677 0298 www.porthouse.ie – Open 11.30am-11pm Mon-Fri, 12.30am-midnight Sat & Sun)

Restaurant

Poulot's

Jean-Michel & Lorna-Jean Poulot opened the old Ernie's restaurant quietly, and have quietly made serious culinary waves, with M. Poulot showing in the kitchen that he is one of the best contemporary cooks, whilst Mme. Poulot shows that she is a master sommelier – she helpfully provides three wine recommendations with each course. The room is superbly comfortable, the service is excellent, and the cooking is precise and involved, with dishes like braised fillet of halibut, glazed carrots, truffle potato gnocchi, smoked bacon and pinot noir butter sauce, fairly typical of a very wordy offering. It reads complicated, but it eats simply and deliciously. (Mulberry Gardens, Donnybrook, D4 ☎ 01-269 3300 www.poulots.ie – Open 12.30pm-2.30pm Tue-Fri, 7pm-10.30pm Tue-Sat)

Restaurant

Queen of Tarts

Dublin Central

Queen of Tarts just gets better and better, so finding a table free in here at any time of the day has become a Major Dublin Event. Their pies are Pie Heaven, with even something as simple as a potato and onion pie rendered with such skill and flavour power and wickedly delicious pastry that one gives thanks to the heavens. The sweet stuff is brilliant: chocolate pecan tart is as rich as it gets – hey, we only live once! – whilst custard berry tart has tangy berries, rich custard and a sweet glaze. QofT is worth weekly visits, and damn the waistline. (Cork Hill, D2 ☎ 01-670 7499 – Open 7.30am-7pm Mon-Fri, 9am-7pm Sat, 9am-7pm Sun)

Market

Red Stables Food Market

This up-and-coming market is one to watch. Managed by Dublin City Council, the market is very choosy about its stall holders, and has secured some real specialists already, such as Joe Condon's omega beef, Burke Farm ice cream, Lynne Swarbrigg's terrific Saucy's relishes and Hemmingway's of Clontarf, just to name a typically adroit and creative quartet of stall holders. An arts & crafts section has recently been added, and this is a superstar in the making. All this and gourmet dog biscuits too. (Red Stables, St Anne's Park, Mount Prospect Avenue, D3. ☎ 01-222 7377 info@redstables.ie www.redstables.ie – Open Sat 10am-5pm)

Off Licence

Redmond's of Ranelagh

Not just one of the best wine shops, but one of the best shops in Dublin, full stop. Jimmy Redmond and his team have been selling great wines and foods for decades, but their vim and vigour remains constant and compelling, and this is a charming, darling place in which to find that must-have bottle. (25 Ranelagh Village, D6 ☎ 01-496 0552 – Open 10.30am-11pm Mon-Sat, 1pm-10pm Sun)

Restaurant

Rhodes D7

Chef Paul Hargreaves worked alongside Gary Rhodes for years before opening up in Dublin 7. In this big, big space, decorated by the artist Deborah Donnelly, he fires out rock-steady cooking that shows the Rhodes' signature of punchy, flavoursome staples-with-a-flourish: rump of lamb with ratatouille; beef with three sauces; duck confit with butterbeans. The big question, of course, is whether an identifiably UK brand will win Dubliners' hearts: old Will Shakespeare, for example, rarely plays for too long in this town. (The Capel Building, Mary's Abbey, D7 ☎ 01-804 4444 info@rhodesd7.com www.rhodesd7.com – Open noon-4pm Mon, noon-10pm Tue-Sat)

Dublin Central

Restaurant

Roly's

People take Roly's for granted now, but it truly was a revolutionary project when it opened, six weeks before Xmas in 1992. No Celtic Tiger then, and very little spending money in the city, which puts the scale and ambition of this restaurant into some sort of perspective. Today, Colin O'Caly and chef Paul Cartwright fire out super-consistent brasserie food to super-enormous numbers of people, and the clamour of the room remains one of the most vividly enjoyable in the city. By the by, we actually reckon Roly's most significant gift to the city lies in the fact that it was the first room where women felt comfortable eating in pairs or in groups. (7 Ballsbridge Tce, Ballsbridge, D4 ☎ 01-668 2611 www.rolysbistro.com – Open noon-3pm, 6pm-10pm Mon-Sun)

Sausage El Supremo

Roy's Italian Sausages

The man who created Ta Se Mahogani Gaspipes restaurant in Dublin 7 all those years ago is now the purveyor of superb sausage snacks at various CoCo markets throughout the city. Roy gets Ed Hick sausages, fine breads from L'Artisan bakery in Navan, makes a superb relish with fried peppers and onions, and serves 'em up to you with a smile. This man is a real gourmet, so don't miss Roy's Italian Sausages at IFSC Wednesday, Marlay Park Saturday, Dun Laoghaire Sunday. (17 Manor Street, D7 ☎ 086-854 2111)

Restaurant

● Saba

So, we started with rice paper spring rolls, then had potstickers, then a very chilli-hot soft-shell crab, and a green monkfish curry. And everything about Saba impressed us as very professional, hard-working, amusingly ironic – check out those Honda 50 photos! – and very enjoyable, though we think the room is a little dark. Owner Paul Cadden and chef Taweesak Trakoolwattaana have a very clear focus of what they want to do in Saba, and it makes for a great destination, so long as you don't park outside and get clamped. (26-28 Clarendon Street, D2 ☎ 01-679 2000 feedback@sabadublin.com www.sabadublin.com – Open noon-late Mon-Sun)

Mexican Foods

● Sabores de Mexico

The great thing about Gus and Teresa Hernandez's stall in the Temple Bar market is that you can buy their sublime foods to take away – champagne habaneros; spicy catsup; jalapenos en escabèche; salsa adobo – and you can also grab a wonderful taco or fajita or burrito to nibble on as you circumnavigate the market, or even just to eat as you linger by the stall and enjoy that craic as all the regulars chew the gossip with Gus and Teresa: boy but this is one lively stall! Gus and Teresa now also have meseca, the masa harina used to make echt tortillas, and do enquire about their cookery classes and Mexican cookery trips. (56 Manor Street, Stoneybatter, D7 ☎ 01-272 2022 meromerocafe@hotmail.com)

Preserves

● Saucy's Super Sauce Kitchen

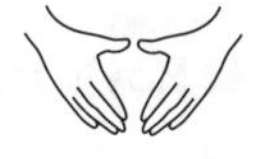

Lynne Swarbrigg makes wickedly flavourful relishes and sauces and curds. Try a hit of that spicy tomato and apricot ravishing relish and you will be blown away by the most meticulously configured series of tastes: this is so good you eat it straight from the spoon. Lynne sells at Howth and Dun Laoghaire on Sunday and at Raheny's intimate Red Stable market on Saturday, and you can also get Meadowsweet Apiaries fine honeys from her stall. (Unit G5, Spade Enterprise Centre, North King Street, D7 ☎ 01-617 4825)

Restaurant

● Seven

Seven feels like a private house, with its softly lit nooks and crannies, but staff are professionally turned out and the food is slick. Well-achieved dishes such as leg of lamb with green lentils and sweet potato, or whole sea bass with lemon and caper butter, strike the right note, but starters need some work to get up to the level of mains and their choice of expert, classic, puddings. (73 Manor Street, D7 ☎ 01-633 4092 – Open noon-2.30pm, 6pm-9.30pm Mon-Sat. No lunch Sat, but Sun brunch from noon and Sat lunch planned for high summer season)

Dublin Central

Restaurant

● Shanahan's

It's the poshest steak in town, and the price of dinner for a party might force you to sell the boat and the Beamer, but there is no lack of charm about Shanahan's, so long as you can afford it. Service is great, the steaks are unquestionably fab, and arguments about value are beside the point. (119 St Stephen's Green, D2 ☎ 01-407 0939 management@shanahans.ie www.shanahans.ie – Open for Fri lunch from 12.30pm, dinner Mon-Sun from 6pm)

Hotel, Bar & Restaurant

● The Shelbourne Hotel

American chef John Mooney is heading the team at the Saddleroom Restaurant, and we are happy to note that when we first met him, he was browsing and buying in the Temple Bar Market one Saturday. The hotel has been made over at a cost of gadzillions of euro, and one hopes Mooney can restore culinary glamour to a landmark Dublin address. The Horseshoe Bar, of course, is restored as the epicentre of the chattering classes. (Shelbourne Hotel, 27 St Stephen's Green, D2 ☎ 01-663 4500 www.theshelbourne.ie)

Cheesemonger

Sheridan's Cheesemongers

Many credit the Sheridan brothers, Seamus and Kevin, and their partner Fiona Corbett with changing the way Irish people think about, and how they use, speciality cheese. But Sheridan's have actually done more than that. They brought a hipness, a savvyness, a world of culture, to their shops and to retail, and they imbued each and every member of their staff with that culture. We were chairing a food seminar once at which Seamus Sheridan quietly admitted that "We don't really sell food: we are selling a piece of culture". Just as importantly, he said that "People are not just shop assistants, they must be respected. We have an obligation of respect to our staff, and to our suppliers." In those simple nuggets of wisdom, you can see why Sheridan's is the world class act it is. (11 Sth Anne Street, D2 ☎ 01-679 3143 – Open 10am-6pm Mon-Fri, 9.30am-6pm Sat; Also 7 Pembroke Lane, Ballsbridge ☎ 01-660 8231 – Open 10am-6.30pm Mon-Fri, 10am-6pm Sat)

Dublin Central

Restaurant

Silk Road Cafe

What an excellent spot the SRC is. Tucked away in Dublin Castle, tucked away beside the Chester Beatty Museum, it's a place where lovely cooking meets a calm atmosphere to provide an oasis of pleasure. (Mind you, that was somewhat helped by the fact that they like to play Ella Fitzgerald singing *Miss Otis Regrets*, a song and a singer who kinda rings our bell). The food – lamb moussaka; spinach pie; stir-fried lamb; chicken curry – is crisp and clean in flavour, the salads are very fine – courgette and grated carrot; wild rice; chick pea salad – and this is a first class address. (Chester Beatty Museum, Dublin Castle, D2 ☎ 01-407 0770 silkroadcafe@hotmail.com www.silkroadcafe.ie – Open 10am-4.30pm Tue-Fri, 11am-4.30pm Sat, 1pm-4.30pm Sun)

Cafe

Simon's Place Coffee Shop

Simon McWilliams has been cooking good food ever since those dark Dublin days when you never brushed into a billionaire on the street and when you could rent a Leeson Street basement for 40 quid a week. The billionaires have multiplied and the Leeson Street rents have skyrocketed, but Simon hasn't changed, and he does the good thing today as well as ever: big, big sandwiches, hearty soups, and as you scan the posters on the walls all the wonderful events that billionaires don't attend and that the young folk clamour for will be revealed to you. Wicked, like. (George's Street Arcade, D2 ☎ 01-679 7821 – Open 8.30am-5.15pm Mon-Sat)

Swedish Organic Preserves and Cordials

Simply Swedish

Bryan O'Kane's company imports the most delectable Swedish jams and cordials, and if you haven't tasted cloudberry preserve, or lingonberry preserve, well then you simply haven't lived. These are magical delights that more than justify their prices. You will find the range also at Fresh stores in Dublin, and catch Bryan at Marlay Park, Rathfarnham Sat 10am-4pm and at Dun Laoghaire People's Park Sunday 11am-5pm and the new Ballymun market on the first Thursday of the month.
(14 Kilnasaggart Road, Newry, Co Down, NI ☎ 086-382 5011 sales@simply-swedish.com
www.simply-swedish.com

Restaurant & Food Store

Brasserie sixty6

A big, tall, New York-style sort of eating room, with a deli next door, designed by John Kaye, sixty6 serves breakfast, lunch, dinner and brunch at the weekends, In honest brasserie style they focus on finger lickin' comfort food, best exemplified by their rotisserie chicken which is the signature dish, but also by bangers and mash, ham and eggs with hollandaise, and baked beans with pork sausage. They shift a lot of food and a lot of good wines, and sixty6 is ringing a lot of bells for a lot of people. (South Great George's Street, D2 ☎ 01-400 5878
info@brasseriesixty6.com
www.brasseriesixty6.com – Open Breakfast, Lunch & Dinner Mon-Sun, Store open 10am-5pm Mon-Sun)

Bakery

Soul Bakery

William White's bakery has its shop in Ongar Village, but SB also sells at many farmers' markets and distributes breads to some other stores. The breads are healthful, but they are also epicurean and extremely well made. (24 Main Street, Ongar Village, D15 ☎ 01-861 4913
laurence@soulbakery.ie www.soulbakery.ie)

Restaurant

Soup Dragon

With a brand new branch just opened on Ormond Quay, Fiona Fairbrother's friendly Dragon is breathing culinary fire over the northern bank of the River Liffey. These guys are cultured: not only do they reference The Clangers – you remember The Clangers, don't you? – they also reference recipes by culinary god Richard Olney – and all that culture makes its way into funky soups that are a meal in themselves. Splendid. (168 Capel Street, D1 ☎ 01-872 3277 – Open 8am-5.30pm Mon-Fri; Also 16-17 Ormond Quay, D2 ☎ 01-872 9692 – Open 8am-4.30pm Mon-Fri, 11am-5pm Sat, www.soupdragon.com)

Pub

South William

A photo in *The Irish Times* of a bloke eating one of the signature pies in Marc and Conor Bereen's pub, showed that alongside the dish he was tucking into, there was a bottle of HP sauce, and a bottle of Perrier water. Well, there you have it: the quotidian and the luxury brand, the pie in the chic trendy pub, the miner's staple food for the Dublin bling set. Fantastic. Troy Maguire, one of the hottest of the hot young chefs, designed the pies, and they are quotidian – Guinness and beef; bacon and cabbage with parsley sauce – and luxury – chilli bean, avocado and cheddar; duck confit with red cabbage – in equal measure. Real smart, absurdly fashionable. (52 South William Street, D2 ☎ 01-672 5946 info@southwilliam.ie www.southwilliam.ie – Food served noon-10pm Mon-Thur, noon-9pm Fri & Sat)

Dublin Central

Shop

Spiceland

Spiceland is the best shop for Middle Eastern food ingredients, from merguez to flatbreads, from orange flower water to feta, from halal meats to sacks of rices and spices. The atmosphere is wonderfully souk-like. (4 Sth Richmond Street, Portobello, D2 ☎ 01-475 0422 – Open 10am-9pm Mon-Sun)

Sushi Bar

Sushi King

Audrey Gargan liked the take-away sushi bars of Australia so much that she decided to open one of her own when she returned from her travels. The sushi comes in various smart concoctions, such as the Salmon of Knowledge box – what brilliant branding, Irish mythology and Japanese food: wicked! – and there is also the fishy selection, Delish Fish. There are also all manner of maki rolls, and the fish used is top quality. (146 Lower Baggot Street, D2 ☎ 01-644 9836 www.sushiking.ie – Open Mon-Fri, 8am-6pm)

Kitchenware

Sweeney O'Rourke

This is where the professionals get their kitchen kit, but amateur cooks can also shop here, and should your Dualit toaster burn out one of its grills, then this is where you will get a replacement. Staff are wonderfully helpful: when we rang to enquire about a replacement jug for a Waring blender, they explained that they didn't deal in Waring, and they then spent an age finding out that Nisbet's of Cork were the people we needed. Thanks very much, guys. (34 Pearse Street, D2 ☎ 01-677 7212
info@sweeneyorourke.com
www.sweeneyorourke.com – Open 9am-5pm Mon-Fri)

Dublin Central

Wine Shop

Sweeney's Wine Merchants

Finian Sweeney's shop traded on Dorset Street for decades before the move to Glasnevin. It's one of the city's best wine shops, and also has a fantastic range of beers and spirits and lots of informed advice. (Finglas Road, D11 ☎ 01-830 9593)

Restaurant

The Tea Room

The Clarence Hotel has major plans for expansion over the next few years, but before they start altering the skyline there is time to enjoy Fred Cordonnier's cooking in The Tea Room. Following a line of distinguished chefs, Mr Cordonnier's cooking is simply beautiful: West Cork scallops with cauliflower mousseline; wood pigeon in bacon and cabbage; crubeens with potato salad and mustard dressing; Hereford beef cheek braised in stout; fine apple tart with vanilla ice cream. Poised, mature, delicious, some of the city's best food. (The Clarence Hotel, 6-8 Wellington Quay, D2 ☎ 01-407 0800
www.theclarence.ie – Open 7am-11am Mon-Fri, 7.30am-11.30am Sat-Sun, 12.30pm-2.30pm Mon-Sun, 7pm-10.30pm Mon-Sat, 7pm-9.30pm Sun)

Market

Temple Bar Market

So there we are, sitting on the steps at the edge of the TB market, eating a Raha Meats burger – wicked! – having already had a Sabores de Mexico taco – wicked! – and it strikes us that the real secret of the market, which is thronged with shoppers, tourists, the curious, the trendy, the hungry, the epicurean, is that it was created to be a market, not to be a tourist attraction. But, because it is such a fine market, it has become a tourist attraction. Chicken and egg, cart and horse. And, the great thing about the market is that it continues to enshrine and exhibit the optimism, the energy and the originality of the people – Laura, Una, Patricia and many others – who turned Temple Bar into a living, working area, after it had mouldered away for decades. Their achievement has been too much forgotten, but it lives on here, in pulsing, vivid, human interaction, every Saturday. (Meeting House Square, Saturdays www.temple-bar.ie)

Dublin Central

Wine Merchant

Terroirs

The ultimate bespoke, boutique wine shop, Sean and Francoise Gilley's lovely store has an aesthetic quite distinct from any other Dublin shop. Everything is carefully chosen, everything is beautifully arranged, and even buying the most quotidian bottle can feel rather special. Aside from the excellent selection of wines – and anyone searching for a scarce or particular vintage should note that Mr Gilley has the ways and means to find that most arcane bottle for that anniversary or birthday – there are wonderful foods and treats. (103 Morehampton Road, Donnybrook, D4 ☎ 01-667 1311 info@terroirs.ie www.terroirs.ie – Open 10.30am-7pm Mon-Sat)

Restaurant

Thornton's

Kevin Thornton has become the media chef par excellence of the moment, and you can scarcely open a newspaper or magazine these days without Mr Thornton's deep-focus gaze peering out at you. Whatever he does garners attention, and happily he has garnered a lot of attention for the restaurant makeover he has carried out with architect David Piscuska, of the firm 1100 Architect. At last, this room has soul in its style, and it also now has a canape

bar, where you can nibble away on superb small plates at modest cost. The full gastronomic entertainment in Thornton's is, of course, an expensive event, but then this chef is one of the most singular cooks of his generation, and his food is a fastidious exploration of not just tastes, but also techniques and textures, from braised pig head with poitin sauce to foie gras crème brûlée. "What we're doing at the moment is really exciting", Thornton told Shane Hegarty in *The Irish Times*. "It's like I'm 16 and getting out of a cage". That's the stuff. (Fitzwilliam Hotel, St. Stephen's Green, D2, ☎ 01-478 7008
✉ thorntonsrestaurant@eircom.net
🖱 www.thorntonsrestaurant.com – Open 12.30pm-2pm, 7pm-10.30pm Tue-Sat)

Deli & Sandwich Bar

● Toffoli

Elaine McArdle's café beside Dublin Castle has four – four – tables, and the most jam-packed piadinas you ever did eat. They take the wonderful freshly-baked Italian flat bread, and then pack it full of as much good stuff as they can manage, but especially with lots of the thing they sell in the shop – prosciutto, goat's cheese, roasted red peppers and crunchy rocket leaves. There are also good salads – Tuna or The Full House – pizzas with fine thin crispy bases which are made with loving care, Italian and South American wines, and excellent coffees. Very fine. (34 Castle Street, D2 ☎ 01-633 4022 – Open 9.15am-5.45pm Tue-Fri)

Restaurant

● Town Bar & Grill

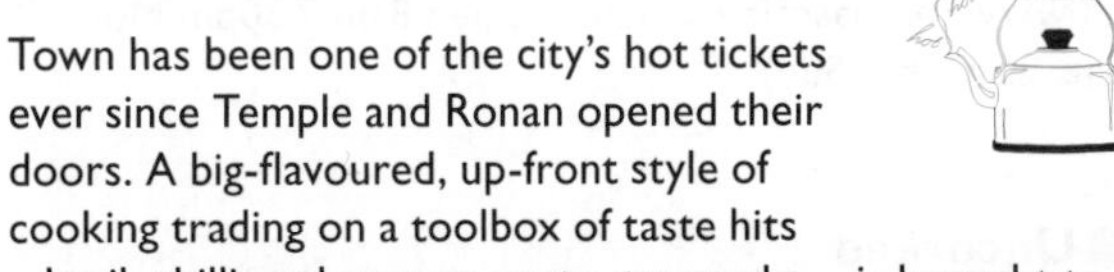

Town has been one of the city's hot tickets ever since Temple and Ronan opened their doors. A big-flavoured, up-front style of cooking trading on a toolbox of taste hits – basil, chilli, red pepper, pesto, tapenade – is brought to bear on a New York Italian-style of food – rabbit fricassee with sage tagliatelle; beef cannelloni with pesto; halibut with Kalamata tapenade; pork belly with Boston baked beans – and the result has been sheer deliciousness. The wines are as carefully chosen as the food, and when put together it means Town is a big night out, whatever the night. A second branch is due to open in deepest Sandyford. (21 Kildare Street, D2 ☎ 01-662 4724
🖱 www.townbarandgrill.com – Open noon-11pm Mon-Sat; 12.30pm-10pm Sun)

Bakery

Traditional Polish Bakery

Karl Tracz's bakery supplies its shop on Capel Street and many other shops and supermarkets, both far and wide, with breads for Ireland's 150,000 Polish residents. Mr Tracz uses a sourdough starter to make the King bread, which is a mix of 30% rye with 70% wheat flour. There is also a dense 100% rye brown bread, as well as cakes and pastries – do try the pastry with sweet cheese which is more than good. (Capel Street, D1 087 270 5136, Ballymount Industrial Estate, Walkingstown, D12 ☎ 01-408 9992 info@polishbakery.eu www.polishbakery.eu 11am-7pm Mon-Sat)

Restaurant

Tribeca

Popular, mainstream cooking, with a new wine bar, Wine Upstairs, just opened. (65 Ranelagh, D6 ☎ 01-497 4174 info@tribeca.ie www.tribeca.ie – Open 10am-11pm Mon-Fri, 11am-11pm Sat & Sun)

Delicatessen

Thomas's Delicatessen

The best delicatessen in the zone offers great foods, great wines and great service. In whatever branch of the operation you look, Thomas's strives to have a definitive selection, but their secret lies in careful editing and choosing, so there aren't a mass of foods and wines, just foods and wines they reckon are the best, and which they are happy to sell to their happy customers. Excellent.
(4 Brighton Road, Foxrock, D18 ☎ 01-289 4101 www.thomasoffoxrock.ie – Open 8am-7.30pm Mon-Sat, 9am-4pm Sun)

Wine Shop

Uncorked

"We are here to help you find the right wine to match your food, mood or occasion" says Richie Barry, and Uncorked is a lively, promising wine venture with lots of chutzpah, and the right attitude to wine, whether you want Lustau sherry or a classed cru from Bordeaux. The French selection is much stronger than the Italian or Spanish range, so Francophiles are sure to find the right bottle, and there is a small but choice selection of funky beers. (Marian Road, Rathfarnham, D14 ☎ 01-495 0000 info@uncorked.ie www.uncorked.ie)

Restaurant, Bar & Function Rooms

The Vaults

Michael Martin's ten vault rooms can hold up to a thousand people, and they cater pretty much for every eventuality, concept and event you can possibly think of, from corporate get-togethers to cooking dinner for yourself and your significant other. But their secret weapon has always been the gifted culinary nous of Mr Martin, so that whilst the food is mainstream stuff– Caesar salad; burger and fries, some very nice pizzas – there is a level of execution that elevates this food into proper cooking, rather than bland catering. With a posse of friends, of course, it is a mighty night out. (The Vaults, Harbourmaster Place, IFSC, D1 ☎ 01-605 4700 info@thevaults.ie www.thevaults.ie – Open noon-11.30pm Mon-Fri, 1pm-2.30am Fri & Sat)

Restaurant

Venu

Charles Guilbaud's basement room divides opinions, but the cooking in Venu is united in praise of a simple, well-focused offer that delivers great tastes and good value for money. They make a great French onion soup, a very fine terrine of duck foie gras, and everyday fare such as steak and chips, or fish and chips are delivered with precision and respect, as one hopes to find in a brasserie. In that regard, the gratin dauphinoise is tops – creamy, garlicky, "everything dauphinoise should be" says Leslie Williams of the Bridgestone parish. Good service, good value, and mighty fun when the room is full. (Anne's Lane, D2 ☎ 01-670 6755 www.venu.ie – Open noon-11pm)

Local Speciality

GUR CAKE

Wine Merchant

The Vintry

Evelyn Jones' shop is one of the very best wine shops and off licences in the city, every bottle carefully chosen, and with gifted staff who know their way around the wine world blindfolded and who know just what you want even if you don't. (102 Rathgar Road, D6 ☎ 01-490 5477 vintry@vintry.ie www.vintry.com – Open 10.30am-10pm Mon-Sun)

Restaurant

Winding Stair Bookshop & Café

Of all the newer openings in Dublin, it is Elaine Murphy and chef Ainé Maguire who seem to have struck the most primal chord with their work in the adorable Winding Stair. Ms Maguire's sourcing is only brilliant – sausages from Sean Kelly in Newport, chorizo from Gubbeen farm; Bellingham Blue from Louth; prawns and crabs from County Kerry, Mount Callan from County Clare, to name just a few – and it really gives the cooking here an edge over others who offer somewhat similar savoury staples. Tying these superb foods to an up-market style of domestic comfort cooking is a superb meld, and this is an exceptional Dublin destination, with superb value and a superb wine list also part of the package. (40 Lwr Ormond Quay, D1 ☎ 01-872 7320 restaurant@winding-stair.com www.winding-stair.com – Open noon-11pm Tue-Sat, 12.30pm-3.30pm Sun)

Dublin Central

Fishmonger

Wright's of Marino

Wright's specialises in exotic fish, so if you are looking for yellowfin tuna, or line-caught sea bass, this is the place. Aside from the exotica, their range of standard fish and shellfish is excellent. (21 Marino Mart, Fairview, D3 ☎ 01-833 3636 info@wrightsofmarino.com www.wrightsofmarino.com – Open 10am-5pm Tue-Thu, 10am-5.30pm Fri, 10am-3.30pm Sat)

Restaurant

Zen Win House

Don't let them give you the Western menu in Zen Win: instead, ask for what everyone else is having, which may be gruel soup, or tofu soup, or the excellent dumplings, and then head up and help yourself to the lovely salads, and dunk the dough sticks into your soup and bite into a Mandarin tea egg. Ultra-cheap, always packed, and a cracking slice of the wild side. (100 Parnell Street, D1 ☎ 01-878 2888 – Open Lunch & Dinner)

Howth

Restaurant

Aqua

Aqua never seems to put a fork wrong. With new chef Tom Walsh at the stoves, the change-over from a long-established crew has been managed with seamless ease, and the cooking remains the best in the zone: braised pigeon with foie gras and salsify is the sort of exquisite flavour and savour combination this kitchen thrives on, and Dover sole on the bone with tomato, lemon and chive shows the classics being gently tweaked into some sort of perfection. Serious cooking, glorious rooms, views out across the water. (1 West Pier, Howth ☎ 01-832 0690 dine@aqua.ie www.aqua.ie – Open 1pm-3pm, 5.30pm-midnight, Mon-Sat; 12.30pm-4pm, 6pm-9.30pm Sun & Bank hols)

Fishmonger

Beshoff's of Howth

Alan Beshoff runs a handsome fish and shellfish shop near the town end of the pier. Beshoff's has a superb range of fish and shellfish and is a key pier-side address. (17/18 West Pier, Howth ☎ 01-839 0766 sales@beshoffs.ie www.beshoffs.com – Open 9am-6pm Mon-Sun, 'till 8pm Thur & Fri)

Café, Deli and Bakery

The Country Kitchen

A café, a food store, and boasting a prominent bakery counter that has loads of good sweet things to take away, this is a valuable place to source good breads and bakes and lots of well-chosen artisan foods. (Main Street, Howth ☎ 01-832 2033 7.30am-7pm Mon-Sat, 7.30am-3pm Sun)

Fishmonger

Doran's on the Pier

Sean Doran's proud boast is that they buy their fish directly from the trawlers who land their fish on the doorstep of this shop and restaurant (see The Oar House) on Howth Pier. (7 West Pier, Howth ☎ 01-839 2419 www.lettdoran.ie – Open 9am-6pm Mon-Sat, 10am-5pm Sun)

Smoked Salmon

Dunn's of Dublin

Peter Dunn has retired from the fish business, having created one of the most distinctive Irish seafood brands, whilst also creating the first Irish Slow Food Presidium for smoked wild Irish salmon. Ken Ecock has taken up the rod and line to drive on this iconic brand. (West Pier, Howth ☎ 01-839 8900 www.dunns.ie)

Wine Bar

Ella Wine Bar

Around the corner from the seaside strip and a bit up the hill, Aoife Healy's Ella is like a northside version of Dalkey's Nosh. It's a classy, deftly-styled and reliable address, with a distinct feminine style, that has a dedicated local following for good, modern cooking, some of which shows nice ingenuity, such as scallops with parsnip purée or crab mornay with Gruyere. (7 Main Street, Howth ☎ 01-839 6264 info@ellawinebar.com www.ellawinebar.com – Open 12.45pm-2.45pm Mon-Sat, from 6pm dinner Mon-Sat)

Restaurant

King Sitric

Go for the classics when in the KS – grilled scallops; sole on the bone; bone-dry white wines from Alsace and Chablis – and you will see why this veteran of more than 30 years in business endures. (East Pier, Howth ☎ 01-832 5235 info@kingsitric.ie www.kingsitric.ie – Open 12.30pm-2.15pm, dinner from 6.30pm Mon-Sat)

Fish Shop

Nicky's Plaice

For many Dubliners, Nicky's is the first and the last port of call for fresh fish and shellfish, so join the queue and join in the – frequently uproarious – craic in this Northside institution, where the service and the customer camaraderie is as superb as the quality of the fish. (West Pier, Howth ☎ 01-832 3557 – Open 10am-1pm Mon, 9am-6pm Tue-Fri, 9am-8pm Thur, 9am-1pm Sat)

Restaurant

The Oar House

Catch of the day means catch of the day in The Oar House – fish directly from the trawlers on the pier – and it has meant that this is one of the northside's hottest tickets. It can be hard to get one of the 40 seats in here even midweek, so powerful is the mix of sharp seafood cookery and truly excellent pricing. They do great – and vanished! – classics like lobster thermidor, but the smart money always goes for the daily specials, whilst the fish'n'chips are knock-out. (West Pier, Howth ☎ 01-8394568 www.oarhouse.ie – Open noon-10.30pm Mon-Sun)

Fishmonger

● Wright's of Howth

Mark Wright oversees this spiffingly fine fish shop, which is one of the stars of the Howth pier. A wonderful array of sparklingly fresh fish and shellfish is housed in a handsome store and sold with sagacious charm. (14 West Pier, Howth ☎ 01-832 3937 sales@wrightsofhowth.com www.wrightsofhowth.com – Open 9.30am-7.30pm Mon-Sat, 9.30am-6pm Sun)

"I would like my readers to share with me the belief that food and wine must be an essential aspect of the whole life, in which the sensuous-sensual-spiritual elements are so intimately interwoven that the incomplete exploitation of any one can only result in imperfection."

RICHARD OLNEY

Lusk

Apple Juice, Vinegar & Wine

● Llewellyn's Orchard Produce

David Llewellyn makes red wine. In north Dublin. It sounds impossible – trying to get German-style white wine grapes to ripen is Ireland in virtually impossible, never mind red wine grapes – yet somehow he manages it, and offers cabernet sauvignon-merlot blends and 3 white wines, producing about 500 bottles each year. But aside from this quirky hobby, Mr Llewellyn is primarily an apple grower and juice maker, and from his juice range he spins off cider, cider vinegar and a very fine cider balsamic vinegar, which is a mighty, almost treacly treat – drizzle it on fish or risotto to get the flavours to explode. A terrifically inventive artisan, his juices and juice products should not be missed at Temple Bar and Dun Laoghaire markets, as well as Brook Lodge in Wicklow. (Quickpenny Road, Lusk ☎ 01-843 1650 pureapple@eircom.net)

Dublin North

Malahide

Restaurant

● Bon Appetit

Oliver Dunne has retained the title of Patsy McGuirk's long-established Malahide restaurant, but changed everything else, creating two restaurants in the space by adding in Café Bon, (see below) and Bon Appetit itself. Mr Dunne is one of the leaders of the younger pack of Irish chefs, and first alerted Irish eaters to his skills when he wowed! food lovers in Ranelagh's Mint restaurant, before heading back home to the northside and this elegant series of rooms in a beautiful Georgian terrace. His food is involved, precise and expert: warm salad of rabbit, globe artichokes, broad beans and cep vinaigrette, or pan-fried brill with roasted cauliflower and lime purée, celery gnocchi and red wine sauce, are typical of the games with texture and flavour, and the subtley constructed but firmly flavoured food that is his trademark. But this is not just cooking from the head: this is actually heart-warming haut cuisine, and those terms actually do belong together. Prices are very fair for such elaborate and lovingly-crafted food, and the sky itself is the limit for what this chef can achieve. (9 St James Terrace, Malahide ☎ 01-845 0314 www.bonappetit.ie – Open 7pm-9.30pm Tue-Sat)

Restaurant

Café Bon

Andy Turner heads up the kitchen in the stylish basement Café Bon, and his food is pretty much faultless. Cannelloni of ocean trout and brown crab, with buttered leeks and shellfish bisque is a star dish, so damned good you won't share a spoonful. Foie gras parfait is pitch perfect, and to prove they know what they are about, you can order a rare steak and that is exactly what you will get. Roasted vegetable tart with wild mushroom and Madeira ragout is wickedly tasty, and if you bring along a younger person they show their true mettle by cooking some nice simple fish and chips for the 6-year-old in your life. Hot chocolate and orange fondant is a show-stopper of a dessert, and typical of a restaurant that is really pushing the envelope with ideas and precise execution. (9 St James Terrace, Malahide ☎ 01-845 0314 info@bonappetit.ie www.bonappetit.ie – Open 6pm-10.30pm Mon-Sat, noon-3.30pm, 6pm-9.30pm Sun)

Traiteur

Foodware Store

Aisling Byrne's excellent traiteur is the sort of place that might persuade you to give up cooking for yourself. Their cooked dishes, salads, cakes and bakes, and a terrific array of freezer food – last time we took away some fine pork with sage and white wine – is all top-notch, hand-made food with real flavours. Domestic cooks who find Xmas particularly trying should note that they do a terrific range for the festive season. Invaluable. (Old Street, Malahide ☎ 01-845 1830 info@thefoodwarestore.ie www.thefoodwarestore.ie – Open 9.30am-6pm Mon-Sat)

Café & Garden Centre

Garden Works

There are two Garden Works stores, here at Mabestown, and at Clonee out in deepest County Meath, and they are beloved amongst keen gardeners, not just for being excellent plantspeople, but also for having exceptionally good food halls in which to shop and eat. Well-kept secrets, but then that's gardeners for you, isn't it? (Mabestown, Malahide ☎ 01-845 0110 info@gardenworks.ie www.gardenworks.ie – Open 9.30am-5pm Mon-Fri, 9.30am-5.30pm Sat, noon-5.30pm Sun & bank hols. Late opening Thur, 'till 8pm Apr-June, Oct-Dec)

Wine Shop

● Gibney's Off Licence

Gibney's is a classy wine shop, and the winner of national wine shop awards, thanks to Siobhan Gibney's energy and enthusiasm and a really crack crew who make finding the right bottle a joyful voyage of discovery. There is a characterful and very busy pub next door run by the family. (New Street, Malahide ☎ 01-845 0606 www.gibneys.com – Open 10.30am-11.30pm Mon-Thu, 10.30am-12.30am Fri & Sat, 12.30pm-11pm Sun)

Restaurant

● Hush Brasserie

A popular food destination in the centre of the village, Hush serves nice modern food that is accessible – fajitas; burgers; tiger prawns with chilli jam – and the polish of the presentation is exact. (12a New Street, Malahide ☎ 01-806 1928 – Open Lunch & Dinner)

Farmers' Market

● Malahide Farmers' Market

The Saturday market has moved back to the GAA club, in the centre of town, and takes place both inside the hall and outside in the courtyard. It's a typically diverse and well-organised market by Sean McArdle, who now oversees a total of 10 markets throughout the city and county. (Saturday 11am-5pm, Church Street, side of St Sylvester's GAA hall, Malahide www.irishfarmersmarkets.ie)

Naul

Organic Herbs

● The Herb Garden

Denise Dunne stocks more than 140 varieties of organic herbs in her Herb Garden nursery, a dazzling array that you can enjoy by buying plants, seeds and cut herbs, and there are also tours of the garden for groups keen to know more about growing and using these indispensible culinary totems. (Forde-de-Fyne, Naul ☎ 01-841 3907 www.theherbgarden.ie)

Organic Vegetables

● McNally Family Farm

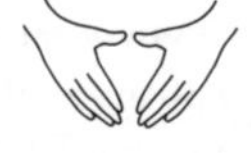

Jenny McNally sells at both the Leopardstown and Temple Bar markets, bringing the bounteous organic produce she and her husband Patrick produce to the hungry market hordes. Look out in particular for the unusual potato varieties that the McNallys, in common with many other organic growers, love to produce. (Balrickard, Ring Commons, Naul ☎ 01-841 3023)

Portmarnock

Wine Shop

Jus de Vine

Tommy Cullen's shop is no mere wine retail unit. Hell, this shop is an entire world of wine, under one roof. It's a sensational shop, whether you want to explore the boss's penchant for the wines of the Rhone Valley, or you want to just grab a cool bottle for Friday night. The range is staggering, but anyone who feels bewildered by the choice can rest assured that excellent staff will be able to decipher just exactly what it is you want (7 Portmarnock Town Centre, ☎ 01-846 1192 – Open 10.30am-10.30pm Mon-Sat, 12.30pm-10.30pm Sun)

Restaurant

The Osborne Restaurant

The restaurant of the hotel and golf complex has always offered serious, cheffy cooking, plush food in a plush room. (Portmarnock Hotel and Golf Links, Portmarnock ☎ 01-846-0611 www.portmarnock.com – Open 7pm-9.45pm Mon-Sun)

Skerries

Deli & Cafe

Olive

Peter Doritty and Deirdre Fahy ran Café Irie in Temple Bar for a decade before heading northside to open up the acclaimed Olive at the end of 2005. It's a cult shop, spoken of in terms of great respect by the people who supply it, never mind the folk who come here for lovely bites and panini and other good things to enjoy in the café. Good wines, good cheeses, lovely olives (of course!) and a one-stop-shop for good things in Skerries. (86 Strand Street, Skerries ☎ 01-849 0310 www.olive.ie – Open 8.30am-7pm Mon-Sat, 9am-5pm Sun)

Restaurant & Accommodation

The Red Bank

Terry McCoy is one of the great veterans of the Irish restaurant world. Indeed, they breed them for longevity on the Northside, for McCoy's colleague Aidan McManus is still going strong in Howth, and Patsy McGuirk has only recently sold in Malahide. These vets do the right thing, the right way, and it is significant that all three are distinguished fish cooks, blokes who treat fish with respect and cook it in the classical fashion. That fashion means their metier and their style is not fashion-focused, and long may Mr McCoy remain true to his instinct and his profession. (5-7 Church Street, Skerries ☎ 01-849 1005 www.redbank.ie – Open 6.30pm-9.45pm Mon-Sat, 12.30pm-4.30pm Mon-Sat)

Wine Merchant

Red Island Wines

Red Island is where the serious wine lovers in Skerries head to for a brilliant selection of wines and good advice. (Church Street, Skerries ☎ 01-849 4032)

Gastropub

Stoop Your Head

You can't book a table in SYH, but no one who turns up for Andy Davies' sharp seafood cooking minds the wait should the place be full, which it frequently is. Smart locals come back again and again to have prawns in garlic butter, or cod in beer batter, and whilst there are non-fish dishes such as chilli or fillet steak, you would need to have your head examined to pass up on the sort of seafood cooking that seems to restore the soul by virtue of its simplicity and sweetly savoury goodness. (Harbour Road, Skerries, ☎ 01-849 2085 – Food served noon-3pm, 5.30pm-9.30pm Mon-Thu, noon-3pm 5.30pm-10pm Sat, 12.30pm-3pm, 4pm-8pm Sun)

Swords

Bakery

La Boulangerie Francaise

Florence and Damian Cusack's bakery has a shop at Applewood Village in Swords and they sell also at Temple Bar on Saturdays. Damian cheffed for some years before winding up baking at La Maison des

Gourmets in Dublin, and when the chance came up to open at Applewood and work for themselves, they went for it. The range extends beyond their seriously good breads and baguettes to include viennoiserie, tartines, quiches, sweet tartlets, all showing the true culture of breadmaking with superb artisan accomplishment. (Unit 77, Applewood Village Square, Swords ☎ 086-102 2786 – Open 7am-7pm Tue-Fri, 9am-5pm Sat & Mon)

Roadside Take-away

The Chuck Wagon

Martin Crosby's gastronomic oasis is a roadside van that resides on the old N1 between Dublin and Belfast, and many truckers and ordinary decent non-truckers will still detour off the new tarmac to restore body and soul with one of those legendary bacon and sausage soda bread sandwiches. A genuine legend, no less. (Turvey Hill, Swords ☎ 085-702 5446 – Open 7.30am-5.30pm Mon-Sat)

Restaurant

The Old Schoolhouse

A staple of Swords right from the days when the village was still a village and not the urban conurbation it has since become, the Old Schoolhouse offers fine cooking served with charm and professionalism. (Coolbanagher, Swords, ☎ 01-840 2846 info@oldschoolhouse.ie www.oldschoolhouse.ie – Open 6pm-10pm Tue-Sat, 12.30pm-2.30pm Sun)

Dublin North

The Ward

Chocolates

Chez Emily

Helena Hemeryck and Ferdinand Vandaele's chocolate company now has two chocolate shops, here and a second store in Ashbourne, and you will also find them at the Saturday Temple Bar market where they have been stall-holders from the very early days. The chocolates, truffles, Turkish Delight and fruit pates are superbly made, and beautifully presented and packaged. Perhaps the best way to try them is to select an empty box and then fill it, and in this way you can work your way through the entire range of flavours and adorable textures. (Cool Quay, The Ward ☎ 01-835 2252, Main Street, Ashbourne, Co Meath Helena@chezemily.ie www.chezemily.ie)

Blackrock

Market

Blackrock Market

Home to a new Rudd Brother's shop, run by Andrew and Simon Rudd of the celebrated food-producing family of County Offaly, you can get everything in here from foods-to-go to select olive oils to their own smashing sausages. The Blackrock Market is presently changing its direction from a general market to one which will focus more exclusively on a dedicated food and wine offer. (Open weekends, Blackrock centre)

Traiteur

The Butler's Pantry

The development of Eileen Bergin's TBP from a single-store traiteur to a confident, classy chain of shops and an excellent distribution system, is one of the best food news stories, and one of the best food business development stories, we know of. Over the span of 20 years, Mrs Bergin has effortlessly mapped out the changing ways in which we eat, and has not just kept abreast of the changes, but read them and understood them, and satisfied them. Food for Tuesday supper, food for children, food for parties, you name it and the Pantries always have something that is just right. Their secret is revealed by a quote from M.F.K. Fisher, on one of their early brochures: "Almost every person has something secret he likes to eat." Mrs Bergin knows your secrets.
(53 Mt Merrion Avenue, Blackrock ☎ 01-288 5505
www.thebutlerspantry.ie; Also 1 Montpelier Place, D'Laoghaire ☎ 01-284 3933)

Wine Importer

Burgundy Direct

Conor Richardson could pass himself off as a Burgundian, so well-informed, so deeply immersed, is he in his specialist field of wine importing. The notes he issues after tasting trips to assess each vintage, and the charming, succinct thumb sketches he creates of each of the growers he buys from, are wine writing of a very individualistic, stubborn, idiosyncratic hue. In other words, he is just like a Burgundian farmer-winemaker. But he doesn't do only stockbroker-priced Burgundies.

Recent investigations have led to Italy and, most recently, a tranche of superb Rieslings. (8 Monaloe Way, Blackrock ☎ 01-289 6615 ☝ www.burgundydirect.ie)

Patisserie

● Cakes & Co

Joannie and Rosanna's cake company, Cakes & Co, is the leading supplier of bespoke novelty and celebration cakes on the southside. No desired representation is beyond their sugarcraft skills, and the results genuinely have to be seen to be believed. But, it isn't mere artifice, designed to be oohed! and aashed! over and then binned – these cakes are for eating and enjoying as well as for creating that big splash. (Jane Cottage, Newtownpark Avenue, Blackrock ☎ 01-283 6544 ☝ www.cakesandco.com)

Wine Merchant

● McCabe's

The McCabe brothers' wine shop has always been a beauty, wth a superb range of wines culled from the four vinous corners of the world, and with excellent staff who know their way with a corkscrew. The company also runs The Gables restaurant in Foxrock, but the great Mount Merrion store remains their flagship. (51-55 Mount Merrion Avenue, Blackrock ☎ 01-288 2037 ☝ www.mccabeswines.ie – Open 10.30am-10pm Mon-Sat, 12.30pm-8pm Sun & bank holidays)

Dublin South

Supermarket

● Superquinn

The Quinn family have sold up their ownership of the Superquinn chain, so whilst the dynamic Fergal Quinn may not be racing around the stores these days, the fundamental food offer and concept remains the same. The primary focus is on high-quality fresh foods, something other supermarkets are steadily moving away from as they seek to have everything they sell with something akin to the shelf-life of a CD. This focus makes Superquinn enduringly valuable. (Blackrock Shopping Centre, Blackrock ☎ 01-283 1511 ☝ www.superquinn.com – Open 8am-9pm Mon-Fri, 8am-8pm Sat, 9am-8pm Sun)

Cookery School

● Valentia Cookery

Linda Booth has exciting new plans afoot at her bespoke cookery school. She has a 3,000 square foot premises

in Blackrock and developments are well under way to begin classes in summer 2007, with ambitious plans for a widely expanded range of courses to follow later in the year. Chances are the school will have a new name – The Dublin Cookery School, perhaps? – so keep your eyes on what should be a vital new addition to culinary education from this gifted cook and teacher. (25 Avoca Park, Blackrock ☎ 01-278 2365
valentiacookery@eircom.net)

Dalkey

Farmers Market

● Dalkey Farmers' Market

An indoor market run by Coco Markets, with a good mix of interesting stallholders. (Heritage Centre, Fri 10am-4pm)

Café

● Idle Wilde Cafe

Dublin South

A good, funky, friendly food space just off the main street, with helpful, polite service and good savoury eating. (20 St. Patrick's Road, Dalkey ☎ 01-235 4501 – Open 8am-6.15pm Mon-Sun)

Pub

● IN

A groovy, super-styled pub with some groovy cooking, the food in In can hit all points between Korean pickles to fillet steak. The more sober dishes are often better realised, but fair play to their ambition. (115 Coliemore Road, Dalkey ☎ 01-275 0007 www.indalkey.ie – Open 10am-12.30am Mon-Sun)

Restaurant

● Nosh

Nosh never seems to put a foot wrong. Come in for a quiet dinner with a friend, and it's ace, the food and space just right. Send a bunch of friends and family in who are on a visit to the city, and they will tell you that it was ace. The Farrell sisters – like the Kemp sisters of Itsa-bagel – just know how to do the right thing, and how to keep on doing it with consistent excellence, creating the quintessential neighbourhood restaurant. (111 Coliemore Road, Dalkey ☎ 01-284 0666 www.nosh.ie – Open noon-4pm, 6pm-late Tue-Sun, brunch served Sat & Sun)

Wine Merchant

On the Grapevine

Gabriel and Pamela Cooney run two fine southside wine stores, the original store sited just off the main street in Dalkey, with a second store on Blackrock's Booterstown Avenue. (21 St Patrick's Road, Dalkey ☎ 01-235 3054 www.onthegrapevine.ie)

Pizzeria

Ragazzi

Good pizzas and great craic are the timeless format of this favourite local Italian eaterie, whose flirtatious waiters are the stuff of local legend. (109 Coliemore Road, Dalkey ☎ 01-284 7280 – Open 5.30pm-10.30pm Mon-Sat)

Restaurant

Thai House

Tony Ecock's Thai House restaurant is a model of consistency and customer satisfaction. Like Yoichi Hoashi's Aya restaurant, Mr Ecock understands that communication with customers is vital, so there are Thai House newsletters to keep everyone informed, and a helpful website through which many people make bookings. Then there is the attention to detail with both food and service that has allowed them to build a core audience who enjoy this excellent Thai cooking and its superb value for money. A model restaurant, focused on service and satisfaction. (21 Railway Road, Dalkey ☎ 01-284 7304 www.thaihouse.ie tony@thaihouse.ie – Open from 5pm Mon-Sat, from 4pm Sun)

Delicatessen

Thyme Out

This most excellent deli-cum-traiteur is run with skill and circumspection by David and Berna Williams. Their cooked-food offers run the gamut of classic beef, chicken, fish and vegetarian dishes, and they also provide an excellent sandwich and sweet things offer. There are also good wines, a freezer service, and they will cook for pretty much any event going, which explains how they have prospered over the last five years. "The pleasure of home cooking with none of the effort", they promise, and they deliver just what they promise. (2a Castle Street, Dalkey ☎ 01-285 1999 thymeout@eircom.net www.thymeout.ie – Open 9am-7pm Mon-Sat)

Restaurant

Winenot

Last time in Winenot, we ate samosa with prawn, spinach and ricotta with a red pepper sauce; red snapper on shaved fennel with mandarin and caper berries; tagliatelle with wild boar sauce; risotto with mussels and cos lettuce; roast duck breast with spinach, orange and fried potatoes. It was superb, and so were the Italian wines, and the staff were so funky we could hardly believe it, and Winenot is a new star in Dalkey. (1 Coliemore Road, Dalkey ☎ 01-235 2988 winenot@eircom.net – Open 5.30pm-10.30pm Tue-Thu 5.30-11pm Fri & Sat, 4pm-9.30pm Sun)

Dun Laoghaire

Restaurant

Alexis Bar & Grill

Dublin South

Onion soup with cheddar gratinée. Braised beef short ribs Reform. Organic sirloin with chips and bearnaise. Peppered duck with confit potatoes. Smoked haddock risotto with poached egg. Jane Russell's sausages with mash and onion gravy. It's back to the future time, folks, in the company of Alan O'Reilly and his brother, Patrick. Alan is one of those blokes who always reads a market before it knows what direction it will go in. He created Morels, and Blueberry Café, and gave folk what they wanted before they knew they wanted it. Now, with Alexis Bar & Grill, he is doing it again. Interestingly, the move back to the future coincides with Paul Flynn doing something similarly eclectic in Balzac – these smart blokes cannot be wrong. And who was Alexis? Just ask your waiter. (17-18 Patrick Street, Dun Laoghaire ☎ 01-280 8872 info@alexis.ie www.alexis.ie – Open 5.30pm-10.30pm Mon-Sat, 1pm-8pm Sun)

Farmers' Market

Coco Markets

10,000 food lovers can't be wrong! Stroll in to the People's Park on a Sunday afternoon, and the sight of the Southside at table is magnificent to behold. Jackie Spillane organises this CoCo – County Council – market, and it is one of the happiest sites on the planet. There are wild and wonderful teas from Kingfisher, and cloud berry jams from Simply Swedish. Roy Kinsley is cooking his irresistible sausages,

Robert Mitchell has his great Edible Icon pasties. There are foods from the California Market Bakery, Caribbean specialities from Jennylynd's Caribbean Corner, and there is wheat grass juice and Susi sushi from Yoshio Miyachi, and there is lamb from Ticknock Farm, and sweet things from Piece of Cake bakery. Jane Russell has sausages, Jane Murphy has goat's cheeses, Liz Keegan has smashing eggs, Jens Krumpe has a queue waiting to buy his organic meat. Shall we eat olives or Gallic Kitchen pies? Or Italian food, or Chinese food on skewers, or felafels or Lebanese cooking. "Every job I have ever had has been leading to this job!", exclaims Jackie Spillane. Right job, right time, right place. 10,000 food lovers – that is the incredible number that come to the market on a summer Sunday – can't be wrong! (Dalkey, Fri 10am-4pm; Marlay Park Sat 10am-4pm; Dun Laoghaire Sun 11am-4pm; Dundrum, Fashion Avenue, Sun noon-4pm. Contact Jackie Spillane, Dun Laoghaire-Rathdown County Council ☎ 01-205 4700 market@dircoco.ie www.dlrcoco.ie)

Dublin South

Cookery School

Cook's Academy

Vanessa and Tim Greenwood's cookery school, in a smartly restored Georgian house near the Dart station, offers everything from afternoon courses and Friday night cooking for singles, all the way through to professional courses for those who want a career at the stove. A wine appreciation course has recently been added, tutored by Rebecca Scaife, and CA is a very professional outfit. (Charlemont Terrace, Dun Laoghaire, Co Dublin ☎ 01-214 5002 info@CooksAcademy.com www.cooksacademy.com)

Farmers' Market

Dun Laoghaire Farmers' Market

A Coco Market, and here is a typical reaction from a Bridgestone reader which we simply have to quote in full: "I have just moved back to Ireland after 15 years in New York - how the place has changed !! When I left the food was hit and miss but now I am back living in Dublin and surrounded by markets, cheeses, olives and all sorts of stuff to eat and drink. It's fantastic. I have been checking out the markets for the past two weekends and have particularly enjoyed Dun Laoghaire on Sundays - it's close to me and it's a treat. I had great falafel from a charming Palestinian gentleman, a fantastic rack of lamb from a German man who was so enthusiastic and informative about organic meats, I know more now about meat than I ever did !! He was so helpful and he had a great accent too - half German, half Tipperary, a charmer !! The cheeses from Sheridans were just delicious and I finished my day off with a real cornish pastie and farm cider in the People's Park from the market. I am so excited about this market having just discovered it, it will be my weekly place now !" A satisfied customer, happy in the new food loving Ireland. (The People's Park, Dun Laoghaire, Sundays 11am-4pm, see for Coco Markets above)

Deli & Take Away

Gourmet Food Parlour

Here lurks something truly savvy. Lorraine Byrne and Lorraine Heskin opened GFP in summer 2006, and almost a year later there are queues out the door for their sandwiches and soups and salads and antipasti plates – roast chicken with Caesar dressing on bagel; smoked salmon with cream cheese; Club sandwich; croque monsieur, and if you can wait 15 minutes they do a mighty burger. There are excellent jars to divert you as you wait for your sandwich, and foods-to-go to persuade you, as you enjoy some olives and a glass of wine at 4pm, that you actually don't need to cook this evening. Well smart. (7 Cumberland Street, Dun Laoghaire ☎ 01-280 5670 www.gourmetfoodparlour.com – Open Mon-Fri 8.30am-6pm, Sat 10am-6pm)

Butcher

J Hick & Sons

The best bratwurst, Lukanika and chorizo you can buy are all for sale here, which means there is a queue out the door on Saturday mornings, when early birds also snap up the great value belly pork and the porcetta, a delicious cut of rolled pork neck which loves a slow, five-hour roast: that's your Sunday dinner. Their kassler is, of course, legendary, but then optimum quality touches everything in this benchmark butcher's shop address. (15A, George's St Upr, Dun Laoghaire ☎ 01-284 2700 www.thepinkpig.com)

Fishmonger

The Ice Plant

Fresh fish are brought daily from Howth and sold in this little shed at the very end of the pier. (Dun Laoghaire Pier ☎ 01-280 5936 – Open 10am-5pm Tue-Fri and Sat am)

Restaurant

Real* Gourmet Burger

The southside strike at the new hamburger revolution that includes Bobo's on Wexford Street in the city, Real* is a family-friendly, sharp-service, wonderfully handsome room which is well focused – tiny wine list, one type of beer – and which is making a real effort to rescue the noble hamburger from its current peril. Early days yet for an obviously ambitious company, but clearly time to sell any McDonalds stock in your portfolio. Expect to see this brand all over the country in double-quick time. (The Pavilion, Dun Laoghaire ☎ 01-284 6568 www.realgourmetburger.ie)

Glasthule

Restaurant

Caviston's Deli & Seafood Restaurant

Peter Caviston's shop and restaurant is as much of a legend as the man himself, and Peter Caviston is quite a legend in Irish food circles. As creative as he is gregarious, as serious as he is light-hearted, we reckon this man should be given the freedom of the city for services to Irish food, for he has done more to champion Irish seafood than anyone else, and he has done it in the most fundamental way: by selling brilliant seafood in his shop, and by cooking brilliant seafood in the restaurant beside the shop. Shops with seafood restaurants are commonplace nowadays, but Caviston's was the first, and for us it remains the best, and the most unique seafood restaurant you can find. Get there early or you won't get a table for lunch, even though they do three sittings per day. (59 Glasthule Road ☎ 01-280 9245 www.cavistons.com – Restaurant open three lunch sittings per day: noon, 1.30pm, 3pm Tue-Fri; noon, 1.45pm, 3.15pm Sat)

Wine Merchant

Mitchell's

Southside sister of the great Dublin wine merchants, a company whose selection and service has always been of benchmark quality. For more on the company, see the entry for Mitchell's in central Dublin. (Glasthule Road ☎ 01-230 2301 www.mitchellandson.com – Open 9.30am-7pm Mon-Thur, 9.30am-8pm Fri, 10am-7pm Sat)

Butcher

Danny O'Toole

Tom O'Connor heads up this small but supremely adequate butcher's shop, the second of Danny O'Toole's shops to specialise in meats which are produced to organic standards. It not uncommon to see folk in here spending 20 minutes spending a huge amount of money buying every manner of meat, such is the obvious – and obviously unsatisfied – demand for meat of this quality and provenance. We would love to see Mr O'Toole take a leaf from the emerging meat plutocrats, and begin to offer meat of specific breed and feed – not just organic, but organic Dexter or Hereford or Galloway. We've no doubt he has been thinking of it already. (1 Glasthule Road ☎ 01-284 1125 – Open 9am-12.30pm Mon, 9am-6pm Tue-Sat)

Restaurant

Rasam

Nisheeth Tak's slinky Indian restaurant, up above the Eagle Pub, is a classy operation. A large and very stylish room offers dishes collected from the subcontinent – Baigun cheese bhaja frok Kolkotta; tandoori quail from Haryana; gosht awadh from Awadh; safaed maans from Rajasthan – and the result of this cherry picking is a menu which is far removed from the conventional, unauthentic Indian cooking which is so widespread, and so unreal. We like the fact that there are tiffin dishes and even street and highway food, and it's a fine room either for dinner for two or for a party with friends. (18/19 Glasthule Road ☎ 01-230 0600 www.rasam.ie – Open 5pm-11pm Mon-Sat, 10.30am-4.30pm Sun)

Deli & Wine Shop

64 Wine

A brand new deli, run by Gerard Maguire and Richard Moran, 64 Wine is handsome and focused, and the selection of foods and wines in the shop shows fastidious sourcing, with cheeses from Sheridan's, olive oil from The River Café, and prepared foods such as good duck confit, alongside a terrific array of wines which show a strong leaning towards organic producers. The wine area is beautifully appointed and set up for tastings, which the team hope to do every Saturday, when you will have a chance to pair up terrific foods with terrific wines. (64 Glasthule Road, Glasthule, Co Dublin ☎ 01-280 5664 info@64wine.com www.64wine.com – Open 10.30am-7pm Mon-Sat, 'till 8pm Fri)

Glenageary

Indian Takeaway

● The Bombay Pantry

Whenever we stay in Glasthule with our friend, a visit to the original Bombay Pantry, up at that windswept shopping centre at Glenageary, is always on the agenda. The cooking has always been some of the best Indian food in town, and as the chain has grown – there are now four shops, with Rathmines, Clonskeagh and Fairview added to the original – quality has never dipped. The proof of their pudding is going to sound controversial in our time-addicted age, but service in the 'Pantry is SLOW. They don't rush things. They give the food the time it needs, and the results are a joy to behold, and explains why Vivek Sahni and his crew are celebrating a decade in business. So, we'll have the Goan fire house lamb, please, karahi paneer, two coriander naans and tarka dal. Grand, so. (Glenageary Shopping Centre, Glenageary ☎ 01-285 6683. Also at 14 Rathgar Road, Rathgar, D6 ☎ 01-496 9695; 107 Clonskeagh Road, Clonskeagh ☎ 01-260 7885, 38 Philipsburgh Ave ☎ 01-884 0033 www.bombaypantry.com – Open from 5pm)

Goatstown

Wine Shop

● Bin No 9

Andy Kinsella's shop is a little south-side jewel, with 500 select wines arrayed throughout the shop, further proof of the independence of spirit in the Dublin wine world that gives the scene such energy. Andy specialises in Old World finds, along with the emerging stars of South Africa, and such select editing and sound advice, makes a pleasure of finding the bottle your dinner table or party table needs. (9 Farmhill Road, Goatstown ☎ 01-296 4844 Andrew@BinNo9.com www.binno9.com – Open 10.30am-10pm Mon-Sat, 12.30pm-8pm Sun)

Killiney

Tea Merchant

● Kingfisher Tea

Colm Hassett's teas are elixirs for the gods, almost 70 varieties of blends, tonics and brews that show the glory and majesty of global teas, from the precious Pai Mu Tan white tea to organic Rooibos. It was the Japanese Gen Mai Cha, tea with toasted rice grains, that first turned us on to the extraordinary Pandora's Box of delights that Mr Hassett selects and imports, and once you taste the variety, and the tea blending expertise, that this man demonstrates, then the world is suddenly your cuppa. Dazzling. (121 The Sycamores, Shanganagh Road, Killiney, Co Dublin ☎ 01-272 1856/087-662 5189 info@kingfishertea.com www.kingfishertea.com)

Leopardstown

Farmers' Market

Leopardstown Organic Market

Tucked snugly into the grandstand of the Leopardstown race track, the Friday market is all things bright and beautiful. There are breads from Blazing Salads – look out for Leon's sourdough fruit loaf – and sweet cakes and bakes from Jackie and Philip – look out for the apple and cinnamon crumble. The Soul Bakery has herb and onion breads, whilst An Tartisan has nice orange teabread. Noirin Kearney from County Kildare has chocolate brownies and much more, whilst Siobhan from Susi Foods has ace sushi. The Out of the Blue stall has fish so fresh it's still wriggling, whilst Suha has felafels and Relihan's from Adare have a rake of porky products. Prue & Simon have their great sausages – don't miss the new shop in the Blackrock market run by Andrew and Simon – and market stars The Real Olive Co and The Gallic Kitchen are thronged with hungry punters. Jenny McNally persuades us to try both Sarpo Yona and Remarka potatoes, whilst David McEvoy is there with turkeys, geese and other good things. Paddy Jack has his cheese brought up from County Laois, and over everything there is the huge presence – and the huge organic vegetable selection – of Denis Healy of County Wicklow. Latest arrival is the Leitrim Organic butcher. Fantastic Friday fun, fantastic Friday shopping. (Racetrack, Friday 11am-7pm)

Markets

Sean McArdle Markets

Leopardstown is just one of a series of markets run throughout Dublin city and county by Sean McArdle. There are now a total of ten markets, with full details on their website. (☎ 087-611 5016 www.irishfarmersmarkets.ie)

Monkstown

Wine Merchant

Enowine

The original branch of the wine importers and restaurant, whose HQ is now in the IFSC. See their entry in Dublin Central. (23 The Crescent, Monkstown, Co Dublin ☎ 01-230 3500 – Open 11am-9pm Mon-Sat, 12.30pm-8pm Sun; Also at Custom House Square, IFSC, D1 ☎ 01-636 0616 info@enowine.ie www.enowine.ie)

Gastropub

The Purty Kitchen

The Purty Kitchen does as good a pub lunch as you will get anywhere in Ireland, which explains why this ancient bar is perennially packed to the rafters. Sheenagh Toal's cooking doesn't mess about: she just cooks good, straightforward food, and it hits the spot, whether you have fish and chips – both cooked perfectly – or even an old warhorse like surf'n'turf, where good shelled prawns come on top of a sirloin, cooked rare as requested, and with a plate of shallow-fried garlic potatoes. Bring the kids on Sunday and they will gobble up everything in front of them, whilst you can relax with a good bowl of chowder and a fine crab sandwich on their excellent brown bread. Great value for money completes the picture of a supremely well-run and sublimely professional outfit. Next door to the Kitchen they run the Food & Wine Emporium, where you can take away a selection of the dishes offered on the menu, along with good wines at very keen prices, and they also have a wine delivery service of their wines via www.purtywines.com. (Old Dun Laoghaire Road, Monkstown ☎ 01 284 3576
info@purtykitchen.com www.purtykitchen.com)

Dublin South

Wine Merchant

Searson's

Charles Searson's wine company is a serious wine business, with a meticulous shop, a brilliant list of wines, a lengthy list of agencies and customers, and superbly notated annual en primeur offers. And yet, the heartbeat of this fantastic wine business is that it isn't the slightest bit, well, serious. Searson's understand that wine is, first and foremost, about enjoyment. Sure, if you have enough money to invest in big clarets they can get you those trophy bottles

which come, ominously, with "POA" after their names. But they will also get you a case of Chateau Beaumont for 100 euro a case, and the shop list is filled with bargains, from the smashing Roederer brut premier to the Three Monks Taltarni from Victoria to the bargain Rueda Eylo from Spain. You could shop here for a lifetime and get everything you need whilst being right up to speed with the wine world. That's what we call service.
(6a The Crescent, Monkstown ☎ 01-280 0405
sales@searsons.com www.searsons.com – Open 10am-7pm Mon-Wed, 10am-8pm Thu & Fri, 10am-7pm Sat)

Mount Merrion

Shop and Café

Michael's Food & Wine

"99% ingredients, 1% skill" It takes nerve to be that honest about how you do what you do, but Michael Lowe and Mary O'Keeffe have always had an openness about them, ever since they opened their wine shop and then their eaterie, here in the heart of Mount Merrion, and they aren't afraid to tell you how they do what they do. But what they do, they do superbly well: indeed so well that you wish more people would use less skill and trust more to ingredients. There are excellent antipasti dishes which congregate artisan ingredients on a single plate, fine bruschetta done just right, good pasta and risotto, and nice salads. Everything tastes direct, true and unpretentious, and value for both food and wine is at a premium. The wine shop is packed with superb bottles, and Michael's is an exemplary example of how discrimination and savvyness can turn something simple into something special.
(57 Deerpark Road, Mount Merrion ☎ 01-278 0377 – Shop open 10am-6pm Mon-Sat, 'till 9pm Thu & Fri. Café open noon-2.30pm Mon-Wed, noon-9pm Thu & Fri)

Rathcoole

Restaurant & Shop

Avoca

It's hard to resist any store that has a pink, poured concrete floor, and the Pratt family's Dublin county flagship is well-nigh irresistible on many more counts. The shop is fabulous, the self-service restaurant – the Birdcage Café – is fleet and the food is delicious. And in Egg restaurant, they have created a waiter service restaurant that brings together all the merits of Avoca Inc.: smart contemporary cooking, well thought-through and well executed, and with great views thrown in for free. Crab salad is served in a Kilner jar and is perky and chilli-hot; there are classics such as fisherman's pie, served with green beans and roasted tomatoes, and a very popular sirloin steak which comes with crispy-dry fries. The lightness, brightness and airiness of the store is a tribute to great design, and successfully up-scaling to this size is a great tribute to Simon Pratt and his crew. "A little oasis of good taste" is how Mr Pratt described his ambitions for Rathcoole before the store opened. Fortunately, they over-delivered. (N7 Naas Road, Rathcoole ☎ 01-257 1800 Egg Cafe Reservations ☎ 01-257 1810 rathcoole@shop.avoca.ie www.avoca.ie – Open 9.30am-6pm Mon-Sun, 'till 8pm Thur)

Stillorgan

Restaurant

China-Sichuan

One of the best loved southside restaurants, the C-S has such a devoted following that trying to get a weekend table in here is well-nigh impossible. They have captured and kept their audience – and indeed they are now serving the children of their original audience, which explains why the place is so crammed – via expert and detailed Chinese cooking that has true authenticity – we will eat the black bean and tofu any time of the day or night. So long as we can get a table. (4 Lwr Kilmacud Road, Stillorgan ☎ 01-288 4817 – Open 12.30pm-2pm Mon-Sat, 1pm-2.30pm Sun, 6pm-11pm Mon-Sun)

Local Speciality
DUBLIN LAWYER

Butcher

Fenelon's Craft Butchers

A highly regarded butcher's shop which is amongst the leading craft butchers in the city and the county, Fenelon's attracts a demanding, choosy, food-loving audience who happily rely on the charcuterie and sourcing skills of this creative team. (6 Stillorgan S.C., Stillorgan ☎ 01-288 1185 www.fenelons.ie – Open 8.30am-6pm Mon-Wed & Sat, 8.30am-9pm Thu & Fri)

Tallaght

Coffee & Tea

Irish Village Markets

This fantastic new collaboration between South Dublin County Council and Irish Village Markets – who also have markets in Monkstown on Saturday and on Anglesea Road on Thursdays – sees some of the brightest marketeers taking to Tallaght's High Street on Fridays. Jane Russell, Prue & Simon, Blazing Salads breads, the Gallic Kitchen, Seamus Kirk and lots more excellent producers can all be found here. (Main Street, Tallaght, 10am-4pm Fri)

Coffee & Tea

Java Republic

David McKiernan's coffee roasting company has been the most visible and dynamic coffee company over the last decade, inspiring new entrants like Ariosa Coffee and Cork Coffee Roasters to establish bespoke coffee roasting companies to challenge the bland monolith that existed in the Irish coffee world. But McKiernan has also challenged the global corruption in coffee that exploits coffee growers, so he deals direct, buying arabica beans, and paying well above the C-contract price on the world market. Great brews, great ethics, up the Republic! (Citylink Business Park, Old Naas Road, Tallaght ☎ 01-456 5506 www.javarepublic.com)

County Galway

GALWAY CITY

Restaurant

Ard Bia

There are many alephs in Galway city – points from which you can see and understand this wild, youthful, self-conscious city – and Aoibheann McNamara's first floor café/restaurant/art space is one of the very best alephs in town. You can't imagine this democratic mix of food, wine, culture and whatever-it-is-you-fancy working anywhere else other than here. But it's success isn't just because it's appositely bohemian. Its success is based on understanding good foods, nice wines, and knowing how to serve them properly, and with a lot of charm, and that is what has made it first port of call for many locals and visitors. Aoibheann and her team have just taken over the wickedly atmospheric Nimmo's, down by Spanish Arch, so see the entry for that also, and they also run the William Street art gallery. (2 Quay Street, Galway ☎ 091-539 897 ✉ ardbia@gmail.com 🖱 www.ardbia.com – Café open 10am-5pm Mon-Sat, noon-6pm Sun. Restaurant open 6.30pm-10.30pm

Galway City

Café and Flower shop

Budding Café

The Budding is buzzing. You might feel like you are gate-crashing a private party when you walk through Heneghan's Flower Shop to find the café, but you aren't. Blue stone walls, flagstone flooring, and a conservatory style are home to one of Galway's best kept secrets, a café with only eight tables, and a simple board menu spells out what they do, nice savoury things like a crostini trio of basil, mozzarella and sautéed mushrooms, or a good savoury tart served with baby potatoes and salad. Even though it's a small busy cafe, you could spend the afternoon here and not feel the time pass by, such is the charm of the setting and the atmosphere. (Sea Road, Galway ☎ 091-588821 – Open daytime)

Café

The Cobblestone Cafe

Tiny but cosy, friendly but intimate, the CC is like a cosy

old style country kitchen where you always want to pull up a chair. The cooking is Mediterranean-vegetarian: felafels with olive salad; fresh tomato soup with croutons, hummus, roasted peppers, and there are classic Mediterranean puds such as Tunisian orange cake and lemon polenta cake. It's always popular, so get there early for lunch. (Kirwan's Lane, Galway ☎ 091-567227
✉ katewright@eircom.net – Open Day-time)

Restaurant

● Da Roberta

This humungously busy Italian restaurant in Salthill has successfully spawned a sister restaurant just up the street – Osteria da Roberta – and together the Robertas do the simple things well. Good breads, good pastas, very good pizzas are what the regulars turn up for time after time, and everything is cooked and served with charm by Sandro and Roberta. Just make sure that you have a reservation for the weekend. (Da Roberta, 169 Upper Salthill, Galway ☎ 091-585808, Osteria da Roberta,
157 Upper Salthill, Galway ☎ 091-581111
✉ daroberta@eircom.net – Open noon-11pm Mon-Sun)

Restaurant

● Da Tang Noodle House

Saturday afternoon, circumnavigating Galway with the children, and the need for noodles suddenly seizes you. Lucky you: you are in the right city. The Da Tang noodles are ace: punchy, fiery, vivid, served in a tiny room which means that if there are five of you – there were five of us – you won't be able to sit together. No matter. You are here for a body-charging blast of noodle profundity, and Da Tang delivers, and has delivered ever since Catherine and Du-Han first opened their doors. And check out the very smart paintings by the boss, which are really rather fetching pieces of modern abstraction. (2 Middle Street, Galway ☎ 091-788638 – Open Lunch & Dinner)

Fishmonger

● Deacy's Fish Shop

The centre of bustling, busy, boisterous Galway is home to Deacy's Fish Shop, where Michael Deacy sells local fish from nearby Rossaveal, in Connemara. Michael also supplies fruit and vegetables, and is a member of the Deacy family who also own Ernie's Fish Stores. (11 High Street, Galway ☎ 091 562515 – Open 9am-6pm Mon-Sat)

Café

Delight Gourmet Food Bar

David Lawrence's little space is spick, span, professional and dedicated, giving Delight the edge over Galway's raft of coffee and food shops. There is real application evident here, and sharp cooking – great salads – including an unusual breakfast salad – lovely imaginative sandwiches ranging from baked ham and brie to Peking duck and eastern hummus, with lots of good sweet things and Illy coffee and excellent juices and smoothies. Fabulous-Food-Fast: yes indeed. (29 Upr Abbeygate Street, Galway ☎ 091-567823 ✉ delightgfb@eircom.net – Open Day-time)

B&B

Devon Dell

Berna Kelly's B&B is one of the best, with one of the very best breakfasts you can eat in Ireland, and the most meticulous housekeeping. (47 Devon Park, Lower Salthill, Galway ☎ 091-528306 ✉ devondell@iol.ie 🖱 www.devondell.com Open Feb-Oct. No credit cards.)

Craft Butcher

Martin Divilly

Martin Divilly belongs to that younger generation of charcutiers who are driven, dedicated and dynamic. He has superb beef – mainly hand-picked Hereford and Angus which is dry-aged – and a terrific range of prepared meats and meals and deli foods in a pristine store. (Unit 9/10 Westside Shopping Centre, Galway ☎ 091-523947 – Open 8.30am-7pm Mon-Thu, 8.30am-8pm Fri, 8am-6pm Sat)

Fishmonger

Ernie's Fish Stores

After 30 years of selling fresh fish, this family shop has diversified into becoming what Ernie Deacy describes as a 'rarity' shop. In addition to a range of fish, they sell organic wines, organic produce, fruit and vegetables and Fair Trade Goods. The fish offer includes herrings and organic salmon from Clare Island. (Sea Road, Galway ☎ 091-586812 – 9am-6pm Mon-Sat)

Hotel

The G

Love it, loathe it, but admit that you can't ignore it. The G has proven itself to be one

of the pivotal design statements in contemporary Ireland, so that those who love it can overlook its terrible location, whilst those who loathe it cite the location as just one of the reasons why it does nothing for them. Well, we love the chutzpah of the public rooms, with their lurid design elan, and the bedrooms are the best we have ever seen in Ireland. We would have preferred a home-grown restaurant to the imported Santini Italian restaurant, but it does a decent job, albeit at high prices. Mary McKeon and her crew work hard to keep this graciously eccentric operation on peak form, and there is always a moment of sublime self-congratulation as you glimpse those sea horses again. (Wellpark, Galway ☎ 091-865 200 www.theghotel.ie)

Market

The Galway Saturday Market

Traders come and go from Galway's iconic market, establishing successful businesses and moving on, or maybe establishing successful businesses and yet maintaining a market stall. A core of vegetable growers have been trading here for years, abetted during the high season by many other casual traders. Recently, the fishmonger Stefan Griesbach has been the big hit of the market, and his success shows that there is space for new blood and a hunger on the part of customers for dynamic new traders.

Galway City

So, what to buy? Well, presuming you have the Kurt Cobain t-shirt and more cannabis-scented incense than you can handle, do check out the famed olive bread from Dave Holland's Bread Stall. Paul will be there with Boychik doughnuts, and Ann Marie McKee will have superb chocolates. Of course, you need green olives stuffed with anchovies from The Olive Stall, and a large bowl of Madras curry to fortify you as you shop. Gearoid de Brun's wild Aran salmon will solve the problem of how to start dinner, and some good hummus from the Hummus Stall will be tickety-boo.

• Breckish Dairies. Huge Zyderlaan has been selling the splendid Breckish dairy cow's and goat's milk cheeses in the market since 1979. Look out for their particularly fine yogurts, which can be bought in McCambridge's during the week.

• Cait Curran's Organic Vegetable Stall. Cait edits the magazine *Organic Matters* (www.organicmattersmag.com) – and when she isn't at the keyboard she is producing a magnificent array of organic fruit and vegetables for her wildly busy stall. Look out for great brassicas, lovely fresh heads of cos and bags of funky leaves, great potatoes and other tubers, and Cait also has a selection of organic imported fruit.

• Dirk Flake. Dirk's organic vegetables, grown out west at Aughinish, are one of the stars of the market.

• Joachim Hess. Joachim's organic vegetables and excellent fresh breads are not to be missed.

• Sheridan's Cheesemongers. They may be busy taking over sections of Galway's eating and drinking culture, but that doesn't mean the Sheridan's crew don't still pay homage to where their culinary journey began back in 1995. So, Saturday morning they set up the trestle table and line up their magnificently affineured cheeses.

• Yummy Crêpes. "Roll up! Roll up! Last 2,000 crepes!". It's not enough just to be a great food expert in the Galway Market: you also have to be an entertainer, and entertainment is what they deliver at YC. The craic is great. The crêpes are superb. (Beside St Nicholas Church galwaymarket@eircom.net www.galwaymarket.net – Sat 8.30am-4pm & Sunday 2pm-6pm)

Bakery

The Gourmet Tart Company

Michelle and Fintan Hyland's company is really putting on the style these days. Breads, bakes, cakes and tarts – and don't miss their all-butter croissants – all have a confident style and swagger that shows how much this company has grown and gotten better. They were always good bakers, but it's the patisserie-level, no short cuts, finish that today pulls them ahead of the posse and makes GTC's savoury and sweet baking a real fixture of the city. The shop is also a good lunch option for a drink and a freshly made sandwich. (7 Lower Abbeygate Street, Galway ☎ 091-588384 – open daily, seven days. Also in the Limerick and Ennis market)

Patisserie & Coffee Shop

Goya's

Emer Murray has few peers in the world of Irish patisserie. A perfectionist by nature, Ms Murray pours heart and soul into her café and her baking and cooking – take it from us, this girl works too hard – but what on earth would we do without her hands-on approach? Definitive excellence is her signature, whether you are in here for a loaf of brown bread, a bowl of stew, or to discuss with the patron how much you are willing to spend on your wedding cake, one of Ms Murray's specialities. Genuinely indispensable. (2/3 Kirwans Lane, Galway ☎ 091-567010 🖰 www.goyas.ie)

Fishmonger

Stefan Griesbach

Stefan's fish stall has been the wow! of the Galway market in recent times, offering a dazzling selection of piscine perfection, and reason on its own to come to the market. Stefan has begun to travel to other Galway markets inland, with exactly the same wow! effect, and his success proves that the market needs new blood, and new people to raise the standards as effectively as this perfectionist fish seller has done. (Stefan Griesbach ☎ 086-3488591)

Bakery

Griffin's Bakery

You need only look at the queue that is a permanent, Monday-to-Saturday fixture of Jimmy Griffin's shop, to know how good this bakery is, and how much it is beloved of Galway food lovers. The sweet baking is charmingly domestic, the bread baking is ambitious and agrestic, and between the two of them Griffin's hits the spot. (21 Shop Street, Galway ☎ 091-563683 griffinj@iol.ie 🖰 www.griffinsbakery.com – Open 8am-6pm Mon-Sat)

B&B

The Heron's Rest

A darling little B&B, from whose windows you can easily toss a pebble into the Corrib – not that we recommend you do. Sorcha Molloy makes some of the finest, funky breakfasts we have enjoyed in recent times, so location, creativity and style make this a key Galway address. (16a Longwalk, Spanish Arch, Galway ☎ 086-337 9343 msorcha@gmail.com 🖰 www.theheronsrest.com)

Restaurant

Holywell Café

The all-conquering County Clare concept moves north to Galway, and already the Holywell signature of bumper flavours and bumper portions – this is Tyrolean cooking, not conventional Italian cooking – and bumper value is sweeping all before it. Four starters, six pastas and nine pizzas are all they need to convince you that you have to tell all your friends, and come back yourself sometime soon. A brilliant concept, brilliantly executed, and just the right addition to Galway. (Bridge Mills, O'Briens Bridge ☎ 091-566231 – Open noon-11pm)

Hotel

● The House Hotel

Do you know, they really missed a beat when they called this hotel "House". They could – and should – have called it "Home". We have felt more looked after in House than in any other hotel of recent times: the staff go the extra mile, and you can see from the packed public rooms that we are not alone. "A house is not a home", says the old song. This House most definitely is a Home. (Lwr Merchant Road, Spanish Parade ☎ 091-538900 info@thehousehotel.ie www.theHousehotel.ie)

Pub/Restaurant

● The Huntsman Inn

This frantically busy pub across the road from The G is a super-slick piece of work. When the office workers crowd out the place – not to mention the car park – at lunchtime, this machine hums into action, and the speed of service has to be seen to be believed. But it's not just speed that pulls in the punters: the food is simple but professionally delivered, and the entire operation is comfortable in its skin. (164 College Road, Galway ☎ 091-562849 www.huntsmaninn.com – Open 8am-9.30pm Mon-Sun)

Galway City

Restaurant

● Kappa-Ya

Yoshimi Hayakawa and Junichi Yoshiyagawa run the best Japanese restaurant in Ireland, This talented pair have proven themselves worthy successors to West Cork's legendary Shiro Japanese Dining House, which blazed a trail for genuine Japanese cooking under the late Kei Pilz. Now, in a room not much bigger than the old Shiro, Junichi cooks with calmness, precision and verve, and Yoshimi looks after everyone in such style that leaving is such sweet sorrow. And whilst we love the pure Japanese dishes, it is Mr Yoshiyagawa's brilliant improvisations with Irish artisan ingredients that strike us as some of the most original cooking in the country. (4 Middle Street Mews, Galway ☎ 086 3543616 kappaya@eircom.net – Open noon-6pm Mon-Fri. Dinner by reservation only)

Restaurant

The Malt House

The Malt House has been garnering awards for its wine list, but teetotallers would enjoy the experience of eating here, thanks to a swish room, smart, polite staff and an aura of professionalism that lets them pull off complicated stuff – such as their signature seafood dish for two people, which arrives on a triple layer plate with roasted fish, prawns and scallops on top, served with basmati rice, then a layer of crab, shrimps, smoked salmon and a timbale of cod, haddock and salmon, with a final layer of Clarinbridge oysters. This is great fun to eat, and comes with an array of sauces, but starters such as mille feuille of asparagus and smoked cheese, or puds like coconut cheesecake are just as adroitly delivered. (Olde Malt Mall, High Street ☎ 091-567866 ✉ info@themalthouse.ie 🖱 www.themalthouse.ie – Open Lunch & Dinner)

Shop

McCambridge's

They smartened up the wine shop in the legendary McCambridge's a while back, but the shop has none of that look-but-don't-touch design self-consciousness that is rampant today, Instead it remains a brilliant local shop, with local style and local service, but which just happens to be in the centre of town. It is packed with lovely things to eat and drink, and local foods such as Brekish dairy and Magnetti pasta. (38/39 Shop Street, Galway ☎ 091-562259 🖱 retail@mccambridges.com 🖱 www.mccambridges.com – Open 8.30am-9pm Mon-Sat

Local Speciality

CONNEMARA LAMB

GALWAY OYSTERS

Restaurant & Fish'n'Chip bar

McDonagh's Seafood House

P.J. and Mary McDonagh's family business has been around for more than a century, though what began as a fish shop – at a time when Quay Street was known locally as Fish Street because it was lined with so many fish sellers – is now a seafood restaurant and a fish'n'chip takeaway. Both are extremely popular with both locals and visitors. (22 Quay Street ☎ 091-565001 ✉ fish@mcdonaghs.net 🖱 www.mcdonaghs.net – Restaurant open 5pm-10pm Mon-Sat, Fish'n'Chips noon-11pm Mon-Sat, 5pm-11pm Sun)

Wine Bar

Martine's Quay Street Wine Bar

Part of the McDonagh family empire, Martine's is a favourite for many visitors who want to inhale and inhabit the Quay Street bustle. Nice wines, simple cooking. (21 Quay Street, Galway ☎ 091-565662 www.winebar.ie)

Fishmonger

Mermaid

Ali Jalivandi sources his fish from south coast day boats in order to get optimum quality. Many of the best restaurants in Galway source their fish from Ali. (67 Henry Street, Galway ☎ 091-586641 – Open 8am-5pm Mon-Fri, 8am-4pm Sat)

Shop

Morton's of Galway

Desperately seeking something new? Believe us, you will find it in Eric Morton's shop. This man and his crew have an ability to winkle out and discover the newest and the coolest foods and wines, and they sell them in a shop that, since it extended, is even more stylish, comfortable and biddable. The staples of bread, cheese, fish and meats are all here in prime pomp, together with super food-to-go and the chicest collection of designer gourmet grub. One of the stars of the west coast. (Lower Salthill, Galway ☎ 091-522237 sales@mortonsofgalway.ie www.mortonsofgalway.ie)

Galway City

Restaurant

Nimmo's

Galway's funkiest room is now operated by Aoibheann McNamara, who has made a formidable reputation in Ard Bia over the last several years, and who has brought a wilfully eclectic Middle Eastern mix of dishes to this great address. Yogurt baked chicken with a chickpea, feta and coriander salad with harrisa; Cypriot baked lamb and potatoes with cumin spiced tomatoes; spanakopita with organic leaf, hummus and roasted Mediterranean vegetables are typical of the food focus, sort of Diana Henry meets Paula Wolfert in the souk, and you can begin with a mezze plate and finish with superb orange and cardamom cake, or baklava. Fantastic wines include the Roaring Meg pinot noir, from New Zealand. Now, there's a bottle to drink when in Galway. (Spanish Arch, Long Walk, Galway ☎ 091-561114 6-11 – Open 6pm-11pm Tue-Sun, open lunch Fri-Sun)

Wine Shop

The Noble Vine

Noel O'Loughlin's selection of wines is available from the shop at Terryland as well as Burren Wines in Bal-lyvaughan, Ferguson Wines in Clifden and Stewart Wines in Sligo. In addition to the interesting and little known wines he imports, Noel also manages a vineyard – Do-maine d'Espere, in St. Jean de Serres – where more than 150 people have bought plots, ranging from 30 acres, to a single row producing 80 bottles per year. Organic status is aimed for, and Le Noblevine is a fun operation, whether you simply want to drink or you have a dream of having your own slice of terroir. (Terryland Retail Pk, Headford Road, Galway ☎ 091-565749 www.theNobleVine.com)

Deli & Cafe

Olio & Farina

Liam and Maria Payne ran The Blackthorn in Gort for many years before switching focus and taking up the hip Olio & Farina franchise. "It's just like walking into a shop in Italy" is how our Galway mates describe the totality of the O&F concept, and the shop at the front with the oils and salamis and gifts and lovely whatnots opens up into the Lite Bites café at the rear, where Liam and Maria want "to keep it simple and keep the quality". They have hit the ground running, and smart Galwegians have found another funky, food-fixated address to satisfy their endless curiosity. (50 Upper Abbeygate Street, Galway ☎ 091-539742 www.olioefarina.com – Open 9.30am-6.30pm Mon-Thur, 9.30am-8pm Fri, 9.30am-6.30pm Sat)

Restaurant

Oscar's

Michael O'Meara is just about the wildest cook we know. In a surrealist room he serves up food that seems to come from the mind of a surrealist, but don't imagine he is some sort of crazy dreamer. Both O'Meara and his wife, Sinead, are disciplined and professional, but they allow themselves the liberty of doing things their own way. So, for starters he offers everything from crisp potato skins to chicken yakitori to frog's legs with tarragon. Mains can feature prawn and chilli sambal, a Thai red beef curry or Hereford steak with Café de Paris butter. It sounds un-likely, and yet he pulls it all off with gas in the tank, whilst Sinead demonstrates that she has few equals at front-of-house. (22 Upper Dominick Street, Galway ☎ 091-582180 www.oscarsgalway.com)

Restaurant

● Park Room Restaurant

The dining room of Eyre Square's Park House Hotel is always sparkling in appearance, staffed by witty, knowledgeable crew who know their stuff, and the cooking is consistent, reliable and tasty, such a contrast to the indifference and uniform blandness of other Galway hotels. You can order chicken liver pâté, then prawns with steak, and both will be pleasing dishes shown appropriate respect. Once upon a time all hotel dining rooms exhibited this care. (Park House Hotel, Forster Street, Eyre Square, ☎ 091-564 924 parkhousehotel@eircom.net – Open Carvery lunch and bar food, Dinner & Sun Lunch)

Fishmonger

● The Seafood Centre @ Galway Bay Seafoods

The Seafood Centre is the factory shop of the well known Galway Bay Seafoods. The Centre offers a huge variety of local and exotic fish, aiming to serve both the local and ethnic communities by providing a comprehensive range of very fresh fish. (New Docks, Galway City ☎ 091-563011 – Open 9am-5pm Mon-Sat, closed lunch 1pm-2pm on Mon & Sat)

Cheesemonger, Delicatessen & Wine Shop

● Sheridan's Cheesemongers

Sheridan's is one of those essential organisations that is not simply part of the food culture, it is an essential organisation that defines the food culture. They sell cheese, they sell good foods, they sell wine, but that is actually the least of what they do. Sheridan's sells culture, and let's spell that with a big c: Culture. If you want to understand contemporary Irish food culture, you need do no more than walk in the door – or walk up the stairs to the wine shop and wine bar – and be served by one of their brilliant members of staff, and all will be apparent to you. These guys are gourmets. They are dynamic business people. They are democrats in terms of taste, in terms of how they work – they maintain fastidious market stalls everywhere along with the shops – and in terms of what they choose to sell. Sheridan's make life better for everyone, simple as that. (16 Church Yard Street, Galway shop ☎ 091-564829, wine shop ☎ 091-564832 www.sheridanscheesemongers.com – Shop Open 9.30am-6pm Mon-Fri, 9am-6pm Sat, (and 1pm-6pm Sun June-Aug only), 2pm-9pm Tue-Fri, noon-8pm Sat)

Gastro Pub

Sheridan's on the Docks

"Are you the Italian waiter?". "Yes." "Okay, well I've been told that I have to ask *you* for an espresso."
Only in Galway. Only in Sheridan's. Irish bars generally have zero service. In Sheridan's you get bespoke service, right down to the espressos. Here is a bar which is so radical in its ambit that at weekends they will sell as much of the sublime Galway Hooker ale – one of the best new drinks to have appeared in Ireland in the last five years, brewed north of Galway up in Roscommon – as they will sell pints of Guinness. But then, Sheridan's customers aren't the standard Irish pub customer, and this isn't the standard Irish pub: this is the Irish pub reinvented for the 21st century, in all its modern, magnificent glory. (New Docks, Galway city ☎ 091- 564905
✉ info@sheridanscheesemongers.com
🖱 www.sheridanscheesemongers.com – Open from 4.30pm Mon-Thur, from noon Fri & Sat, closed pub hours)

Butcher

C.R. Tormey & Sons

Galway City

John Tormey's shop exhibits all the experience and expertise that is the hallmark of the Tormey family shops in Mullingar, Tullamore and here in Galway. Beautifully prepared and beautifully presented, whatever you buy at Tormey's is failsafe-good, though their own beef is always the speciality. (Unit 17 Headford Shopping Centre, Headford Road, Galway ☎ 091-564067
✉ tormeysm@gmail.com)

Restaurant

Tulsi

Indian cooking in Ireland remains a conservative genre, and the unchanging Tulsi outlets – there are several more in Dublin and elsewhere – offer a pleasant, familiar ethnic experience. (3 Buttermilk Walk, Middle Street, Galway ☎ 091-564831 – Open noon-2.30pm, 6pm-11pm Mon-Sat (closed 11.30pm Fri & Sat) 1pm-10pm Sun)

Restaurant

Vina Mara

Eileen Feeney's restaurant has carved out a fine reputation as offering something that operates in between the more avant garde food offers in the city and the more conventional. The cooking is solidly based on Mediterranean staples and signatures with modern tropes – braised lamb shank; cod with piquillo peppers – and there has always been a hungry ambition evident in Vina Mara. (19 Middle Street, Galway ☎ 091-561610 info@vinamara.com www.vinamara.com)

Wine Shop

● The Wine Buff

Tony and Eleanor Grealy do a really good job here at the Wine Buff, on the promenade at Salthill. Whether you choose the Braidot pinot grigio at under a tenner or push the boat out a bit for the Colbois Chablis at a few euro shy of twenty, you will get typicity, interest, singularity and value for money, especially that pinot grigio which is a steal. Good service, good delivery, and a model wine shop that can introduce you to the true culture of wine. (The Promenade, Salthill, Galway ☎ 091 586550 tony@thewinebuff.com www.thewinebuff.com – Open 1pm-8pm Mon-Wed, noon-8pm Thur, noon-9pm Fri, 11am-8pm Sat)

Wine Shop

● Woodberry's

Declan and Sandra Owens' wine shop is another choice element of the Middle Street Mews culinary oasis. Lovely wines, with a strong leaning towards the New World, great service, and it's always such a sweet experience to be buying a bottle or a case in Woodberry's. (3 Middle Street Mews, Middle Street, Galway ☎ 091-533706 woodberrys@eircom.net www.thomaswoodberrys.com)

"It is the relationship between you and the earth, between you and the grower, between you and your care and responsibility for what your customers eat."

BERNADETTE O'SHEA *PIZZA DEFINED*

Aran Islands – Inis Meain

Restaurant and Suites

Bialann & Seomraí Só Inis Meáin

The de Blácam family have a distinguished history of creativity and endeavour on Inis Meain, and now Ruari and Marie-Therese de Blácam's Inis Meáin restaurant and suites promises a thrilling new concept. Sean de Blacam has designed a long building, using island stone and lots of glass, and in addition to a 30 seater restaurant there will be a series of own-door suites. Mr de Blácam plans to use island fish, shellfish and produce, and he enjoys a considerable reputation as a creative chef, so prospects bode well for this striking adventure opening in summer 2007. (Inis Meain ☎ 086-826 6026 www.inismeain.com – Open seasonally)

B&B

An Dún

A pretty B&B and restaurant owned by Teresa and Padraic O Fatharta, and the perfect base from which to explore the intimate particularity of this glorious island. (Inis Meain, Aran Islands ☎ 099-73047
anduninismeain@eircom.net
www.inismeainaccommodation.com)

B&B

Mairin Concannon's B&B

Another lovely B&B in which to base yourself as you get to the soul and lonely spirit of the island. (Moore Village, Inis Meain, Aran Islands ☎ 099-73019)

Aran Islands – Inis Mór

Smoked Seafood

Aran Salmon

Gearoid de Brun's smoked fish is sold at the Saturday Galway Market and also through retail outlets. Mr de Brun favours a light smoking, and uses extra elements, such as Guinness, truffles and peat smoking, to supply contrasting and complementary flavours to the smoked fish. (Kilronan, Inis Mor ☎ 099-61240)

Guesthouse

Kilmurvey House

We stayed for a few days at Kilmurvey House in summer 2006, and we had the best time ever. Of all the dining rooms we ate in during that year, none matched the sky-high energy and brio of this room, packed with happy holidaymakers eating the most delicious – the most delicious – food, served by a crack team of young women who over-delivered in every department. We swam in Kilmurvey Bay – and got stung by a jellyfish: be careful! – climbed up to Dun Aengus, walked up the hill to the pub, hired the bicycles and cursed the selfish minibus drivers who make the roads so dangerous, and who behave with such bad grace. But, back in Kilmurvey, we forgot about those twits immediately, and chilled out in the unique bliss that is Aran. Treasa Joyce runs the most special B&B you can find: don't on any account miss it. (Kilmurvey, Inis Mór, Aran Islands ☎ 099-61218
kilmurveyhouse@eircom.net
www.kilmurveyhouse.com)

Guesthouse & Restaurant

Man of Aran Cottage

A summertime lunch, eaten on the verandah at the rere of Man of Aran, is something that is hard to beat. Nice food, gentle sea breezes, good calm service, a lovely domestic spot that every visitor has to visit, and do note that Joe and Maura also have three rooms for guests for those who want to prolong the pleasure. (Kilmurvey, Inis Mór, Aran Islands ☎ 099-61301
www.manofarancottage.com – Open Mar-Oct)

Guesthouse

Mainistir House

Joel d'Anjou has been working hard to upgrade Mainistir, so whilst the exterior still needs some work, the rooms inside are being enlarged and are being decorated with M. d'Anjou's inimitable style: this guy can take stuff from Dunnes Stores and make it look like Casa Armani. The vegetarian feast every evening represents the best value meal on the island, and for those guests who get into the groove that M. d'Anjou weaves, you will likely have an unforgettable time, whilst others simply don't see what there is to make a fuss about. (Kilronan, Inis Mór, Aran Islands ☎ 099-61351 mainistirhouse@eircom.net
www.mainistirhousearan.com)

Aran Islands –Inis Oirr

Restaurant & Study Centre

The Fisherman's Cottage

We had an early-morning fishing venture with Enda Conneely, last time we stayed on Inis Oirr, and it was the brilliant end to a brilliant Aran Islands adventure. We hauled in the pollock and mackerel, and felt we were kings of the waves as the boat bobbed about within view of the village. The night before we had enjoyed a lovely simple dinner in the restaurant – mushroom and thyme leaf tart; lemon sole with herb butter and floury potatoes and monkfish flamed with brandy – and we were sorry we had no urgent excuse to stay longer and maybe do a cookery course or two in the Foodwise Cookery School Enda and Marie have built beside the restaurant. The courses concentrate on wholefood cooking for health, but the feeling of exhilaration that comes from Fisherman's Cottage surely comes from the holistic approach of this most talented, unclichéd couple and their singular way of working. (Inis Oirr, Aran Islands
☎ 099 75073 ✉ foodwise@eircom.net
🖱 www.southaran.com – Open April-Sept 10am-4pm, 7pm-9pm)

Galway County

Guesthouse

Radharc an Chlair

A pretty bungalow up the hill is where Brid Poil runs her much-respected B&B, and food lovers adore the dinners this gifted cook prepares. (Inis Oirr, Aran Islands
✉ bridpoil@eircom.net ☎ 099-75019)

Athenry

Bakery

Foods of Athenry

Siobhan and Paul Lawlor's Farm House Bakery unites two mighty talents – she is a former computer programmer, whilst he has given up minding the cows to make the breads – and the result is some very fine baking. We like the brown soda and treacle bread, the scones and those Mom'n'Pop style apple tarts (they hand-peel the apples each morning). The breads are available in local supermakets, and is the house bread used by famous seafood pub Moran's of the Weir. (Oldcastle, Kilconieron, Athenry
☎ 091 848152 🖱 www.foodsofathenry.ie)

Ballinafad

Hotel and Restaurant

● Ballynahinch Castle

Ballynahinch may be the most relaxing castle in the world, an oasis run with superb control, calm and decorum by Patrick O'Flaherty, who oversees a superbly friendly crew who manage to make everyone feel welcome, and special. There is more than a bit of magic to the Ballynahinch spell, and food lovers will easily declare it as one of their all-time favourite places to eat and stay in Ireland – the latest letter received at Bridgestone Central as we were writing this book simply said: "Thought I would drop you a note to agree on how outstanding Ballynahinch Castle is. The food was superb". Everything chimes sweetly, from service to cooking to value, and it is the most democratic space in the west. Outstanding is right. (Ballinafad, Recess, Connemara ☎ 095-31006 bhinch@iol.ie www.ballynahinch-castle.com – Open all year, except Feb)

Ballinasloe

Farmers' Market

● Ballinasloe Farmers' Market

Kicking off on Fridays at 10am, the BFM is a vital stop for local produce, and don't miss Stefan's superb fish counter which has proven to be one of the big draws amidst all the other must-have delights from West Coast artisans. (Croffy's Centre, Main Street. Ballinasloe – Fridays 10am)

Organic fruit and vegetables

● Beechlawn Organic Farm

Padraig Fahy is a restlessly energetic, ever-smiling, hard-working organic grower, a man who orchestrates and organises local farmers' markets, when he isn't urging the compost to bestow its goodness on his own fruit and vegetables, or else scooting around in his car delivering his weekly basket delivery scheme. A planned expansion of the area under tunnels at the farm should see lots more lovely Ballinasloe vegetables spreading happiness and culinary contentment to Padraig's markets, so look out for this superb produce in the Loughrea, Ballinasloe and Athlone markets, or sign up for the basket scheme. (Ballinasloe, info@beechlawnfarm.org www.beechlawnfarm.org)

Farmhouse Cheese

● Killeen Farmhouse Cheese

Marian Roeleveld's Killeen goat's milk cheese is a beauty, but, like other westerly cheeses such as Mill House or Carrowholly or Derrymore, it remains relatively little known. The milk is pasteurised, but the flavour is fulsome and sweet, and the texture achieved by the cheesemaker is sinuous, subtle, extremely expert. This is a really fine cheese, so hunt it down in good stores. (Killeen Milhouse, Ballyshrule, Ballinasloe ☎ 090-9741319 ✉ haske-marion@iolfree.ie)

Spice mixes

● Kylemore Acres

Diana and Richard Murray are tireless, painstaking people, and their diligence shines through in the diverse but uniformly excellent Kylemore herb mixes, rubs and marinades that form their product list. These mixes show true epicurean expertise, and they deliver balance, roundness and piquancy to any dish, whether you are marinating a steak or elevating a lamb stew into something extraordinary. You will find the KA sachets in all good butchers and fishmongers. (Kylemore, Laurencetown, Ballinasloe ☎ 090-965 5857 ✉ sales@kylemoreacres.com www.kylemoreacres.com)

Butcher

● Leitrim Organic Butcher's Shop

The Leitrim Organic Producers first brought their mobile meat stall to the Ballinasloe Market, but it has quickly developed into a stand-alone shop open Thursday, Friday and Saturday in Crotty's Yard, where Declan Carroll prepares and sells fresh, organic symbol meats. (Crotty's Yard, Ballinasloe ☎ 071-9640869 ✉ info@leitrimorganic.com www.leitrimorganic.com)

Ballyconneely

Smokehouse

● The Connemara Smokehouse

Graham Roberts is a talented, inquisitive, creative fish smoker, and he has brought this family firm smack up to date with great new products, such as honey roast smoked tuna, and has seen his

hard work rewarded with a brace of awards and with customers such as Rick Stein of Padstow sourcing his smoked tuna. The range of smoked fish includes an exceptional smoked wild salmon, smoked mackerel, smoked cod and also kippers. Mr Robert's company is a model, artisan, west coast, fish smoking specialist with a true signature to everything he does. (Bunowen Pier, Ailebrack, Ballyconneely ☎ 095 23739
info@smokehouse.ie www.smokehouse.ie)

Clarenbridge

Restaurant

Claire's Tearooms

Claire Walsh has style. Masses of it. You only need to walk in the door of this lovely tearoom – which also houses her daughter, Kiersey McGrath's home furnishing shop – to see that everything Ms Walsh puts her hand to is done stylishly. The food is simple, stylish, quotidian things like bacon and leek quiche with salad – but done perfectly, done with flair. Half the attraction of Claire's is the fact that it makes you feel so hip and wholesome to be here, attributes that the food accentuates and congratulates. Pure darling. (Clarinbridge ☎ 091-776606 – Open 10.30am-5pm Tue-Sat, Sun 1pm-5pm)

Pasta

Magnetti Pasta

The Magnetti company's fresh pastas have been a staple of delis and good food shops in recent years, as well as their own family restaurant, Trattoria Magnetti on Quay Street. But their development of a new range of filled raviolis – pumpkin ravioli; seafood ravioli; sunblush and black olive ravioli; a smashing porcini, ricotta and gorgonzola ravioli – is really exciting, and with developing distribution these should become more widely available. The fresh pastas and the pasta sauces are a godsend for the busy house, giving real quality in double-quick time. (Unit 1A Clarenbridge Business Park, Clarenbridge ☎ 091-776580
pasta@magnettifoods.com
www.magnettifoods.com)

Restaurant

The Old School House Restaurant

Kenneth Connolly's ever-popular restaurant at the edge of Clarenbridge offers some lovely comfort cooking, in dishes such as filo-wrapped West Clare goat's cheese, or braised shank of lamb with carrot and parsnip purée, or roast fillet of pork with champ and a mustard grain sauce. This is unpretentious, true cooking, served by sweet-natured staff in a comfortable room, and the excellent value for money explains its enduring popularity. Make sure to book for the weekend and Sunday lunch. (Clarenbridge ☎ 091-796898 ✉ kenc@iol.ie – Open 6.30pm-10pm Tue-Sun; 12.30pm-2.30pm Sun)

Cleggan

Seaweed Relishes

● Cleggan Seaweed Company

The seaweeds of the West of Ireland grow in the cleanest, purest waters in Europe, and Cleggan preserve them without processing or washing out any of their mineral richness. They then dry them and bottle them as condiments or preserve them in the most wonderful pickle – use it wherever you might use capers or gherkins. Beautiful simple packaging, great food. You can find their little bottles in Sheridan's and the Connemara Hamper. (Cleggan Fishing Village, Connemara ☎ 095-44977 ✉ info@clegganseaweed.com 🖱 www.clegganseaweed.com)

Clifden

Shop

● The Connemara Hamper

Eileen and Leo Halliday's shop truly is a hamper: wander around it and you will find yourself picking and choosing lots of delicious treats and surprises, and that's before you even decide which bumper sandwich or roll it is that you want from their blackboard selection. TCH is a wonderful store, a real food lover's tonic. (Market Street, Clifden ☎ 095-21054 ✉ info@connemarahamper.com 🖱 www.connemarahamper.com – Open daily)

Fishmonger

● Duane's Fish Shop

The local port for Clifden is Rossaveal, and this is where Duane's source much of their fish. In the summer, however, local boats supply them with mackerel, pollock, crab and lobster; indeed fresh summer crab is one of their specialities. They also sell the excellent wild smoked salmon prepared by Clarke's of Ballina. (Main Street, Clifden ☎ 095 21804 – Open 10am-6pm Mon-Fri, closed Mon off season, 10am-5pm Sat)

Cooked Food To Go

High Moors Foods

Hugh and Eileen Griffin were the restaurateurs of choice for visitors to Clifden for many years, and whilst daughter Claire continues the family tradition in Steam, Hugh and Eileen still like to keep their hand in by growing and cooking vegetable dishes and other treats for folk renting holiday homes in and around the town. All we can say is that the HM vegetables we ate in past years were amongst the best we have ever enjoyed, and all they cook is true and delicious. (Dooneen, Clifden ☎ 095 21342 – 30 hours' notice required for orders. Food to be collected between 5pm & 6pm)

Guesthouse

Quay House

Paddy and Julia Foyle's iconic house has no equal in Ireland, in terms of style, design, hospitality, in terms of sheer sang froid. It's a collection of fine old houses down by the port, gathered together and decorated by Mr Foyle in the most inimitable way, decorated with the humour and wit that characterises this singular couple and their quiet sense of genius. Let's call them outrageous – immoderate; extravagant; extraordinary. Yes, outrageous will do nicely. An icon address that you will never forget. (Beach Rd, Clifden, Connemara ☎ 095-21369 res@thequayhouse.com www.thequayhouse.com)

B&B

Sea Mist House

Sheila Griffin's lovely house, in the centre of town, offers both beatific comfort, and a taste of the town's specialities, with lots of fine treats from local butcher, Des Moran, along with other good things from the shops of George Mannion and John Malone, all adding up to one of the happiest breakfast rooms – and happiest B&B's – we know of. (Clifden, Connemara ☎ 095-21441 sgriffin@eircom.net www.connemara.net/seamist)

"Britain – like other Western countries - is fifty years into a mass experiment in human nutrition. We're all eating basic foods that have been stripped of the antioxidants, trace elements and essential fatty acids that once promoted good health. Is it any wonder that our body maintenance systems are breaking down in middle age or earlier?"

GRAHAM HARVEY, *WE WANT REAL FOOD*

Coffee Shop

Steam

Claire Griffin and Alan King have one of the best food offers in Connemara, and there is a meticulous sense of care about everything this couple do – just look at the time and effort lavished on a simple cup of hot chocolate, for instance (our kids' all-time favourite!) and you realise that you are in the capable hands of talented, motivated people. Lunch in the courtyard is a treat, and everything is delivered with such style, from Connemara Smokehouse salad to Thai noodles to the best ham sandwich in the West. (Station House, Clifden ☎ 095-30600 – Open 10am-6pm Mon-Sat)

Galway County

Internet Café

Two Dog Café

Day-trippers to Clifden flock to the town's many and indifferent places to eat, but hip travellers know that it is cult addresses like the Two Dog Café that show you the true spirit of this left-field town. Superb Illy coffee, great sounds – where else will you hear The Grateful Dead these days? – and smart food in the shape of excellent sandwiches, wraps and paninis make TDC one of those places that offers something close to the true zeitgeist of wild Connemara. And don't you just love that contact address: kennel@twodogcafe.ie!! (Church Hill, Clifden ☎ 095-22186 kennel@twodogcafe.ie www.twodogcafe.ie – Open 10.30am-5pm Tue-Sat Jan-May & Oct. Mon-Sat June-Sep. Closed Nov-Dec)

Gort

Fish and Chip Shop

Kettle of Fish

Gort is known locally as "Little Brazil", having welcomed many Brazilians into the town in recent years. It has, of course, a good Brazilian food store, at the north end of the town, but what it also has is a very fine chipper – Kettle of Fish. This is fish'n'chips in the English style, which is to say good crisp, dry frying, hand-cut chips and proper respect. If you are navigating the N17 KoF is a brilliant quick-stop if you need to keep moving whilst you munch your way through a bag. (The Square, Gort ☎ 091-630300)

Kilcolgan

Oysters

Michael Kelly Shellfish

Diarmuid Kelly's company are superlatively efficient suppliers of oysters; one call and that basket is at your door in double-quick time, so have the lemon, the brown bread and the O'Hara's Stout all ready. (Tyrone, Kilcolgan ☎ 091 796120 kellyoysters@eircom.net www.kellyoysters.com)

Galway County

Kinvara

Pub

Keogh's Bar

We wish the bar was a little smarter in Keogh's, a little more shipshape and sparkling, because it's an atmospheric pub and the food is tasty, so it's easy to see why locals like it so much, and it is the best bet in Kinvara. Some steamed mussels, maybe a nicely finished vegetarian lasagne or some Burren lamb will do just the trick. Evening meals start at 6pm. (The Square, Kinvara ☎ 091-637145 keoghsbar@eircom.net www.kinvara.com/keoghs)

Smokehouse

Kinvara Smoked Salmon

Declan Droney's Kinvara salmon company's history has been one long, sustained, richly deserved shout of success. 95% of the

salmon produced is organic, and 65% of their business now is done in the UK, supplying blue-chip retailers such as Waitrose and Fresh & Wild. Everything that goes out of Kinvara Central shows an utterly fastidious approach to artisan food production: care in the fish quality, care in the smoking and the gravadlax curing, care in the packaging and care in customer relations. In truth, every artisan company could and should be run like Kinvara, a business built on deliciousness, and commercial savvy, and knowing what counts. (Kinvara ☎ 091-637489
info@kinvarasmokedsalmon.com
www.kinvarasmokedsalmon.com)

Loughrea

Café Deli

● Fare Green Food

FGF is a real wee cracker of a shop. Maureen and Irene are two busy mums with a passion for food, and their selection of things to eat and things to buy is ace. Local organic foods nestle alongside Fair Trade goods and they have a strong focus on healthy, energy foods, as well as making a wickedly good cup of coffee. "Fresh, natural and ready to go", is what they say, and is just what they do. (Westbridge, Loughrea ☎ 091-870911
maureenfynes@yahoo.co.uk– Open 8am-6.30 Mon-Fri, 9am-6pm Sat, open Sun seasonally)

Galway County

Market

● Loughrea Market

Local grower Padraig Fahy is organiser and mainstay of the Loughrea Market, which has lots of good local foods and visiting marketeers. (Barrack Street – Open Thurs 10am-2pm)

Restaurant

● Slatefort House

There is more than a touch of magic to Slatefort, which somehow remains one of the best kept secrets in County Galway. Its sheer remoteness may explain that – it would help greatly if they had some accommodation – but eating here is well worth the drive. Maura Winters' cooking is expressive and tactile: panfried squid stuffed with prawns, and crab claws in a tangy lemon & orange cream are dishes that taste every bit as good as they look. Seabass is ovenroasted with prawns and cherry tomatoes whilst good vegetarian choices such as homemade pasta with mushroom and smoked cheese are very fine. A rhubarb crumble, just out of the oven, is superb. Great staff, lovely setting, worth the considerable detour. (Slatefort, Bullaun, Loughrea ☎ 091-870667 – Open 6.30pm-11pm Tue-Sun, 1pm-3pm Sun)

Leenane

Café

Blackberry Café

The Blackberry may sound distinctly businesslike in these high-pressure days, but Sean and Mary Hamilton's café is a place to switch off the blackberry and switch on to some true, simple cooking and the stupendous natural beauty of the Leenane fjord. (Leenane, ☎ 095 42240 – Open afternoon and early evening, noon-4.30pm, 6pm-9pm Wed-Mon)

Country House

Delphi Lodge

Peter Mantle's sublimely situated country house is the quintessential country house destination for sportsmen. an archetype of the 19th-century country house experience of claret, good cooking, good cheer and a bag of birds or a fish or two. If sport isn't your thing, this also happens to be a house beloved of folk who couldn't tie a fly to save their lives. (Leenane ☎ 095-42987 res@delphilodge.ie www.delphilodge.ie)

Letterfrack

Craft Shop & Café

Avoca

Across the road from Ballinakill Bay, the westerly Avoca is home to the best Irish crafts and is an indispensible daytime stop for good savoury and sweet cooking as you sweep along the western seaboard. (Letterfrack ☎ 095-41058 info@avoca.ie www.avoca.ie – Open 9am-6pm Mon-Sun. Closed Jan 15-Mar 15)

Restaurant and Cookery School

Pangur Ban

John Walsh is a good cook, indeed he is rare amongst Irish chefs in having a true feel for diverse ethnic cuisines, and in being able to concoct them with accuracy and energy. Pangur Ban is a sweet stone-fronted cottage, staff are swish, the art works are classy, and the food completes this very artistic milieu. Even with the traditional sirlon steak, for instance, Mr Walsh spices up some black-eyed beans as the untraditional accompaniment, and he has fun everywhichway – lamb shank braised in ale; lemon sole with Swiss chard; hake with brie; tagliatelle with roast pumpkin. Spirited cooking, and a very good fit for the Connemara spirit. (Letterfrack, Connemara ☎ 095-41243 pban@indigo.ie www.pangurban.com – Open 6pm-9pm Mon-Sun. Limited hours low season)

Country House

● Renvyle House Hotel

We admit it: we're the sort of family who are devotees of Renvyle. The kids love all the things to see and do. The adults love the cooking and the chill-out. Ronnie Counihan and chef Tim O'Sullivan do a mighty job here, in this spendiferous location, and the entire team seems to us one of the happiest crews around, serving delicious cooking to relaxed holidaymakers. Dinner is truly special, breakfast is one of the best in the West. (Letterfrack, Connemara ☎ 095-43511 info@renvyle.com www.renvyle.com)

Country House

● Rosleague Manor

Mark Foyle's beautiful hill-top house has become the romantic-wedding destination of the west, such is its pastelly perfection and its drop-dead location. But, if you ain't getting married, it is also a champion country house, boasting excellent cooking, stupendous housekeeping and with a great crew working alongside Mr Foyle. (Letterfrack, Connemara ☎ 095-41101 www.rosleague.com – Open Mar-Nov)

Monivea

Restaurant

● An Scioból Restaurant

An Scioból is the destination of choice in Monivea, which means the punters are all on first-name basis with the staff, and which gives the pretty room great atmosphere. You will have to get there early for Sunday lunch, whilst the dinner menu offered from Wednesday to Saturday evening shows close attention to detail in terms of sourcing – organic salmon; corn-fed chicken; good fresh fish – and in terms of the precise, delicate cooking. (Monivea ☎ 091-849765 – Open 5pm-10.30pm Wed-Sat 12.30pm-7pm Sun)

"There is poetry in the fat fingers of cooks."

NICHOLAS FREELING

Moycullen

Restaurant

● White Gables

Kevin and Anne Dundon do a superb job in White Gables, maintaining a superbly manicured room – even the loos are smart – and cooking old classic dishes with true care and fizz. Order anything from the menu – chowder; black and white pudding with mustard sauce; carrot and orange soup; roast duckling; monkfish with garlic butter; lemon sole with tartare sauce – and the level of execution is unerring, the flavours are punchy and satisfying, and how nice to see a restaurant that still cooks beef Wellington. "Everything works for this restaurant, from setting, staff and great food", wrote our reporter, after a darling night out. And in White Gables everything has been working well for a mighty long time. (Moycullen Village ☎ 091-555744 info@whitegables.com www.whitegables.com – Open 7pm-9.30pm Tue-Sun 12.30pm-3pm Sun)

Galway County

Wine Merchant

● Mad About Wine

Ivan Edwards' wine shop in mushrooming Moycullen has grown and developed over the last four years, and the passionate interest of this gifted sommelier turned wine merchant shines through in enthusiastic advice and an always interesting and ever-developing wine selection. Ivan is slowly adding more foodstuffs to the shop's selection, and he sells a mighty amount of fresh Yew Tree loaves from Oughterard every Saturday morning, so you can get your daily bread and your weekend bottle in one easy, fun visit. (Main Street, Moycullen ☎ 091-868882 ivanedwards@eircom.net www.madaboutwine.ie. Closed Sun & Mon)

Oranmore

Restaurant

Asian Fusion

Charlie Chan was for many years the foremost Chinese restaurateur in Galway, with a big bustling place called the Royal Villa, and before that he cooked in the acclaimed Dragon Court. Now, he has down-scaled, moved out to the expanding suburb of Oranmore, and he has up-scaled his menus to pull in sushi, some European foods, and a brace of Chinese classics. (Castle Court, Castle Road, Oranmore ☎ 091-790823 – Open 5pm-11pm Mon-Thu, 5pm-11.30pm Fri & Sat, 1pm-4pm Sun)

Oughterard

Butcher

Finnerty's Butchers

The fact that Billy Morgan's butcher's shop thrives in a small town such as Oughterard, which is also home to the legendary McGeough's, gives you some idea of the skills, not to mention the dedicated audience, this talented butcher has amassed. Food lovers particularly appreciate the boudin-style black pudding, whilst the white pudding and their sausages are deserved prize winners. A beautful shop, with everyone on first name terms (Main Street, Oughterard – Open 8am-6.30pm Mon-Sat, 'till 7pm Fri)

Butcher

McGeough's Butchers

Of all the younger generation of Irish butchers, James McGeough may be the most distinctive and determined. He spent six years at the tough school of German charcuterie and has that experience to thank for his technical skills, and also perhaps for his doggedness. He has become famous for creating air-dried Connemara lamb, but it seems to us that this superb product only represents the tip of his creative iceberg, and that we shall be seeing many wonderful new meat products emerging from Oughterard over the next few years. And whilst he has become famous for the queer gear, he still runs a brilliant butcher's shop where the bangers and the bacon and the Friday-night fillet are all top notch. One of the great Irish artisans.(Barrack Street, Oughterard ☎ 091-552351 fougheast@iol free.ie)

Wine Merchant

Probus Wines

Paul Fogarty's wine company grows steadily and surely, expanding the scope of their wholesaling operation whilst concentrating retail business in the shop in Oughterard. A former sommelier, Mr Fogarty has both an epicurean's appreciation of food and wine and an aesthete's sense of judgement. Put those two together and it makes for an especially fine wine list, packed with wines that enjoy typicity and attitude, and a very sang froid attitude at that. From the Domaine Joliette to the magical Les Cranilles Cotes du Rhone, there is nothing in here – save perhaps the Calabria wines from Oz – we wouldn't recommend, and Probus is one of the best places to buy wine in the west. (Camp Street, Oughterard ☎ 091-552084 www.probuswines.ie)

Bakery

The Yew Tree

Eric Japaud has taken up the ovens at the Yew Tree, and is already producing a range of breads that numbers almost 80 varieties in total, not to mention their cakes, pastries and specialist items such as wedding cakes. The Yew Tree also has both a cheese counter – which concentrates mainly on Continental cheeses – and a deli counter. "Every week there are new styles of bread included in the batch they send me," says Ivan Edwards of Mad About Wine in Moycullen, "and they are so good I have people waiting out the door to get their hands on them." Watch this Yew Tree grow, for there is both ambition and accomplished execution evident here. (Main Street, Oughterard ☎ 091-866986 – Open 9am-6pm Mon-Sat)

Galway County

Recess

Country House

Lough Inagh Lodge

Maire O'Connor's hotel fits snugly and comfortably into the Connemara hills, and it also fits snugly into the Connemara family of individual, distinctive and bespoke accommodation run by talented and painstaking owners. The hotel is charmingly understated in every way, which makes it an even more valuable retreat. (Recess, Connemara ☎ 095-34706 inagh@iol.ie www.loughinaghlodgehotel.ie – Open Mar-Dec)

Roscahill

Garden & Tea Rooms

Brigit's Garden

Jenny Beale and her team oversee the glorious Brigit's Garden, designed by Chelsea gold medallist Mary Reynolds to a seasonal Celtic festivals theme. Beautiful gardens, of course, but also an excellent café with toasties, soups and generous sandwiches, just the ticket after a couple of hours doing what Bob Dylan clearly did on an Irish trip: "As I walked out tonight in the mystic garden...". (Pollagh, Roscahill 091 550905 ☝ www.galwaygarden.com)

Roundstone

B&B

The Angler's Return

Lynn Hill's house is especially pretty and charming, with a darling location abutting the Ballynahinch River. The house seems straight out of House & Garden, so design heads will love it, as will anyone who seeks peace and quiet, and a spot of fishing or wandering around the gardens. (Toombeola, Roundstone, Connemara ☎ 095-31091 www.anglersreturn.com – closed Dec-Jan)

Hotel

Eldon's Hotel

Michelle and Lorraine have taken over the running of Eldon's Hotel, and how marvellous to see two childhood friends setting off in business in a market now dominated by bland multinational chains. They are hard-working young women who are just setting out their stall, but this is just the sort of venture modern Irish tourism needs, personable people brining their personalities to a fine old tourist hotel, offering good value and lots of charm. (Roundstone ☎ 095-35933 ✉ eldonshotel@eircom.net)

Bar & Restaurant

O'Dowd's Seafood Bar & Restaurant

A quaint wee bar which is usually packed to the rafters with well-heeled locals (Roundstone has become something of a Dublin 4-out-west), and tourists who have been told by someone that the chowder is very fine. (Roundstone ☎ 095-35923 ✉ odowds@indigo.ie ☝ www.odowdsbar.com)

County Kerry

Annascaul

Black Pudding

Ashe's Black Pudding

Country Kerry has a rich tradition of pudding making, and there is no finer pudding made in either Kerry or in Ireland today than that made in the tiny space of Ashe's by Thomas Ashe. Beef blood, onions, breadcrumbs, suet, milk, oatmeal, flour, salt, pepper, spices and herbs are mixed together before the Annascaul pudding is baked in a steam oven for over two hours. Baking is the characteristic of the Kerry puddings, and it is a technique the Ashe family have used ever since the pudding was first made as long ago as 1916. A superb, extremely rare and precious artisan Irish food. (Annascaul ☎ 066-915 7127 info@annascaulblackpudding.com www.annascaulblackpudding.sitestogo.biz)

Ballinskelligs

Chocolate

Cocoa Bean Artisan Chocolates

Emily and Sarah have migrated south, bringing their celebrated Cocoa Bean Company down to deepest Ballinskelligs where, in a fascinating example of artisan synergie, they share production premises with Skellings Chocolate. These young women are the most dynamic, self-critical chocolatiers you can find, always seeking out new taste territory. "We want to stay at the cutting-edge", they say. "We aren't going to stagnate!". No chance of that, not whilst Sarah is over conquering the hippest U.K. retailers, whilst Emily is back at base making gin 'n' tonic chocolate bars, and starting to craft new milk chocolate concoctions. The very model of an artisan industry, Cocoa Bean produce dazzling work, offered with dazzling presentation, work that fuses inspiration and intuition, side by side. (The Glen, Ballinskelligs ☎ 066-947 9119 info@cocoabeanchocolates.com www. ocoabeanchocolates.com)

Chocolate

Skelligs Chocolate Company

Colm Healy runs this excellent bespoke chocolate company, the most westerly chocolate company in Europe, and with a little chocolate factory that you can visit, it is well worth the trip way out west to Ballinskelligs to see the chocolates being made, and to buy some of their award-winning range. Presentation is just as beautiful as the chocolates themselves. (The Glen, Ballinskelligs ☎ 066-947 9119 info@skelligschocolate.com www.skelligschocolate.com)

Blackwater

Tearooms

The Strawberry Field

A curious and rather sweet little cottage that cooks very good crêpes, as well as offering for sale some wonderfully abstruse garden furniture and ornaments in cast-iron. Don't think these fine crepes are just for the kids: a flour crêpe with some excellent ice cream and a refreshing cup of tea is great traveller's fare, whatever your age. You will find Margaret and Peter's Strawberry Field by taking the Sneem road at the Avoca store at Moll's Gap. And Avoca is another interesting location in which to have lunch and to break your journey, especially with such dazzling views from the upstairs dining room. (Sneem Road, Blackwater, Moll's Gap ☎ 064-82977 info@strawberryfield-ireland.com www.strawberryfield-ireland.com – Open 11am-6pm Mon-Sun)

Kerry

Bonane

Chocolatier

Benoit Lorge

Kerry chocolate makers like to hide themselves away. Skelligs and Cocoa Bean are both at the end of the earth, whilst Benoit Lorge works from a small shop and chocolate factory half way up a montain. Okay, so it is on the main Kenmare-Glengarriff road, but you get the point. What the chocolatiers don't hide under a bushel is their talent, and M. Benoit is a skilled chocolatier, so stop in little Bonane and buy some or look out for them in good delis. (Releagh Cottage, Bonane, Kenmare ☎ 064-79994)

Caherdaniel

Farmers' Market

Caherdaniel Market

Fancy half a dozen oysters sitting in the garden by the river with your shopping bag full of local handmade foods? Well you can get it here. Every Sunday, in the garden of the Blind Piper there is a small raggle-taggle market. You will find home-made cakes and savouries from Jane Urquhart, Derreensilla Smokehouse mackerel, salmon, and their oysters, Dereenaclaurig Cheese and home-made preserves. (Blind Piper, Caherdaniel – Open 12.30pm-6pm Sundays, May-Oct, weather permitting)

Smoked Foods

Derreensillagh Foods

Tim Youard had a serious food background in the UK, as both a chef in London's Savoy Hotel in the 1960's and as an oyster farmer in Suffolk, supplying culinary luminaries such as Simon Hopkinson of Bibendum, before he and Bronwen made the move to Kerry. Their smokehouse uses an old Scottish Pinney smoker, and they use oak logs from Killarney National Park, so the technique is as traditional as all get out. You will find their smoked salmon, hot-smoked sea trout, smoked mackerel, smoked eel, and smoked haddock at the local markets in Kerry, or you can head to London's Borough Market where they sell. And, should you manage to finally get that table in The Ivy, then you can order the fish there. (Caherdaniel ☎ 087-792 3318 derreensillagh@iolfree.ie)

Kerry

Guesthouse

Iskeroon

David Hare has lately become celebrated as the producer of Ireland's newest generation of television chefs, bringing both Rachel Allen and Clodagh McKenna to the screen. But when he isn't charging around the country's markets with a Sony on his shoulder and a boom mike in his hand, Mr Hare and his wife Geraldine run the most romantic, arcane, remote and design-drop-dead-gorgeous house in the country. Iskeroon is accessed by driving across a beach – yes, really – and the interior design of the house more than lives up to its amazing location. Blissful. (Iskeroon, Caherdaniel ☎ 066-947 5119 res@iskeroon.com www.iskeroon.com)

Local Specialities
THE KERRY COW
DINGLE PIES
VALENTIA SCALLOPS
KERRY MOUNTAIN LAMB

Cahirciveen

Farmers' Market

Caherciveen Market

Westcove Farmhouse cakes and Sneem cheese are foods to look out for in this seasonal market in Caherciveen, which also has good bric a brac. (Contact Barbara Cassidy ☎ 087-296 5874 Community Centre, Thurs, 11am-2pm, Jun-Sept)

Smoked Salmon

Kerry Fish

Liam Quinlan's company specialises in its own smoked salmon, which you can buy from their shops, as well as Field's of Skibbereen. This is a fine product, and keenly priced. In addition to the salmon, a substantial variety of fish are sourced for his two Kerry shops. (Killorglin ☎ 066-9761860, Caherciveen 066-9472686 – Open 10am-6pm, Mon-Fri, 10am-2pm Sat)

Kerry

Bar & Restaurant

QC's

Kate and Andrew Cooke's bar and restaurant has the singular advantage of being serviced by the family's fish wholesale and retail operation, so fish and shellfish is always the first choice here, especially the choices cooked on their char-grill. Whilst there is a Basque flavour to some of the dishes – brill with toasted garlic; hake in olive oil; a tapas plate of seafood – it is never overstated, and they also serve a very good plate of Gubbeen cured meats, a nifty Thai red curry of monkfish and prawns, and there are steaks for the incorrigibly carnivorous. The bar and restaurant are splendidly atmospheric. (3 Main Street, Cahirciveen ☎ 066-947 2244 info@qcbar.com www.qcbar.com – Open low season Thu-Sun 6pm-9.30pm, Easter-Oct Tue-Sun 6pm-9.30pm. May-Aug open for lunch noon-2.30pm. July & Aug open Mon-Sun)

Castlecove

Shop, Bakery & Accommodation

Westcove Farmhouse Shop

What an excellent venture Jane Urquhart's shop, bakery and self-catering accommodation is. Jane specialises in home-made, additive-free cakes and breads – carrot cake; lemon Madeira cake; Norwegian chocolate cake – and some savouries. She supplies local shops and restaurants and sells at the local markets in Waterville, Sneem, Caherciveen and at the Caherdaniel Sunday market. Jane also organises the Caherdanieal Country market which runs from June to September and Christmas. Don't miss making a visit to the shop, where you will find funky clothing and funky crafts alongside the excellent cakes, whilst holidaymakers will find it easy to be tempted by a week or so in the self-catering apartment. (Westcove Farmhouse, Westcove Road, Castlecove ☎ 066-947 5479 westcovefarmhouse@oceanfree.net www.westcove.net)

Castlegregory

Farmhouse Cheese

Dingle Peninsula Cheese

Maya Binder's cheeses are perhaps the most distinctive and original of all the Irish farmhouse cheeses. Using sea vegetables to flavour the raw cow's milk, she makes her Diliskus cheese with flecks of dilisk which are cut up and added to the curds, and another which takes the Morbier idea of a central line of ash, but instead uses a central line of dilisk, a brilliant improvisation. The cheeses are washed with salted whey, and are matured in a wonderfully characterful cheese room. Lookout for Diliskus, Beenoskee and Kilcummin in good shops and at farmers' markets. (Kilcummin, Castlegregory ☎ 066-713 9028)

Seafood, Relishes and Charcouterie

On The Wild Side

Olivier Beaujouan trained originally to be a charcutier in his native Tours – he still makes a mighty sausage and a fantastic boudin noir when he has a moment – but it is his inspired improvisations with sea vegetables which have brought this gifted artisan to fame. His pickled kombu, his tartar of kelp, his pickled sea spaghetti, his smoked dilisk and his astonishing tapenade of sea vegetables, are amongst the most unusual and original of Irish artisan foods, and they have deservedly won culinary awards, and in the last couple of years they have inspired a number of other artisan companies to look to the oceans and the seashores for these vital health foods. Only brilliant. (Kilcummin, Castlegregory ☎ 066-713 9028 seatoland@hotmail.com)

Dingle

B&B

The Captain's House

A sweet and lovely B&B rght in the heart of the town, with terrific baking – oh, those scones! – and wonderful breakfasts from Mary Milhench. (The Mall, Dingle ☎ 066-915 1531 captigh@eircom.net www.captainsdingle.com – Open 15 Mar-15 Nov)

Restaurant

The Chart House

Jim and Carmel McCarthy's restaurant is on a roll these days, with chef Noel Enright firing out fabulous food from an outfit that may be ten years old, but which feels more like ten years young. Sesame-seed turbot with a fondue of fennel, leek and tomato; duck leg confit on butterbean mash; fillet of pork with brandied apricots; sirloin with black pudding mash – this is exciting cooking with every element slightly juxtaposed and counterpointed, and it makes for great eating. The room is run by the McCarthys with zest and unflappable poise, and it is one of Dingle's glories. (The Mall, Dingle ☎ 066-915 2255 charthse@eircom.net www.charthousedingle.com – Open 6.30pm-10pm Mon-Sun, closed Mon & Tue off season, and restaurant closes 7 Jan-Valentine's Day)

Bakery

Courtney's Bakery

Courtney's is a great bakery, where they are hard at work from six in the morning creating good things. (Green Street ☎ 066-915 1583 gene.courtney@gmail.com – Open 8am-6pm Mon-Sat, closed Thurs)

Kerry

Market

Dingle Local Produce and Craft Market

This market sells produce and crafts from the Dingle peninsula, plus some organic foods and speciality foods from further afield. In high summer there can be as many as thirty stalls selling cheeses, cooked foods to go, baking and home-grown vegetables, as well as crafts and local cosmetics. (Contact Mary Devanne ☎ 066-915 1474 The Harbour, Dingle, Fridays 9.30am-4pm)

Seafood

Dingle Bay Shellfish

Ted Browne has a epicurean's appetite and a chef's skills, which explains why his prepared crab meat and cooked crab claws are so damned good. He mixes the cooked brown and white meat together to get the ideal mix, both in terms of taste and texture, and in comparison everyone else's crab meat is strictly second rate to this benchmark seafood. His frozen prawns are also of superb quality, and not pumped with water, he smokes some very fine salmon and, being an environmentalist as well as an epicurean, he produces superb compost from all those shells. Fantastic. (Ballinaboula, Dingle ☎ 066-915 1933 tbrowne@indigo.ie)

Guesthouse

Emlagh House

A grand new house, close to the road as you come into Dingle from the east, and one where good taste and restraint work hand in hand with blissful comfort to create a fantastic destination. Marion and Grainne Kavanagh are superb hosts, and Emlagh is one dazzling house. (Emlagh, Dingle ☎ 066-915 2345 info@emlaghhouse.com www.emlaghhouse.com – Open 10 Mar-1 Nov)

Guesthouse with Restaurant

Gorman's Clifftop House

With nine guest rooms and a popular restaurant that enjoys spectacular views out over the sea on the north side of the Dingle peninsula, it's no surprise that Vincent and Sile Gorman's restaurant with rooms is so popular. (Glaise Bheag Ballydavid, Dingle ☎ 066-915 5162 info@gormans-clifftophouse.com www.gormans-clifftophouse.com – Open 6pm-9.30pm Easter-end of Sept. Off season for reservations only)

B&B

Greenmount House

John and Mary Curran have been busy renovating their ever-popular guesthouse, which is one of the fixtures of hospitality in frothy Dingle. (Upper John St, Dingle ☎ 066-915 1414 ✉ greenmounthouse@eircom.net 🖱 www.greenmount-house.com)

Shop

An Grianan

Fanny Binder and Michelle Flannery's excellent wholefood shop is one of the key addresses in Dingle for good foods and for good local foods. Whilst they no longer host a farmers' market outside the shop, they do hold winter markets when the local Dingle market is closed. (Green Street, Dingle ☎ 066-915 1910 ✉ michelleflannery@eircom.net – Open 9am-6pm Mon-Sat)

B&B

Milltown House

Mark Kerry's house has one of the best locations in Dingle, or in fact just outside of Dingle, for you cross over the bridge on the Ventry road then swing left to drive down to the house, from where you can look across the water to the town itself. It is a comfortable, stylish house, and quietly grand. (Dingle ☎ 066-915 1372 ✉ info@milltownhousedingle.com 🖱 www.milltownhousedingle.com)

Ice Cream

Murphy's Ice Cream

Here is an indicator of just how serious the Murphy brothers, Sean and Kieran, are about their work and their shops. Head into their shop, either here in Dingle or in Killarney and – order an espresso. Yes, coffee. And, now, just taste that cup of sheer perfection: sheer, utter perfection. That's the kind of blokes they are: they could coast by on the strength of their superb ice creams, but they don't. Every detail of what they do is obsessed over, examined, worked on, perfected, and that applies to the coffee just as much as the ice creams. But, of course, the coffee can wait until after you have had an ice cream, so try to decide from the sixteeen or so different flavours that they create, made using the best – and the most

expensive – ingredients. An inspirational artisan company and, to cap it all, Kieran Murphy writes a very fine blog – a readable blog, characterised by brevity and wit – at icecreamireland.com. (Milseoga Uí Mhurchú Teo, Sráid na Trá, An Daingean ☎ 066-915 2644
✉ sean@murphysicecream.ie
🖱 www.murphysicecream.com – Open 11am-10pm Mon-Sun, closes early evening off season)

Restaurant

Out of the Blue

Tim Mason and his crew, with Jean-Marie Vireaux in the kitchen and manager Irene Grobelaar, continue to do the good thing here in the tiny OOTB. Since opening in 2001 they have honed and sharpened and improved this smashing restaurant and bar each and every year, and the key to their success lies in the fact that they only cook seafood, so nothing distracts from their sharply tuned focus of offering the freshest fish cooked in the simplest way. For fish lovers, the really good news is that it isn't all fashionable fillets: you can get pollock – a superb and under-rated fish that eats deliciously – with a potato crust, or a warm salad of haddock with smoked tuna, and even the almost-forgotten rock cod. And, if your boat has come in, you can also splash out on crayfish. Superb wines match superb cooking in a true Dingle star. (Waterside, Dingle ☎ 066-915 0811 ✉ info@outoftheblue.ie
🖱 www.outoftheblue.ie – Open 12.30pm-3pm, 6.30pm-9.30pm Mon-Sat; noon-3.30pm, 6pm-8.30pm Sun. Open every day except Wed. Closed Nov-Feb)

Kerry

Pies

Píog Pies

Here are the votes of the jury concerning Brid ni Mhathuna and Steven Neilings' Piog Pies. The Beef and Guinness Pie? "Excellent". The Kerry Lamb Pie? "Superb". The Seafood Pie? "Wicked". Well, there you have it. The jury would also like to add that they noted that Piog are "excellent pies, with great fillings and great buttery pastry. Yum". So, a new star is born. Vegetarians should note that there is also a vegetarian pie with braised lentils with carrots and onions in tomato sauce. This is a brilliant new venture, with skill in the making abetted by the use of superb organic ingredients. (Dingle ☎ 087-794 4036
✉ sales@piogpies.com 🖱 www.piogpies.com)

Kenmare

Restaurant
Bacus

Gerry O'Shea is creating quite an empire of food and drink addresses in Kenmare. In addition to Bacus, he runs the excellent Prego and the new Kenmare Food Company, a deli and wine shop. He has managed to make these businesses work by attending carefully to the small details – if he makes a traditional breakfast he uses Gubbeen bacon, Sneem black pudding and makes an ace potato cake, for an example – and also by always having fantastic staff, the sort of cool young people who are masters of the art of service, despite their tender years. In Bacus, the bistro style of cooking suits the small room perfectly – lamb cutlets with turnip fries; ray wings with caper and lime butter; cod crusted with oatmeal and dill; classic moules mariniere. It's the kind of cooking that goes superbly with the Irish craft beers they sell, and there is no more sharply customer-focused bistro in the town. (Main Street, Kenmare ☎ 064-48300 ✉ www.bacus.ie – Open 9am-4pm, 6pm-10.30pm Tue-Sun)

Restaurant
The Breadcrumb

Manuela Goeb's bakery is one of the best things to have happened to Kenmare's gourmet central food culture since whenever. Bringing the rigour and purity of Germany's splendid culture of baking to a Mediterranean template of savoury and sweet baking has created a range of breads which is simply superb. They use a stone hearth oven and sourdough starters, which results in breads with true crust and crumb, and excellent eating quality that shows through in true tactility. The sweet things are no less expert, and this is a brilliant craft bakery that deserves your closest attention. (O'Shea's House, New Road, Kenmare ☎ 064-40645 🖱 www.thebreadcrumb.com)

B&B
Hawthorn House

Noel and Mary O'Brien's B&B is a beauty, a statement of just how a B&B should be, thanks to its charm, the true sense of care, and the lovely cooking. Excellent. (Shelbourne St, Kenmare ☎ 064-41035 ✉ hawthorn@eircom.net 🖱 www.hawthornhousekenmare.com)

Juice and Coffee Bar

Fruit and Bean

Run by Vanessa Foley, who used to cook in Cafe Indigo when it was open in the town. Fresh juice, good coffee and excellent soup. (Henry Street ☎ 064-42106 – Open 9.30am-5.30pm Mon-Sun)

Bar

The Horse Shoe Bar

Paul Bevan runs a good show in the Horse Shoe, with local foods, including Gubbeen bacon, used wisely and a genial, relaxed atmosphere. (3 Main Street, Kenmare ☎ 064-41553 – Open noon-3pm Mon-Fri, 5pm-9.30pm Mon-Sun)

Café

Jam

James Mulchrone made a great name for himself as a working chef in Kenmare before opening up the hugely popular Jam café. As you would expect of a perspicacious, hard-working food lover, he does things right, so breads, savouries and salads are all a treat, and the only difficulty you will find is the perennial one of every seat being occupied by some local food lover. (6 Henry Street, Kenmare ☎ 064-41591 info@jam.ie www.jam.ie – Open Mon-Sat 8am-6pm)

Farmers' Market

Kenmare Farmers' Market

This is a new Kenmare indoor market which plans to open all year. Producers who would like to take part should contact Vince at ☎ 086-3128262. (Wed-Sun 10am-6pm, 7 days during July and Aug, An Cro, Bridge Street)

Deli & Wine Shop

Kenmare Food Company

A new food and wine venture from Gerry O'Shea, of Bacus and Prego, the Kenmare Food Company promises to bring the best Irish artisan foods and lots of well chosen wines to town. To have a deli and wine shop has been a long-held ambition of Mr O'Shea, and one can expect the sharp, courteous service that graces his other destinations. (22 Henry Street ☎ 064-79800 www.thekenmarefoodcompany.com – Open 8am-8pm April & May, 8am-10pm Jun-Sept, 9am-6pm Oct-Mar)

Restaurant

The Lime Tree

Tony and Alex Daly's restaurant is one of the perennial performers of Kenmare's dynamic food culture. It's a winningly pretty series of rooms in a lovely old house that dates back to 1832, and the cooking is consistent and modern and has many champions: smoked haddock risotto with hen's egg; confit belly of pork with capers and raisins; beef fillet with fondant potato; turbot with basil mash and asparagus. (Shelburne Street, Kenmare ☎ 064-41225 limetree@limetreerestaurant.com www.limetreerestaurant.com – Open 6.30pm-10pm Mon-Sun, Mar-Nov)

Restaurant

Mulcahy's

Bruce Mulcahy's cooking has flair, panache and a well-understood cosmopolitanism, and he serves it in a hip, modern room that is a sheer delight. His take on modern classics such as crab crème brulée; scallops with capers and raisins; cod with garlic pomme purée; or lamb with lamb shank tartlet is always bracingly original and fresh, both in concept and execution, and it makes for cooking that is both good to eat and good to think. A classic modern Irish restaurant with modern Irish cooking. (Henry Street, Kenmare ☎ 064-42383 – Open 6pm-10pm Mon-Sun, closed Tue & Wed off-season)

Kerry

Pub

O'Donovan's

Gerry Foley always puts something special on the plate in O'Donovan's. It can be simple food - liver and onion gravy with mash; fish and chips; bread and butter pudding; good vanilla ice cream – but the care in the execution is every bit as keen as the value for money. (Henry Street, Kenmare ☎ 064-42106 – Food served noon-9pm Mon-Sun, closed Thu off season)

Restaurant

Packie's

Martin Hallissey is a fine chef, with a culinary style that is as far removed from cheffy grandstanding as you can possibly get. His food is subtle, understated, deep-flavoured and abidingly simple – lemon sole on the bone with toasted almonds and caper butter; lobster salad with homemade mayonnaise; rack of lamb with lentilles de Puy, mint and redcurrant sauce – but he makes his ingredients sing with freshness and flavour, and there are few restaurants where the mix of cooking, service and ambience is so sweetly and powerfully realised as in Packie's. (Henry Street, Kenmare ☎ 064-41508 – 6pm-10pm Mon-Sat. Weekends only Nov-Dec. Open one week before Christmas. Closed mid Jan-mid Feb)

Shop

The Pantry

A great wee wholefood shop, filled with lovely things and essential necessities, and with lots of good organic produce from local growers, such as Billy Clifford, arrayed outside the front window of the shop. (Henry Street, Kenmare ☎ 064-42233 pantry@gofree.indigo.ie – Open 9am-6pm Mon-Sat, 11am-3pm Sun)

Hotel

The Park Hotel

Francis and John Brennan's hotel is one of Ireland's classic addresses. A grand old railway hotel that today boasts a luxurious spa – Samas – it is recognised the world over for superlative service, and for that unique Kerry style of wit and welcome. And don't imagine that it is just for billionaires and high-roller Americans, for it isn't, and even having just a cup of tea in here is always something special. (Kenmare ☎ 064-41200 info@parkkenmare.com www.parkkenmare.com – Open 18 Apr-30 Nov & 23 Dec-2 Jan. Weekends only in Nov)

Wine Importer

Mary Pawle Wines

Mary Pawle only sells organically produced wines, and the organically – and bio-dynamically – produced wines she sells are fantastic. The pioneering spirit that led Mary and Ivan to establish their company back in 1997 is hungrily evident a decade later, as they hunt down classy wines such as the ace chenin blanc from Milton Vineyards in N.Z., or the vivid Domeine la Batteuse of Bernard Delmas, or the brilliant quaffers such as Domaine de Brau or Can Vendrell, from Spain. The very model of a boutique, bespoke wine company. (Gortamullen, Kenmare ☎ 064-41443 www.marypawlewines.com)

Gastro Bar

The Purple Heather

Grainne O'Connell's lovely bar and restaurant is quite unlike any other. It's a bar that doesn't feel like a bar, and a restaurant that doesn't feel like any other restaurant. Add to this unique ambience some seriously delicious domestic cookery – smoked salmon pâté; Purple Heather omelette; crab meat on brown bread; Guinness fruit cake – and you have a real stormer of an address, the sort of place people return to time and time again to eat exactly the same thing they had the last time. Only brilliant. (Henry Street, Kenmare ☎ 064-41016 oconnellgrainne@eircom.net – Open 10.45am-7pm Mon-Sat)

Country House

Sallyport House

Sallyport is a grand and very comfortable B&B-meets-country-house, just on the outskirts of the town. Sallyport is always a good choice when eating in the food mecca of Kenmare. The house is always very popular with visitors from the United States. (Kenmare ☎ 064-42066 port@iol.ie www.sallyporthouse.com)

Hotel

Sheen Falls Lodge

A calm, glam, high-end hotel, the SFL has always been distinguished by a very confident, very international ambience and by amazingly high standards of service. (Kenmare ☎ 064-41600 info@sheenfallslodge.ie www.sheenfallslodge.ie)

Guesthouse

Shelburne Lodge

Maura and Tom Foley's house is one of the most beautiful small country houses in Ireland, and breakfast here is regarded by many food lovers as one of the very best you can enjoy. Mrs Foley's love of furniture, of design, and of art sings throughout this lovingly cared-for house, and design heads are likely to be so smitten by it that they simply won't want to leave. The hospitality from the Foley family is warm and true, the icing on a most singular cake. (Killowen, Kenmare ☎ 064-41013 shelburnekenmare@eircom.net www.shelburnelodge.com – Open Mar-mid Dec)

Traiteur

● Truffle Pig Fine Foods

Andrew and Lindsey Hill's traiteur specialises in cooked foods-to-go, rotating a range of classics such as lamb shanks in red wine, moussaka, Irish stew, cassoulet, Greek-style chicken and many other smartly delivered staples. The shop also has excellent local foods – look out for Valentia ice cream. (The Square, Kenmare ☎ 064-42953 ✉ aghill1@msn.com – Open 9.30am-6pm Mon-Sat)

Wine Shop

● Vanilla Grape

Alain Bras has created a fine jamboree of a shop in VG, packed with the distinctive wines that this master sommelier has made a virtue of discovering throughout his career. His latest project is to create a school of wine, and there could be no better teacher than this authoritative wine lover. In addition to great wines, the shop has a myriad of foods and treats that will make anyone's day better. (12 Henry Street, Kenmare ☎ 064-40694 ✉ vanillagrape@eircom.net 🖰 www.vanillagrape.com – Open 8.30am-6pm Mon-Sat)

Killarney

Restaurant

● Bricin

There is a popular restaurant upstairs in this handsome craft shop, a short stroll up the High Street. (26 High St, Killarney ☎ 064-34902 ✉ bricin@eircom.net – Open 12.30pm-3pm, 6pm-9pm Tue-Sat)

Restaurant

● Cellar One Restaurant

Gloria Swanson would feel right at home descending the dramatic staircase down into Cellar One, and any Hollywood star would revel in the funky, wild, red-carpet glam of this hip restaurant. The food has full-on-flavour bistro punch – duck wontons with balsamic reduction; roast chicken stuffed with feta and oven-roasted tomato; Skeghanore duck with braised red cabbage. Service is as outstanding as one expects in a Treacy family hotel. (Town Centre, Killarney ☎ 064-31855 🖰 www.theross.ie – Open 7.30am-10am & dinner, 6.30pm-9.30pm Mon-Sun)

Butcher

The German Butcher

Armin Weise's small butcher's shop a few miles from town is worth the detour in order to get your hands on the best German-style charcuterie you can find in Ireland. (Fossa, Killarney ☎ 064-33069 www.germanbutcher-shop.com – Open 8am-6pm Mon-Fri, 8am-4.30pm Sat)

Restaurant

Gaby's

Gaby's enjoys the best of Killarney. It has what is perhaps the best cooking from Geert Maes, a dedicated chef whose seafood cookery can only be described as masterful, especially his cooking of shellfish such as lobster and scallops, which is in a class of its own. But the waiting staff in Gaby's exhibit that Killarney superciliousness that treats you as if you are simply a number needing to be processed – they need to wake up, and to realise they need to be as dedicated and focused as the kitchen of this distinguished restaurant. (27 High Street, Killarney ☎ 064-32519 www.gabysireland.com – Open 6pm-10pm Mon-Sat)

Café

Jam

The Killarney outpost of James Mulchrone's Kenmare bakery and deli is a comfortable spot in which to buy good breads and sweet things and also to grab a bite of lunch. (77 High Street, Killarney ☎ 064-31441 info@jam.ie www.jam.ie – Open 8am-5pm Mon-Sat)

Kerry

Hotel

Killarney Park Hotel

Is the KP the best hotel in Ireland? The question may be somewhat pointless, but anytime you stay in the KP, it is a question that you can't help but ask yourself. Where else will you find better staff, better comfort, better cooking? Where else so consistently improves and upgrades – the newest make-over of the bedrooms has to be seen to be believed. What other bar serves such superb food? And what other dining room is simply so charming, so swish? And where else offers such good value for such pristine accommodation and service? Padraig and Janet Treacy's hotel is a world beater. (Kenmare Place, Killarney ☎ 064-35555 www.killarneyparkhotel.ie)

Bar

The Lane Bar

Daytime eating in Killarney can be fairly banal, so the bar food offer in the wickedly stylish bar of The Ross is a vital alternative to the prevailing sameness of so many other places. (The Ross, Town Centre, Killarney ☎ 064-31855 info@theross.ie www.theross.ie – Open 12.30pm-8pm Sun-Thu, 12.30pm-6pm Fri & Sat)

Ice Cream Parlour

Murphy's Ice Cream

The Killarney colony of the Murphy brothers' superlative ice cream empire. If it is an ice cream empire, then they must be the Emperors of Ice Cream. "Let the lamp affix its beam./The only emperor is the emperor of ice-cream". Wallace Stevens would choose a double scoop of mint chip, we would reckon. (37 Main Street, Killarney ☎ 066-915 2644 sean@murphysicecream.ie www.murphysicecream.com – Open 11am-10pm Mon-Sun, closes early evening off season)

Café

Panis Angelicus

A popular daytime eating room in the middle of town and one of the most reliable choices in Killarney. (15 New Street, Killarney – Open 10am-5.30pm Mon-Sun. Open 'till 9pm high season)

Hotel

The Ross

"I just want to say that The Ross is a very good hotel". Well, that was PJ McKenna's reaction after a night in Padraig and Janet Treacy's boutique hotel, and when you can impress the 8yrs-old set, you are onto a winner. The Treacys have developed their operation to include the stellar Killarney Park, and most recently they have bought the Killarney Great Southern. But The Ross is where Mr Treacy grew up, and learnt his trade, and he still likes to work the tables in the swish basement restaurant of Cellar One. Devotees of the old hotel would struggle to recognise this uber hip makeover, but what hasn't changed is the charm of the service and the meticulous attention to detail. We love the style, with its Bridget Riley waves and stripes, and we love the sheer panache of this brilliantly realised hotel. (Town Centre, Killarney ☎ 064-31855 www.theross.ie)

Deli and Bakery

● Jack's

Jack's father and grandfather were bakers before him, and as a modern Irish artisan baker he is both determined to revive some of the traditional Irish bread products – brown soda bread, batch loaves, scones – whilst also casting his net into modern waters such as creating his own version of a San Francisco sourdough, and a spelt bread with organic honey. Celine looks after the deli, where she prepares the salads, stocks all the best Irish farmhouse cheeses, has Janet Drew relishes, and Skelligs chocolate, and together they have a star in the making, all permeated by the wonderful smell of freshly baking bread. (Lower Bridge Street, Killorglin ☎ 066 976 1132 – Open 8am-7pm Mon-Sat, 8am-5pm Sun)

Farmers' Market

● Killorglin Market

Get there early to snap up the best produce and baking at the Friday morning market. (CYMS Hall Fridays 11am-1pm)

Restaurant

● Nick's Restaurant

One of the great champions of good food and good times in all of the county, Nick and Anne Foley's restaurant is a comfortable, family-friendly bar and restaurant, serving good, fashion-free cooking, in hugely generous portions. Let the good times roll. (Lwr Bridge St, Killorglin ☎ 066-976 1219 – Open 5pm-10.30pm Tue-Sun)

Restaurant

● Sol y Sombra

Clíodhna Foley's family have run the legendary Nick's Restaurant for many years, and it's brilliant to see a new generation taking up the culinary challenge in Killorglin, for Cliodhna has opened up Sol y Sombra, whilst her sister has been busy running the Zest Café. The Old Church of Ireland, just behind Nick's restaurant, is where you nowadays break pinchos and enjoy their raciones – larger size tapas – and wines and sherries: prawn and bechamel croquettes; squid with garlic, olive oil and parsley; chickpeas with chorizo, black pudding and pork;

crema catalana. The wine list is a brilliant selection of great Spanish bottles, but do not leave without trying the San Leon manzanilla sherry: it is stunning. (The Old Church of Ireland, Killorglin ☎ 066-976 2357 info@solysombra.ie www.solysombra.ie – Bar open from 5pm-10.30pm Wed-Sun'till 12.30pm Fri & Sat. Winter closed Mon & Tue, Summer closed Tue)

Farmhouse Cheese

Wilma's Killorglin Farmhouse Cheese

Wilma O'Connor makes a truly excellent gouda-style cheese, using the raw milk from their Fresian herd, which when mature has pronounced notes of a rich, fudgy sweetness. There is also a cumin-flavoured cheese, typical of the Dutch style, but for us the unadorned Killorglin has all the flavour potential and promise it needs. You can buy the cheese from the shop at the farm which is just off the Caragh Lake road. (Killorglin ☎ 066-976 1402 www.killorglincheese.sitestogo.biz)

Listowel

Bistro & Accommodation

Allo's

A glorious bar and restaurant, Allo's is the sort of place where you could lock us up and chuck away the key and we wouldn't mind. The bar has a glorious style, and so does the food, for Theo Lynch and Armel Whyte are rock solid professional cooks, firing out sole on the bone with chive and lemon butter; darne of salmon with fennel and lime beurre blanc; lamb's kidneys with wholegrain mustard. (41 Church Street, Listowel ☎ 068-22880 www.alloslistowel.com – Food served noon-6.30pm Tue-Sat)

Farmhouse Cheese

Béal Lodge Dairy Farm

"Creamily rich, with a flaky crumbliness not dissimilar to Wensleydale and a flavour at once sweet and savoury, smooth and sharp, then explosive with fiery piquancy" is how the food writer Diane Curtin described Kate Carmody's Beal Lodge cheeses, made using the organic milk from their own herd. You will find the cheese at local farmers' markets and in local stores. (Asdee, Listowel ☎ 068-41137)

Farmhouse Cheese

● Kerry Farmhouse Cheese

Eilish Broderick continues the distinguished cheese-making enterprise started by her late mother, Sheila. The cheeses are all territorial-style, and the most popular is the cheese Eilish flavours with nettles, so be sure to look out for this when in the Listowel area. (Coolnaleen, Listowel ☎ 068-40245 kerrycheese@netscape.net)

Farmers' Market

● Listowel Farmers' Market

Listowel has always had a lively food scene, and their local market is a great place to find Beal Lodge cheese, Jane Urquhart's baking, local organic produce, free-range eggs and preserves. Every autumn there is a fun food festival throughout the town. (Contact Joanna Watkins ☎ 068-23034 listowelfoodfair@eircom.net www.listowelfoodfair.com – 11am Thur)

Milltown

Shop & Market

● Milltown Organic Market

Every Saturday there is a bustling, busy market in the brilliant Milltown Centre, quite the most atmospheric shop – well, church, actually – in the land. Lookout for Píog pies from Dingle, Moroccan pottery from Isabelle Kirrane, organic produce from Paul and Sarah Caridia of Callinfercy Organics, Italian specialities from Danielli, home baking from Rose Clifford and Maura Ryan, and cheese from Wilma O'Connor of Killorglin amongst many other specialists. (Saturdays 10am-2pm www.milltownorganicmarket.com)

Shop & Market

● Milltown Organic Store

Rebekah van Kan has taken charge at the deeply wonderful Milltown Organic Store, for our money the most atmospheric place in which to shop in Ireland, thanks to its location in a splendiferous old church. Rebekah has shifted the arragement of the shop, so that you first encounter the market stalls that are in use every Saturday for the Milltown Market, and then the shop is at the end of the church. She

is creating a gluten-free section, an organic baby section, and introduces two new products each week, as well as offering a complete selection of organic wines and foods. Going to church was never so much craic, and do not miss the wonderful market held here every Saturday, when the shop is like a festival of good food and great craic. (Old Church, Milltown ☎ 066-976 7869
✉ info@milltownorganicstore.com
🖱 www.milltownorganicmarket.com – Open 10am-6pm Mon-Fri, 10am-2pm Country Market Sat)

Portmagee

Bar, Restaurant & Guesthouse

● The Moorings @ The Bridge Bar

Good unpretentious seafood cookery in a pleasing, unpretentious place is the signature of Gerard and Patricia Kennedy's bar, restaurant and guesthouse. The bar food is simple and straight-ahead, the restaurant cookery is more involved and just as tasty, and the rooms are just the right sort of inexpensive excuse to make a proper night of it in Portmagee. (Portmagee ☎ 066-947 7108
✉ moorings@iol.ie 🖱 www.moorings.ie – Restaurant open 6pm-10pm, Bar open noon-9pm. Restaurant closes Oct-Mar, bar open all year)

Kerry

Sneem

Butcher

● PJ Burns

It was PJ Burns' aunt who first began to make the Sneem black pudding, and today that fine tradition persists in this little butcher's shop in the village. Mr Burns mixes pinhead oatmeal, sheep fat, onions and spices, before baking the pudding in a cake tin for 3 hours, as is the classic Kerry style of pudding making. The pudding is made in the tin, usually at about 15 to 16 pounds in weight each time, and is then sliced when you go in to the shop and order some. And, should you be late arriving into Sneem, and dying for a slice of Burns' black pudding, but you find the shop closed, don't worry. Just knock on the door, politely, and they will open up and sell you what you need. Now, isn't that what shopping is all about? Only precious. (Sneem ☎ 064-45139 – Open 9am-7pm Mon-Sat)

Farmhouse Cheese

Dereenaclaurig Farmhouse Cheese

Harry van der Zanden is the archetype of the artisan cheesemaker, from the time before Irish farmhouse cheeses became successful commercial enterprises. He uses the milk from his herd of Jersey cows to make 10 kilos of cheese a day between May and October. He matures the cheeses in a spotlessly clean cold room adjacent to his farmhouse. Some of the cheeses are flavoured with cumin, some with garlic. Some cheeses are sold at around 4 months, some are matured until almost a year old. Harry then sells them at the local markets on the Ring, and to a few local shops. The cheeses are mildly flavoured, and meticulously well made. It isn't hobby cheesemaking, it is artisan cheese-making, and every dairy farm in the country should be doing it, making local foods with distinct identities and selling them locally. A brilliant artisan enterprise, and look out for Harry with his cheeses at the various markets on the Ring during the summer season.
(Derreenaclaurig, Sneem ☎ 064-45330)

Farmers' Market

Sneem Farmers' Market

A lovely summer market takes place each Tuesday in pretty Sneem. (Tuesdays, 11am-3pm June-Sept plus Christmas)

Kerry

Tralee

Bar & Restaurant

Duinin Seafoods

Paddy O'Mahony's shop is a great place to source wet fish. (Market Place, Tralee ☎ 066 712 1026 – Open 10am-6pm Mon-Fri)

Bakery

Kiely's Cameo Bakery

Jerry, Ari and Ulli, the trinity of talents behind the Life-fibre breads and cakes made by the Cameo Bakery, remind us of the trio that created Roly's Bistro, back in the early 1990's in Dublin. Roly, Colin and John were an unlikely team back then, but they broke the mould and created one of the capital's great success story. Likewise Jerry – the Irish baker – Ari, the Aussie ideas man – and

Ulli, the German nutritionist – seem an unlikely gathering of talents in little Castleisland, But their seed breads have blazed a mighty trail into shops and homes, thanks to their originality and excellence, and one has the strong feeling that this company is only at the beginning of a successful pathway of creativity. (Tralee Road Industrial Estate, Castleisland ☎ 066-714 2944 sales@cameo.iol.ie www.abreadlessordinary.ie)

Shop

Kingdom Food & Wine

If you can't find it in the Kingdom, then it just doesn't exist. Maeve and Pat's shop almost bursts at the seams with great things in every shape and form, from wine and cigars to sandwiches made with their own bread and rare speciality foods from Ireland and everywhere else. This is the shop Tralee always needed, and lucky old Tralee got it, and how! Everywhere you look the Kingdom is crammed with delicious things, selected with a choosy, expert idea, and sold with charm and authority.
Tralee ☎ 066-711 8562 – Open 9am-7pm Mon-Sat, 'till 6pm Sat info@kingdomstore.ie
www.kingdomstore.ie)

Restaurant

Restaurant David Norris

David Norris is a graduate of the Gerry Galvin school of culinary arts, having worked with the great chef in Galway, and he brings the same funky yet classical mode to his work in Tralee, making his restaurant the best choice in town. His tastes incline towards the sweetness of the Mediterranean – warm smoked chicken tart with basil mayonnaise; crab cake with roasted prawns; scallops with coral sauce; potato and goat's cheese cannelloni – but regardless of what he turns his hand to, execution is always precise, service is calm and professional, and value for money for such expert cooking and service is extremely keen. (Ivy House, Ivy Terrace, Tralee ☎ 066-718 5654 – Open 5.30pm-9.30pm Tue-Fri, 7pm-9.30pm Sat)

Farmers' Market

Tralee Farmers' Market

Look out for the wild things from On The Wild Side, amongst lots of other very good local specialities at the weekly Tralee market, held in the town's pretty square. (Town Centre, Fridays 9am-5pm)

County Kildare

Athy

Farmers' Market

Athy Farmers' Market

Jenny Young has the eggs and cheeses and the relishes, Dick Wellwood has the organic vegetables, Helen Gee has her gee-whizz jams, and there are also baskets, trees and bedding plants, scented candles from Derrynine, cakes and breads and tarts from Olive Finlay and local vegetables from Liam Ryan, along with "little nice things" from Susan Manley. Little Nice Things: what an excellent way to describe what you find at the Athy market. (Emily Square, Athy 10am-3pm Sunday)

Farmshop

Castlefarm Shop

Organic farmers have a long tradition of scripting their adventures in print, usually in relatively obscure magazines. But Jenny Young's monthly diary in *Food & Wine* magazine, which is becoming a diary for *The Farmer's Journal*, has brought the highs and lows of Irish farming to a much bigger audience than normal, and it will be fascinating to see how the Journal, bastion of Irish agribusiness, will cope with a perky organic farmer who sells at the Athy Farmers' Market as well as running a farm shop at Castlefarm itself. We have a distinct feeling that Mrs Young is going to be the first female superstar organic farmer in Ireland: watch out for the telly series that will almost certainly come. (Castlefarm, Narraghmore, Athy ☎ 087-6785269
jenny@castlefarmshop.ie www.castlefarmshop.ie)

Kildare

Ballymore Eustace

Restaurant & Gastropub

Ballymore Inn

Georgina and Barry O'Sullivan are the smartest cats in the Irish culinary world. Look at those wonderful pizzas that are part of the Ballymore menu, for instance, which in the early days refined and sythesised ideas by Bernadette

O'Shea, from her book, *Pizza Defined*. But look at that new Greek lamb pizza with yogurt and mint topping? Where did that come from? Did Diana Henry have that recipe in her book, *Crazy Water, Pickled Lemons*. Well, the dish is in the index, but it's not in the book. But then, doesn't Claudia Roden have a lamb pizza in her book, *Arabesque*? Yes she does, but it's slightly different from Mrs O'Sullivan's. So, see what is going on here: new ideas being chased down from every manner of source and inspiration, then refined and given the Ballymore signature of clean, sharp flavours. Food that is good to eat, and food that is good to think. As if that sort of culinary intelligence wasn't enough, the O'Sullivans have sublime taste in art, coach terrific staff, and their makeover of this old bar into a spiffing restaurant with a large food bar at the rere is the most successsful makeover we have seen since The Cellar at the Merrion Hotel. All this, and excellent value for money. Priceless. (Ballymore Eustace ☎ 045-864 585 📫 osullivan@ballymoreinn.com 🖱 www.ballymoreinn.com)

"I always did the opposite of what everybody told me to do."

MYRTLE ALLEN

Ballysax

Organic Chicken

● Organic Chicken

Margaret McDonnell and her husband, Jim, "were typical smallholders. We produced our own vegetables, free-range poultry and always had an interest in good wholesome food", Margaret told Cait Curran in the magazine, *Organic Matters*. Customers for the birds increased, the McDonnells converted to organic production, and today the Ballysax birds are amongst the best-known organic poultry in the country, birds who enjoy a stress-free lifestyle, and who reward us with wonderful flavour and texture and taste, completely unlike the tragic, deracinated flavour of intensively reared poultry. You will find the Ballysax birds in the best butchers' shops, at local farmers' markets, and on the menu at the Ballymore Inn, where Georgina O'Sullivan cooks it with a broccoli and ginger salad and a black bean sauce. Accept no substitute to poultry of this standard, a standard which guarantees animal welfare, sustainable environmentalism, and culinary success.(Martinstown Rd, Ballysax, The Curragh ☎ 087-210 8895 📫 magmcdonnell@eircom.net)

Carbury

Farm Shop

Deirdre and Norman O'Sullivan

The great champions of the Dublin Food Co-Op, where their stall is under a virtual state of siege from hungry shoppers every Saturday, Norman and Deirdre simply do the good thing. They farm organically. they supply their devoted customers with beautiful produce – scratchit, cluck and go eggs (!); multi-coloured beets; big, mucky parsnips, beautiful potatoes, feathery carrots fresh from the ground – and they run a farm shop at the farm. They have their own wind generator, and they use solar panelling. They dispose of sewage via reed beds. They plan to run both tractors and cars on vegetable oil. They are that too-rare breed – smart farmers, happy farmers, independent farmers, cultured farmers. They are food heroes, no less. (Carbury ☎ 046-955 3337 organicveg@eircom.net)

Clane

Café

Zest Café

Some people just open the right place in the right place at the right time. So it was when Mark Condron opened Zest Café back in 2004, in a nifty room beside the shopping centre and at the car park. Today, you can hardly get a table in here, as the population has exploded, and as Mr Condron and his crew continue to do the good thing. The food touches all the modern mood points – chicken Caesar salad; beef burrito; pesto linguini; steak with bearnaise; chicken stuffed with goat's cheese and red onion relish – and it's well done and well served by a lively crew. The right place in the right place, simple as that. (Clane Shopping Centre, Clane ☎ 045-893 222
zestcafeclane@eircom.net www.zestcafe.ie
– Open 8.30am-4.30pm, 5.45pm-10pm Mon-Sat, 1pm-9pm Sun)

Kilcullen

Butcher

Nolan's

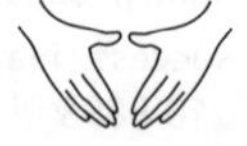

James Nolan's butcher's shop has its own

abattoir and processing room all under the one roof, making for an ideal scenario for producing the highest quality meats. The recent expansion of the shop has created a pristine space in which they have been able to extend their deli offer, and add in a coffee shop, so you can now get their acclaimed charcuterie products, organic fruits and vegetables, as well as luxuries like the best smoked salmon, all the while having a relaxing cup of coffee. That seems pretty ideal to us. (Main Street, Kilcullen ☎ 045-481 229 http://nolansofkilcullen.tripod.com – Open 8am-6pm Mon-Sat)

Sausages

Jane Russell's Original Irish Sausages

With a new range of dry-cure, nitrate-free rashers added to their list of speciality sausages – only Pat O'Doherty of Enniskillen also does a nitrate-free bacon – Jane Russell's company goes from strength to strength. Mrs Russell has built her company in double-quick time, but she has in fact returned to her roots, because she grew up as part of a butchering and bacon-curing family in Clonmel. When she became a sausage maker, she started selling at the Naas market and enjoyed a terrific response, and today she works five markets each week and sells to independent shops and supermarkets as well as some of the SuperValu chain. There is no mystery as to why these sausages sell so well; they are excellent, and once you try them you wouldn't even consider trying a commercially-made sausage. Anyhow, the big guys don't make funky jalapeno sausages, or good Toulouse sausages, or beef and Guinness bangers, or the simple and pure original Irish sausage. (Link Business Park, Kilcullen ☎ 045-480100 straightsausages@eircom.net www.straightsausage.com)

Kildare

Restaurant

L'Officina

The irresistible Dunne & Crescenzi Italian chic has ventured away from Dublin city and into the new Kildare Village Shopping Centre. The food products on sale make L'Officina as good a place to shop as it is to eat, but you really should not miss eating here for the signature style of D&C well chosen and well crafted plates of classic

Italian ingredients makes for great eating. (Unit 35 Kildare Village, Nurney Road, Kildare ☎ 045-535850 www.dunneandcrescenzi.com – Open 9.30am-6pm Mon-Wed, 9.30am-8pm Thu, 9.30am-7pm Fri, 9.30am-10pm Sat, 10.30am-6pm Sun)

Maynooth

Wine Merchant

Mill Wine Cellar

We get regular e-mails from Berna Hatton, of The Mill, keeping us up to speed with their courses and classes, their offers and celebrations, their competitions and whatnots. It's a sign of a wine shop that is dynamic, pro-active, and which revels in the joys and pleasures of the whole culture of the world of wine. Only excellent. (Maynooth ☎ 01-629 1022 info@millwinecellar.ie www.millwinecellar.ie – Open 7.30am-10.30pm Mon-Sat, 12.30am-10.30pm Sun)

Moyvalley

Pub

Furey's of Moyvalley

A popular just-off-the-main-road spot for a bite to eat for travellers. (Moyvalley, Broadford ☎ 046-955 1185 – Food served noon-7.50pm Mon-Sat)

Naas

Farmers' Market

Naas Farmers' Market

The Naas Market brilliantly mixes the market veterans food lovers are familiar wwith and depend upon – Sheridans, Gallic Kitchen, Jane Russell, G's jams, Castleruddery Organics, Denis Healy – with some emerging stars – pies from Edible Icon; chocolates from local chocolatier Jamie O'Neill; Louise O'Hare's What's Cooking traiteur foods; Ffrench's baking and preserves; Seccoto Coffee; Maggie Foley's crepes; Andrea's baking from the former Dobbins Restaurant pastry chef. A brilliantly social market, with a terrific atmosphere, superbly co-ordinated by Siobhan Popplewell. (Friary Lane, beside Storehouse, Sat 10am-3pm)

Deli, Foods-to-go, Café

● Harvest Kitchen

Valerie and Susan's Harvest Kitchen has developed a specialisation in gift hampers over the last few years, collating together some top-notch Irish artisan foods with good wines to make gifts that are an ideal "Thank you!" for anyone in your life. The shop also does a roaring trade in sandwiches, panini and wraps during the day, and it's a vital resource for good foods and wines in busy Naas. (1 Sallins Road, Naas ☎ 045-881793 🖱 www.harvestkitchen.ie – Open 9.30am-5.30pm Mon-Wed, 9.30am-6pm Thu-Sat)

Wine Importer

● Tyrrell & Co

Pretty much the highest compliment you can pay a modern Irish wine list, or a modern Irish wine shop, is to say that it has a good selection of wines imported by Simon Tyrrell. Celebrated in particular for the wines he sources from such superstars of the Rhone Valley as Stephane Ogier, Denis Alary, Serge Férigoule, Yann Chave and others, the Tyrrell portfolio is filled with great wines, with some of them at great prices. But the list is also discriminating in wines from Burgundy, the Loire Valley and South-West France, and their Plume Bleu quaffer is a wee delight. You will find the Tyrrell wines on the very best lists and in the best shops. (Rathernan, Kilmeague, Naas ☎ 045-870882 ✉ simon@tyrrellandcompany.com)

Newcastle

Restaurant

● Cafe La Serre

In La Serre, the café of the Lyons complex, global classics are rendered precisely and smartly – onion soup with Gruyère croutons; smoked haddock risotto with poached egg; duck rillettes; fish and chips; Margaret's roast chicken with mesclun salad; excellent oysters. Richard Corrigan never reinvents the wheel, concentrating instead on consistency and sure-fire flavours. The latest element of the venture is a bakery where Garret Hennessy is head baker: at present the breads can be bought from La Serre as they develop the bakery shop as part of the ongoing development of the village. (The Village at Lyons, Newcastle ☎ 01-627 0007 🖱 www.villageatlyons.com – Open noon-3pm (lunch), 3.30pm-5.30pm (afternoon tea), 6pm - 9pm Mon-Sun, 'till 8pm Sun

Kildare

Restaurant

The Mill at Lyons

Tony Ryan's largesse and Richard Corrigan's amiable chutzpah and culinary savvy have proven themselves to be a tonic for success in the village at Lyons. The complex opened with two restaurants, the very grand The Mill, and the more informal La Serre, a place which has already proven itself to be a big hit for Sunday lunch, when families can mill around the enormous, handsome complex and dream the country estate dream. As one would expect of Mr Corrigan, the food is carefully sourced and simply cooked. In The Mill, Paul Carroll serves crubeens with celeri remoulade and herb salad, pairs chicken wings with hand-dived scallops, roasts black sole on the bone with brown shrimps and a verjuice beurre blanc, and serves the most perfect lamb's sweetbreads with salsify. Superb staff are a key element. (The Village at Lyons, Newcastle ☎ 01-627 0007 www.villageatlyons.com – 5pm-9pm Wed-Thur, 11am-9pm Fri-Sun)

Rathangan

Craft Bakery

Noirin's Bakehouse

Noirin and Vincent Kearney's breads can be found at many of the big Dublin and Leinster markets, and they are worth hunting down for there is a trueness and simplicity to them that is beguiling. From the basic wholemeal brown bread to their ginger bread and their tarts such as pear and almond or pecan, this is honest baking. (Ballinrahin, Rathangan ☎ 045-524 078 www.noirins.ie)

Craft Bakery

California Market Bakery

Kathy and Vince McClean's CMB made a humungous reputation for itself when they were based up in Tandragee, and the move to Kildare simply brings them to within closer range of their many Dublin markets – they do Dun Laoghaire, Marlay Park, Bray, Monkstown and IFSC, but you will also find them in choice shops such as Olive in Skerries, F&B and Harvey Nicks in Dublin. Look out for wickedly good cheese and bacon scones, brilliant poppy seed muffins, whilst fruit baking such as pecan and pear or orange and date are out-of-the-box delicious. (Ballinrahin, Rathangan ☎ 045-252222 www.californiamarketbakery.com)

County Kilkenny

Bennettsbridge

Pottery & Café

Nicky Mosse Pottery

Nicky Mosse's superb spongeware is internationally famous, just as it deserves to be. The tableware unites elegance with an ancient craft form, and it is also terrific fun to use. It is also a treat to visit the mill at Bennettsbridge, to see the work in situ and in progress, and to give your credit card one hell of a hard time. There is a very sweet café in which to take tea or lunch as you try to come to terms with your new-found indebtedness. (Bennettsbridge ☎ 056-772 7105 sales@nicholasmosse.com www.nicholasmosse.com – Open 10am-6pm Mon-Sat, 1.30pm-5pm Sun)

Castlecomer

Pottery

Rosemarie Durr Pottery

We love the wan blue, and jade coloured pottery, which Rosemarie Durr and her husband, Andrew Luddick, produce at the Estate Yard crafts centre in Castlecomer. The tapering of the tableware is very fine and feminine, yet with an elegant tactility that is completely winning. Beautiful, beautiful work in stoneware clay, and a potter and ceramicist who is a star in the making. (Castlecomer Estate yard, Castlecomer ☎ 087-683 3639 info@rosedurr.com www.rosedurr.com)

Cramer's Grove

Ice Cream

Cramer's Grove Ice Cream

Nigel and Carol Harper make superb ice creams. We bought some at the Carrick-on-Suir farmer's market for our kids, and the Madagascan vanilla was awesome, the Bailey's and brown bread was incredible – their mammy

bakes the brown bread! – and the strawberry frozen yogurts were wicked. Ice Cream heaven! There is no mystery as to why the ice cream is so good: fresh milk and fresh cream from their own herd of Holstein Fresians, and lots of TLC, and sheer joie de vivre in the work of these fine, optimistic young folk, who are actually the fifth generation of their family to produce fine food in the south-east of Ireland. These are some of the most exciting and delicious new foods to have emerged during our research for this book, so don't miss Cramer's Grove. (Cramer's Grove, Kilkenny ☎ 056-772 2160
icecream@cramersgrove.com
www.cramersgrove.com)

Ferrybank

Apples and Apple Juice

Vogelaar's Apple Farm

The Vogelaars open their farm shop when the first Discovery is ready on the trees and they close when all the Katjas, Elstars, Cox's Pippins, Jonagolds and Bramleys are all sold. Some of the crop is used to make a very fine apple juice. (Mullinabro, Ferrybank ☎ 051-872544
vogelaart@eircom.net)

Graiguenamanagh

Restaurant and B&B

Waterside

The accommodation is simple in Brian and Brigid Robert's restored mill, beside the river, and Brigid's cooking keeps things nice and simple in the restaurant: broccoli and blue cheese soup; Clonakilty black pudding with apple purée; striploin steak with caramelised onions; darne of salmon with braised fennel. With almost a decade in business in 'Graigue, the Roberts are doing a handsome, happy job. If you are messing about on a boat during the high summer, do note that they serve light lunches, so pull over and tie up. (Graiguenamanagh ☎ 059-972 4246
info@watersideguesthouse.com
www.watersideguesthouse.com – Open weekends in winter from 6.30pm. Open seven days in summer, evenings and Sunday lunch)

Inistioge

Restaurant

Bassett's At Woodstock

Mijke Jansen and John Bassett's restaurant was the hottest ticket in Irish food after opening, thanks to serving an exotic, multi-course menu each evening. That menu is now confined to Saturday nights, when chef Emilio Martin Castilla fires out courses such as deep-fried soft-shell crab; magret of duck with vanilla risotto; foie gras with couscous of cauliflower; tortellini of ceps with a soup of green asparagus. For the rest of the week, an à la carte menu offers many of the same dishes, but served as ordered rather than in a stream of new arrivals. Great cooking, and a superb location in the Woodstock estate near beautiful Inistioge. (Woodstock Gardens, Inistioge ☎ 056-775 8820 www.bassetts.ie – Open noon-4pm, 7.30pm-9.30pm Wed-Sat, 1pm-5pm Sun)

Kilkenny

Shop

Aine's Farm Shop

Aine's is a nice wee roadside shop where you will find Sheridan's comestibles, Ditty's biscuits, G's jams and goodies from Wexford's Stable Diet. There are also home-made brown breads, fruit pies and scones. (Lavistown, Clara ☎ 056-770 2355)

Delicatessen and Take-away

Blueberry Larder

Will and Kerry Fitzgerald's traiteur signals their serious intent with a selection of well dog-eared cookery books lining the shelves as you walk into the shop. It's a top-notch shop whose ambition is to create good food that the customer can pick up quickly, so there are breads and sweet things and a comprehensive range of ready meals – Thai-style fish cakes; chicken and mushroom vol au vent; sausage casserole; seafood pie; Moroccan roasted vegetables. They produce a range of speciality sandwiches, with a classic Reuben amongst the wittily-named selection, and Blueberry is busy and fun and rather good. (2 Market Yard, Kilkenny ☎ 056-776 1456 www.blueberrykilkenny.com info@blueberrykilkenny.com – Open 8.30am-6pm Mon-Wed & Sat, 8.30am-7pm Thu-Fri)

Restaurant

Café Sol

Things are really coming together in Café Sol. The team work hard on sourcing, and they deliver with good cooking, whether you dip in for Sunday brunch – eggs Benedict made with Ballon eggs; baked salmon with tomato confit – or just slip in for a coffee and a cake – homemade tiramisu, a brilliant extra chocolate chocolate brownie – or if you make an evening of it with a good dinner – fillet of hake with spinach; beef fillet with braised oxtail and potato rosti; lamb's liver with red pepper mash; roast cod with potato dauphinoise. A confident signature style is really emerging here, and the people of Kilkenny are flocking to it. (William Street, Kilkenny ☎ 056-7764987 info@cafesolkilkenny.com www.cafesolkilkenny.com – Open 11.30am-10pm Mon-Sat, noon-9pm Sun)

Bar & Restaurant

Carrigan's Liquor Bar

So, let's allow Eamon Barrett to tell us all about Carrigan's: "Finally, we finished off with a couple of coffees in Carrigans Liquor House. It's where the old Caislean Ui Caoimh was and is a wonderful reinvention of a 'Marble city' bar with its beaten zinc counter and embossed metal ceiling. A single very efficient member of staff ran everything like clockwork and the kitchen was putting out food that looked simple and tasty." (2 High Street, Kilkenny ☎ 056-770 3979 www.langtons.ie – Food served 9am-8.30pm Mon-Sun)

Wine Merchant

Le Caveau

The day you walk into Pascal and Geraldine's wine shop is the day your life takes a turn for the better. The selection of wines M. Rossignol imports, and his extensive connections with wine growers in France, means that this company actually has pretty much all the wines your life needs. If you need wallet-bending Burgundies, you are spolit for choice, but start with Vincent Girardin, or Philippe Rossignol or Jacky-Truchot Martin. If you want quaffers for Tuesday night, they are here, from a wide range of producers. And then there are those great specialists, such as Billecart-Salmon from Champagne, Clos Triguedina from Cahors, and many more. The shop is the most charming space in which to browse, service is superb, and delivery is fleet. It would be hard to better Le Caveau. (Market Yard, Kilkenny ☎ 056-775 2166 ✉ secure@lecaveau.ie 🖱 www.lecaveau.ie – Open 10.30am-6.30pm Tue-Sat)

Café

Chez Pierre

Excellent tartines during the day make way for a short and choice dinner menu in Pierre Schneider's sweet little dining space, a rather well-kept Kilkenny secret. (17 Parliament Street, Kilkenny ☎ 056-776 4655 ✉ chezpierrerestaurant@hotmail.com – Open 10am-4.30pm Mon-Sat, from 6.30pm Thu-Sat. Bookings only Thur)

Restaurant

Fleva

Michael Mee is a chef much respected by his peers in the profession, and his first-floor restaurant in the centre city has a devoted following after almost a decade of creating interesting modern cooking. He spins new twists on familiar ideas, like duck confit and orange filo parcels, for example, which mixes two traditions into a neat new filip, or roasted parsnip and curried apple soup, or fried polenta with rocket and pine nut with sesame-coated goat's cheese. He has a fondness for the sharpness of Asian grace notes in his dishes, as in Asian-style roast duck, but otherwise the focus is on classic Mediterranean standards. Stylish room, good service. (84 High Street, Kilkenny ☎ 056-777 0021 ✉ flevarestaurant@eircom.net 🖱 www.flevarestaurant.ie– Open 12.30pm-2.30pm, 5.30pm-close Tue-Sat, 1pm-8pm Sun)

Delicatessen

The Gourmet Store

Padraig and Irene lawlor's shop is virtually beseiged every lunchtime, as the couple are run off their feet catering to a queue of hungry food lovers that almost extends out the door and onto the street. Panini and sandwiches are what everyone is here for, and has been turning up here for ten years in order to get their hands on them, and you can choose from a suggested menu, or make up your own. In quieter moments, it's lovely to have a relaxed browse amidst all the good things they sell. (Main St, Kilkenny ☎ 056-777 1727 ✉ gourmetstore@hotmail.com 🖱 www.thegourmetstorekilkenny.com – Open 9am-6pm Mon-Sat)

Design Shop and Café

Kilkenny Design Centre

Prices are high in this pretty room of the celebrated shop and design gallery, but the best seafood chowder around helps one to overlook the cost. (Castle Yard, Kilkenny ☎ 056-772 2118 info@kilkennydesign.com www.kilkennydesign.com – Open 10am-7pm Mon-Sat, 11pm-7pm Sun and bank hols)

Farmers' Market

Kilkenny Farmers' Market

Located at Gowran Park, the market offers excellent things from The Truffle Fairy, has Helen Finnegan's brilliant Knockdrinna Cheese, local organic vegetables plus a huge selection of imported and local produce from Denis Healy. Noirín's Bakehouse will be there and don't miss the hi-fibre breakfast loaf and the pecan tart. The Gallic Kitchen have fantastic pies and savouries, Pat Hartley has good seafood. The Tinnock Farm Produce is one of the best stalls at any market, and Paddy Jack Cheese from Laois has masses of good things. (Gowran Park, 2nd Sunday of each month)

Hotel

Kilkenny Ormonde Hotel

Mark Gaffney is the chef in the Ormonde, and despite the surroundings of a standard hotel dining room, his cooking is extremely accomplished, and offers very good value for money. Let this man loose on a complex competition dish, such as coriander seed seasoned john dory, with a ragoût of fava beans, wild garlic, morels, tarragon and confit silver skin onions, with crab and basil tortellini and a corn a smoked bacon foam (phew!), and he makes it seem as easy as a walk in the park. We also had one of the best crème brûlées of our lives in here, cooked by pastry chef Mary. (Ormonde Street, Kilkenny ☎ 056-772 3900 info@kilkennyormonde.com www.kilkennyormonde.com)

Hotel and Conference Centre

Lyrath Estate

A big, big-buck, 5-star hotel and conference centre on the north side of town, Lyrath has yet to find its feet and to establish a style of its own, a task not helped by the curious collision of styles and artefacts that they call a lobby. The bedrooms are very good indeed, and Lyrath needs a top-notch manager to pull together all the elements of this big operation, but the food has improved markedly in recent times. (Dublin Road, Kilkenny ☎ 056-776 0088 info@lyrath.com www.lyrath.com)

Gastro Bar

Marble City Bar

A stylish bar which is always busy at lunchtime, the MCB is a good choice for a quick lunch in the centre of the city. (66 High Street, Kilkenny ☎ 056-776 1143 www.langtons.ie – Food served 10am-10pm)

Tea Rooms

Marble City Tea Rooms

The tea rooms at the back of MCB is also owned by the Langtons group, and smart locals tend to favour the cooking in here over the bar food. They do punchy, tasty things such as garlic field mushrooms with ciabatta on a green salad which is particularly good. There is a variety of sandwiches, and interesting side orders like cous cous and beetroot. (66 High Street, Kilkenny ☎ 056-776 1143 www.langtons.ie – Open 9am-9pm Mon-Sun)

"It's inspiration. It's the moment. It's the energy in the kitchen, which is always changing". KEVIN THORNTON

Restaurant

Rinuccini

An Italian restaurant which also offers accommodation in seven upstairs rooms, Antonio Cavaliere's restaurant doesn't do the contemporary River Café style of Italian food, preferring instead the richer, more sedate and comforting classic Italian cooking. (1 The Parade, Kilkenny ☎ 056-776 1575 info@rinuccini.com www.rinuccini.com – Open noon-2.30pm, 5pm-10.30pm Mon-Sat, noon-3pm, 5.30pm-9.30pm Sun)

Sandwich Bar

Sandwich Express

Alan and Sandra, formerly of Zuni, offer an excellent selection of sandwiches that have real imagination and style. (23 Rose Inn Street, Kilkenny ☎ 056-779 5899 – Open 8am-4pm Mon-Fri, 8am-3pm Sat)

Asian Delicatessen

Shortis Wong

Chris Wong seems to cram even more stuff into his shop with every month that passes, making this wonderful shop a brilliant combination of Oriental emporium meets Middle Eastern souk. SW is the best place for ethnic ingredients and for any queer gear that your most arcane recipe calls for, and you can find fresh tofu and exotic vegetables. But, no visit to Shortis Wong is complete without buying the superb street food Chris makes – the best spring rolls and samosas, the best sausage rolls, and we would detour into town just to get our hands on some lamb murtabak. A true star. (John Street, Kilkenny ☎ 056-776 1305 – Open 9am-7pm Mon-Sat)

Wine Merchant

Vendemia Organic Wines

"We've come out!" says Helen Tobler, of her decision to change the name of Vendemia Wines to state just what it is they sell: Vendemia Organic Wines. With the coming out has also come a new shop – Kilkenny's best-kept secret – which is beside their offices at Hebron Road, and this has allowed the brilliant range of organic and bio-dynamic wines to grow steadily, and allowed them to introduce a range of organic olive oils, vinegars and herbs. Dubliners should note that you can buy a good selection of the Vendemia wines at the Saturday Dublin Food Co-op on Pearse Street. (Hebron Road, Kilkenny ☎ 056-777 0225 info@vendemiawines.com www.vendemiawines.com)

Wine Merchant

The Wine Centre

A massive, treasure trove of a wine shop with a jaw-droppingly enormous selection of wines and spirits, a selection so vast it has to be seen to be believed. (John Street, Kilkenny ☎ 056-772 2907 www.wineobsessed.com – Open 10.30am-10pm Mon-Sat)

Restaurant & Townhouse

Zuni

Lunch in the bar, on soft leather sofas, is the new favourite at Paul and Paula Byrne's ultra-hip Zuni. Caesar Cleopatra; prawn and melon salad; smoked salmon and

shrimp on brown bread with wasabi mayonnaise all hit the spot. We ate as well as ever on our most recent visit to the restaurant, and found the savoury cooking from Maria Raftery to be bang up to form, and it's wonderful to see a chef digging into the back pages of cordon bleu to come up with old classics like cod veronique. The dining room remains one of the best in the entire country, but the rooms upstairs are in need of an overhaul.
(26 Patrick Street, Kilkenny ☎ 056-772 3999
info@zuni.ie www.zuni.ie 12.30pm-2.30pm,
6.30pm-9.30pm Mon-Sat; 1pm-2.45pm, 6pm-8.30pm Sun)

Lavistown

Farmhouse Cheese & Sausages & Study Centre

Lavistown Farmhouse

The wonderful Lavistown cheese is, believe it or not, almost 25 years old. It is, thus, one of the pioneers of farmhouse cheese-making in Ireland, its pale white, crumbly deliciousness as distinctively different from any other cheese as the Lavistown sausages are different from any other pork sausages. But that pioneering spirit is nothing new for Olivia and Roger Goodwillie. Their house and farm, and the courses they run and the foods they produce, are all of an holistic totality, and they don't follow fashions, they create them. They use their brawn to make foods, if you like, and their brains to teach and educate people about everything from wild flowers in the Burren to breadmaking to foraging to sedges. And, Olivia is planning a cookery book of Lavistown recipes. Unique. (Lavistown
☎ 056-776 5145 courses@lavistownhouse.ie
www.lavistownhouse.ie)

Piltown

Apple Juice

The Little Irish Apple Co.

Philip and Oren Little's apple company has 60 acres of orchards from which to select the apples that are pressed to make their very fine juices. Jonagored, bramleys and other dessert apples are all used, and look out especially for the organic juice they produce each season. (Clonmore House, Piltown ☎ 051-387109)

Honey

Mileeven

"It all started because we had bees" says Eilis Gough, of Mileevens, "and in 1987 we had a surplus, so that started the business". That business soon grew into the excellent series of Mileeven honey products, a range which the restless Ms Gough is forever working on, most recently creating jars of honey with apple and cinnamon, and honey with sour cherries, and honey with raspberries. In 1997 Eilis bought over the Ownebwee preserves company, which allowed the company to expand into preserves and baking. Everything this gifted artisan touches is blessed with goodness and trueness, and it is a textbook example of how to run a successful company that stays true to its roots – Mileeven is still based where it began all those years ago – whilst being able to innovate steadily and successfully. Worth any Ph.D student's thesis, and every food lover's larder. (Owning Hill, Piltown ☎ 051-643368 mileeven@indigo.ie www.mileevenfinefoods.com)

Stoneyford

Farmhouse Cheese

Knockdrinna Farmhouse Cheese

In the old days, it used to take cheesemakers years to discover the true signature of their cheese and to get to a situation where a particular cheese was associated with a particular style. Nowadays, the new generation of cheesemakers such as Helen Finnegan of Knockdrinna can seemingly create signature-style farmhouse cheeses right from the outset. Helen produces both a semi-hard – Knockdrinna Gold – and a soft – Knockdrinna Snow – goat's milk cheese, and they are superb, with the milk coming from Saanen goats from the herd of Hugh Daniels. The semi-hard cheese is washed with an organic white wine wash, the soft cheese mixes brilliantly with pesto and red pepper. And what is the secret of their sudden success? Partly that cheesemakers like Helen were tutored on a cheesemaking course by the legendary Bill Hogan, of West Cork Natural Cheeses, and this inspirational man has helped the cheesemakers get to this level of expertise in double-quick time. This is proof that one of the most valuable legacies artisan food has in Ireland is the skill level resting with its eminent practitioners. So, Professor Hogan, and Professor Steele, and Professor Ferguson and Professor Grubb should all be co-opted by the NUI, given healthy stipends and gowns and an institute, and allowed to get on with creating the third wave of Irish farmhouse cheesemakers. (Stoneyford ☎ 056-772 8446 ✉ hlanders@esatclear.ie)

Thomastown

Delicatessen

● Food For Thought

Theresa Hayes runs a smashing little shop right in the centre of Thomastown. Full to the brim with a fantastic array of artisan and well sourced food, there is something pleasingly old-fashioned about FFT. There's a great selection of coffee from Union Coffee Roasters, including the knockout Sulawesi Kalossi, a hugely satisfying dark and nutty coffee. There's Dorset cereals, Blakes organic chocolate, Kingfisher teas and an array of Olive oils. Knockdrinna farmhouse cheese from nearby Stoneyford supply the cheese counter. Great service, and Theresa also knows all the food-loving' gossp for miles. (Market Street, Thomastown ☎ 056-7793297)

Wine Academy

● Wine Academy Ireland

Mary Gaynor is one of the best-known wine educators in Ireland and worked for many years as senior lecturer of of the Wine Development Board. In Thomastown she teaches the WSET (Wine & Spirit Education Trust) as well as Intermediate and Advanced wine courses.
(The Quay, Thomastown ☎ 056-772 4894
✉ marygaynor99@eircom.net)

Tullaroan

Bakery

● Oldtown Hill Bakery

Joy and James Moore's artisan bakery began in 1999, and has carved out a neat niche for great breads and cakes, with their ambition being to produce foods that "taste just like your mother's". The range runs from wholemeal soda bread to their trademark fruit tarts and crumbles and there is also a range of speciality baking at Xmas. Lovely stuff. (Oldtown Hill ☎ 056-776 9263
✉ oldtownhill@mail.com)

Urlingford

Organic Farm

Drummen Farm

Charlotte and Ben Colchester run the oldest organic farm in Ireland rearing chickens, turkeys, beef and lambs on homegrown feeds and processing them in their own abbatoir. You can buy direct from the farm. (Islands, Urlingford ☎ 056-883 1411 charlottecolchester@hotmail.com)

Windgap

Organic Vegetables and Poultry

Bia Beo Organics

Excellent organic poultry and geese are joined with organic fruit and veg in this enterprising farm. You can buy from the farm gate or look out for them in Kilkenny and Waterford markets. (Ballyhall, Windgap ☎ 056-775 5072 flaving3@eircom.net)

County Laois

Abbeyleix

Jams, Preserves & Relishes

G's Gourmet Jams

"It's not all money for jam!", says Helen Gee about her dynamic preserves company, G's Jams. "It's hard work too". Well, it sure is hard work when you take as much care as Mrs Gee does, selecting the best fruit and then cooking it in such a way that it emphasises the pure fruit flavours, rather than bundling everything up in a haze of sugar. This is jam making as you would expect it to be practised by a farmer's wife: expert, domestic, artisan, cultured. Helen's march towards jam super-stardom has been helped by the expansion in farmers' markets, and by the growth of the specialist delicatessens that appreciate the extra effort that is in every jar. (Ballypickas, Abbeyleix ☎ 057-873 1058 ✉ gsgourmetjams@eircom.net)

Ballacolla

Farmhouse Cheese

Abbey Organic Cheese Co.

Pat Hyland's Paddy Jack cheese stall is as omnipresent in Ireland's farmers' markets as is Denis Healy or The Gallic Kitchen. Quite how this hard-working man also manages to find time to create cheese, and to smoke cheese, we don't know, but he does both and does them well, with the original Abbey Blue brie remaining our favourite amongst the range. (Cuffsborough, Ballacolla ☎ 057-873 8599 ✉ abbeycheese@eircom.net)

Mountrath

Country House

Roundwood House

Frank and Rosemary Kennan's lovely regency house offers the hospitality of bygone Ireland. Others have state-of-the-art this and that and the other, whilst Frank and Rosemary have good food, good conversation, and an aesthetic

that is almost 19th century, such is its patrician, civilised and civilising aesthetic. Lovely place, lovely food, lovely people. (Mountrath ☎ 057-873 2120
roundwood@eircom.net www.roundwoodhouse.com – Open all year, except Christmas)

Portarlington

Coffee

Seccoto Coffee Roasting

Tom Naughton's bespoke coffee roasting company specialises in small runs of specialist coffees, whether single origin coffees, organic and Fair Trade coffees, or decaff coffees. He makes specialist roasts for customers, so that fine cup you enjoy in Jim Tynan's Country Kitchen or that specialist Xmas roast will have been created by Tom. Tom sells his Seccoto coffees in the Naas farmers' market. (15 Foxrock Court, Portarlington ☎ 057-864 0098
info@seccoto.com www.seccoto.com)

Portlaoise

Restaurant

Eureka Bar & Grill

Kevin Hennessy made a fine reputation when he was operating The Lemon Tree restaurant in the centre of town, and with a move out to the stylishly constructed Comfort Hotel at Midway, hard by the N7, which is planned to be developed as a food hub, there is infinite potential for this most professional restaurateur. Michael Rath, whose graceful cooking has been a feature of many addresses ever since we began to write, is rattling the pans in the Eureka Restaurant in the Comfort Inn, the hotel element of Midway, and you can expect to see the McKennas, en route from West Cork to Belfast, pulling into that big, big car park to get some vital sustenance. The Food Court of the hotel is still in the early stages of development as we write, but a good supermarket is planned alongside a noodle bar, a sandwich shop, a burger stop and other popular new brands. (Comfort Inn, Togher Roundabout, Portlaoise ☎ 057-862 1090
www.comfortinnhotelportlaoise.com – Open 7am-10am (breakfast) (8am-11pm at weekends), 12.30pm-3pm (lunch), 3pm-5pm (snacks), 5pm-10pm (dinner) Mon-Sun)

Wholefoods

● The Fruit'n'Nut Place

The Wellwood family's great wholefood store is one of the original of the species in Ireland, and today it remains one of the best after twenty years' service. (1 Lyster Square, Portlaoise ☎ 057-862 2239 – Open 9.30am-6pm Mon-Sat)

Town House

● Ivyleigh House

Dinah Campion's house is one of the most pristine town-houses you will find anywhere, and offers one of the very best breakfasts, along with true hospitality. (Bank Place, Portlaoise ☎ 057-862 2081 www.ivyleigh.com)

Restaurant

● The Kingfisher

Khurshid Googee has been serving good Indian specialist food to the happy folk of Portlaoise for a decade now, a longevity that reflects the care the kitchen takes in preparation of its dishes, and the bustling, lively ambience of this old Bank. (Main Street, Portlaoise ☎ 057-866 2500 inquiries@kingfisherrestaurant.com www.kingfisherrestaurant.com – Open noon-2pm Wed-Fri, 5.30pm-11.30pm Mon-Sun)

Restaurant & Food Store

● The Kitchen & Food Hall

Jim Tynan has been the Midlands culinary purveyor par excellence for almost 25 years now. Old timers like us can still remember the tiny room that originally held the The Kitchen. Today, it has grown organically into a splendid dining space, with one of the country's very best shops – The Food Hall – facing onto Hynds Square, as part of the complex. The sheer hard work that goes into masterminding this complex is breathtaking, with so much baking and making, soaking and curing, arranging and making beautiful, sourcing and selecting, but Jim and his crew –and the staff here are amongst the very best – seem to manage to skip through it all with a joie de vivre inspired by the thrill of creative cooking: they never cut a corner nor take a shortcut. As unmissable as it gets in the world of Irish food. (Hynds Square, Portlaoise ☎ 057-866 2061 jim-kitchen@eircom.net – Open 8.30am-5.30pm Mon-Sat)

County Leitrim

Aghacashel

Pub

The Mountain Tavern

Roisin McDermott's bar is noted for cooking and serving locally-sourced foods, and Ms McDermott is an enthusiastic player in the local culinary culture. (Liscarbin, Aghacashel ☎ 071-964 1302 – Food served noon-8pm Mon-Sun during high season. Limited hours off season, check before travelling)

Ballinamore

Cakes

Cannaboe Confectionery

Whether you want a re-creation of the Sagrada Familia for your wedding, or a Bart Simpson cake for the boy in your life, Sharon Sweeney will rise to the challenge with her jaw-dropping sugarcraft skills. (Willowfield Road, Ballinamore ☎ 071-964 4778 info@cacamilis.com www.cacamilis.com)

Ice Cream & Sorbets

Ballinamore Ice Cream

An exciting new company producing hand-made ice creams and sorbets, Anne Marie sells at the popular Boyle market. (Ballinamore ☎ 071-964 4080)

Carrick-on-Shannon

Accommodation

Ciúin House

Fiona and Barry Reynold's super-stylish house, with its emphasis on contemporary design and subtle luxury, is an exciting new addition to one of the fastest-growing towns in the country. (Hartley, Carrick-on-Shannon ☎ 071-967 1488 info@ciuinhouse.com www.ciuinhouse.com)

Country House

Hollywell Country House

Rosaleen and Tom Maher's country house has been a staple of the Bridgestone Guides ever since we first stayed here in the early 1990's. It is everything a country house should be – comfortable, distinctive, characterful, and with superb hospitality from the owners. (Liberty Hill, Carrick-on-Shannon ☎ 071-962 1124 ✉ hollywell@esatbiz.com – Open 1 Mar-31 Oct)

Farmers' Market

Market Yard Farmers' Market

A dynamic farmers' market takes place here every Thursday, in the beautiful Market Yard, Indeed it is hard to think of another market that has such an enviable location, so it's a special place to find great foods. (Market Yard, Carrick-on-Shannon, Thurs)

Gastropub

The Oarsman

Ronan and Conor Maher have hospitality in the blood, and it shows. Their folks run Holywell Country House, just over the bridge, and before that they used to run the hotel in town. The gene for good food and instinctive hospitality is in clear evidence in the dedicated work of these talented brothers, and whether you pop in for a bar lunch – one of the best in the entire country – or make a night out of it and enjoy Lee Mastin's cooking upstairs in the restaurant, you will find food that has great style, and service and hospitality that has even greater style. The Maher brothers are, we reckon, going to be one of the great forces in the North West: they are only at the starting gates now, and whilst their achievement in The Oarsman is already considerable, it is really only the beginning. (Bridge Street, Carrick-on-Shannon ☎ 071-962 1733 ✉ info@theoarsman.com 🖱 www.theoarsman.com – Food served noon-3.30pm Mon-Wed, noon-2.30pm Thurs-Sat, 6.45pm-9.45pm Thurs-Sat)

Wine Merchant

Slattery's

Rio and Tom Slattery opened their wine shop and deli in 2005, and have prospered over the last couple of years, a happening business in this happening town. They have a great selection of wines and some very interesting local foods. In addition they have a busy hamper business and have lots of vinous and edible gifts. With backgrounds in hospitality and business in Ireland and overseas, the Slatterys have just what is needed to power a valuable asset to the town, (Main Street, Carrick-on-Shannon ☎ 071-965 0535 ✉ sales@finefoodwithwine.com 🖱 www.finefoodwithwine.com)

Dromahair

Farmhouse Cheesemonger

● Cheese Etc

The next time you buy a piece of perfect farmhouse cheese from Trevor and Myra Irvine's Cheese Etc stall, perhaps in the St George's Market in Belfast, or in Boyle or Manorhamilton or at Coleman's Nursery in Templepatrick, take the time to pick up their simple brochure and take the time to read its short but passionate manifesto. "Our own philosophy is simple", they write. "We take the time to learn about each cheese we sell". Cheese selling, as an art form, is actually all about taking time, understanding when each cheese is ready, understanding how each cheese is developing. And that is why there is always a huge queue at the Cheese Etc stall, because folk know that Trevor and Myra have taken the time each cheese needs to be perfect. And that is what they sell to you: a slice of perfection. Inspiring. (Carrowcrin, Dromohair ☎ 071-962 2121 ✉ cheeseetc@eircom.net. Belfast St Georges on Fri & Sat, Boyle Farmers Market, Manorhamilton Farmers Market and Coleman's Nursery Templepatrick on the last Sunday of the month.)

Farmhouse Cheese

● Tullynascreena Goat's Farm

Michael and Marika Tolksdorf deservedly pulled in a Gold Medal at the British cheese awards in late 2006 for their Tullynascreena organic goat's cheese in oil, and they also went home with a bronze medal for their Tullynascreena organic fresh goat's cheese. That is a mighty achievement – and one echoed by other new cheesemakers like Knockdrinna and Glebe Brethan – but it will be no surprise to the fans of these fantastic cheeses. They are wonderfully fresh, tactile and clean in taste, and the Tolksdorfs are already so busy that they have no time to sell at any markets, so expect to find the Tullynascreena cheeses in good delis in the future. (Dromahair ☎ 071-916 4590)

Dromod

Bakery

● Dromod Homemade Boxty

Timmy Faughnan supplies a number of the local SuperValu shops with his breads – and these are not to be missed. He makes a potato bread, and little round pancakes which are made to his mother's recipe, as well as a health bread. But the jewel in the crown is the Boxty, a dense, starchy cake of potatoes which can be fried, toasted or microwaved. The Real McCoy. (Station Road, Dromod ☎ 071-963 8535)

Drumkeerin

Farmers' Co-Operative

● Leitrim Organic Farmers Co-Op

John Brennan heads up this pioneering organisation of local organic growers, many of whom supply organic meat to the Co-Op's travelling butcher's shop, which sells at local markets, has a store in Ballinasloe, and now travels to Dublin to the Leopardstown market. This method of retailing organic meat direct to customers is a brilliant innovation, and one that can get top quality organic meats out of the conventional system and into a high-value specialist retail market. (Drumkeerin Enterprise Centre, Drumkeerin ☎ 071-9640868 ✉ leitrimorganic@eircom.net)

Drumshanbo

Food Production Units

● The Food Hub

Leitrim has always had a pioneering role to play in Ireland's speciality food culture, for it has long been a favourite home for organic producers, and it has been a pivot of the Green Box eco-tourism concept. The Food Hub aims to capitalise on this pioneering spirit by creating a base where artisan scale food enterprises can be assisted to get off the ground and into production. It's a visionary idea, but we have no doubt they can steal a march on all those guys in West Cork and Offaly and elsewhere: just give them a couple of years. (Carrick Road, Drumshambo ☎ 071-964 1848 ✉ ifdel@iol.ie
🖱 www.thefoodhub.com)

Bakery

Jinny's Bakery

Sinead McGuire and Pascal Gillard bring backgrounds in catering and hospitality and a master's degree in food science, respectively, to their boutique bakery, and that mix of energies is already paying off with a bakery brand that already boasts a signature style with its breads, scones, cakes and a particularly fine carrot cake. Pascal joined the business Sinead had started after several years as an inspector with IOFGA, and this energetic couple really relish their work. For the present time the breads are available in stores in Leitrim, Sligo, Cavan, Longford and Roscommon, but one senses that it is only very early days for an ambitious and well-executed venture. Do note that Pascal and Sinead also have self-catering cottages – McGuire's Cottages, for rental, overlooking Acres Lake just outside Drumshanbo. (Carrick Road, Drumshanbo ☎ 071-964 1033 sinead@jinnysbakery.com www.jinnysbakery.com)

Local Speciality
ORGANICS

Kinlough

Restaurant with Rooms

The Courthouse

Piero and Sandra Melis's lovely restaurant with rooms is one of the stars of the North West, serving superb Sardinian-influenced cooking, with lovely wines, and offering simple, comfortable accommodation in this most charming village. (Main Street, Kinlough ☎ 071-984 2391 thecourthouserest@eircom.net www.thecourthouserest.com – 6.30pm-10pm Wed-Mon, 12.30pm-2.30pm Sun. Open seven days during high season, and closed at 9.30pm low season)

Manorhamilton

Shop

The Co-Op Shop

A small but perfectly formed destination address where you can find the gorgeous produce of lots of local organic growers who live and farm in the county. (Manorhamilton ☎ 071-985 5609 – Open 9.30am-6pm Mon-Sat)

Farmers' Market

● Manorhamilton Farmers' Market

Myra Irvine sells soups and smoothies as well as perfectly matured farmhouse cheeses at the Cheese Etc stall, and she is joined each first Friday by other talented producers and stallholders in The Bee Park. (1st Friday each month 10am-2pm)

"We have developed on the philosophical basis that small is beautiful, aiming at quality, which is quality in a business relationship as well."

ROD ALSTON

Rossinver

Herbs

● Eden Plants

Rod Alston is one of Ireland's elder statesmen of organics, and his herb company, and his vegetable gardens, have represented the pinnacle of organic food production, in terms of excellence and sustainability, for many years. Mr Alston is also a very fine early music specialist. (Rossinver ☎ 071-985 4122 ✉ rodalston@eircom.net)

Cakes

● Grass Roof Café

The GRC is the café and restaurant of the Organic Centre, and in addition to serving daytime foods, and catering for the participants on the many courses the centre runs, they also have fun food evenings, when the kitchen gets a chance to explore new cuisines. Recent events have wanderered over the culinary world, from the flavours of Hunan to a herb extravaganza via the flavours of Eastern Europe. (The Organic Centre, Rossinver ☎ 071-985 4338 ✉ organiccentre@eircom.net 🖱 www.theorganiccentre.ie – Open 11am-4pm weekdays, 9.30am-4.30pm weekends. Closed late autumn-St Patrick's Day. Hours can vary to check before travelling)

Organic Centre

The Organic Centre

A non-profit company with charitable status, the Organic Centre has been offering superb courses in organic production since 1995. Under the benificent control of the brilliant Hans Wieland, their series of celebrations, seminars, days out and study days offer an exhilarating series of opportunities to discover everything from 150 varieties of spuds on their potato day to an evening of Middle Eastern food with belly-dancing. The OC brilliantly joins up all the dots between organic food production, education, and experience, and it is, thus, a truly holistic organisation. They practice what they preach. (Rossinver ☎ 071-985 4338 organiccentre@eircom.net www.theorganiccentre.ie)

Speciality Food Company

Rossinver Grass Roots Organics

The Rossinver company products comprise a range of specialist sausages – lamb with rosemary and cranberry; lamb with mint and garlic; pork with apricot and paprika; and pork with parsley and sage – as well as a demon range of relishes and handsomely packaged porridge oats. You will find them at local farmers' markets in the North West – Carrick-on-Shannon, for instance, and in shops such as McMorrow's in Manorhamilton. The Rossinver foods are the delicious result of a collaboration between three organic groups working under the Atlantic Organics brand, and it is another example of organics discovering the power of collaboration, and getting into the market-place to get directly to customers. (The Organic Centre, Rossinver ☎ 071-985 4015 info@atlanticorganics.com www.atlanticorganics.com)

County Limerick

Adare

Restaurant

The Wild Geese

The Wild Geese is the prettiest restaurant in Ireland, in the prettiest village in Ireland. And, in chef-owner David Foley and f-o-h Julie Randles, it has a team who are more than a match for their gorgeous surroundings. Ms Randles is one of the best hospitality purveyors in all of Ireland, a woman who raises the businesss of front-of-house to an art form, and Mr Foley is one of the most interesting cooks currently at work anywhere in Ireland. His cooking at first seems overly cheffy – medallions of monkfish topped with crabmeat on a pea and saffron risotto; roast Barbary duck with a spring roll of confit duck leg with Savoy cabbage and a red wine jus are typical dishes from his repertoire, and they sound over-egged at first – but everything in The Wild Geese eats simply, because ingredients are pristine, and because the pairings on the plate are so rigorously thought-through, and then cooked-through with such precision, that a clear, calm culinary picture emerges. Beautiful food, happy times, unforgettable place. (Rose Cottage, Main Street, Adare ☎ 061-396451 wildgeese@indigo.ie www.thewild-geese.com – Open 6.30pm-10pm Tue-Sun (closed Sun off season)

Annacotty

Restaurant

Copper & Spice

The second branch of Bryan and Seema Conroy's restaurant, Copper & Spice, is unusual in that it offers Thai, Japanese and Korean dishes alongside its core offer of Indian specialities. But it is more than unusual in the fact that the different cuisines are rendered authentically, thanks to Mrs Ryan's exacting culinary standards. Most recently, they have introduced a buffet lunch offer on Sundays in Annacotty, which makes for a relaxing afternoon enjoying excellent food. This is some of the best ethnic eating in the West. (The Mill Bar, Annacotty Village ☎ 061-338791 copperandspice@eircom.net www.copperandspice.com – Open 5pm-10.30pm Tue-Sat, 12.30pm-4.30pm Sun)

Ballingarry

Artisan producer

The Green Apron

Theresa Storey makes a range of wonderful preserves, chutneys, jellies, jams, marmalades, mixes, relishes and rubs, each one just as impressively tactile, individual, easy to use and enjoyable to eat as the other. You will find the Green Apron foods at the Limerick Milk Market on Saturday morning, and don't leave the market without them. (Derryclough, Ballingarry ☎ 069-68524 storeytd@tinet.ie)

Restaurant & Country House

The Mustard Seed

Dan Mullane's gorgeous country house and restaurant is one of the glories of west coast hospitality. Indeed this distinguished address is one of the glories of Irish hospitality, and one of the glories of Irish interior design. If you want an Irish country house experience, but you want it at a level that encompasses professional service and international style, then the Mustard Seed is for you. The main house, Echo Lodge, is a glorious piece of Victoriana, and the newer suites in the modern wing are brilliantly comfortable and swish. The cooking is contemporary yet somehow agelessly classical, the dining room blessed with Mr Mullane's endless grace and hospitality. (Echo Lodge, Ballingarry ☎ 069-68508 mustard@indigo.ie www.mustardseed.ie – Open all year, except first two weeks in Feb)

Drumcollogher

Organic College & Market

Organic College Market

"Towards the way of knowledge" is the slogan of the small – 60 student – Organic College. The courses are dedicated to sustainable farming, and co-operative rural living. Visitors can visit the gardens made and maintained by the students, and there is also a market for produce from the College each Friday in the centre of town. In a recent tribute to the late, great David Storey, College director Kim McNamara quoted Mr Storey, in an epithet that could and should apply to everyone in agriculture: "His advice to students and young people thinking of entering farming was always positive and practica. 'Follow the dream however unfamiliar the landscape or challenging the terrain. Go for it! But with the two eyes open'." Amen to that. (Drumcollogher ☎ 063-83604 ✉ oifig@organiccollege.com 🖱 www.organiccollege.com)

Glen-O-Sheen

Farmhouse Cheese

● Oisin Farmhouse Cheese

Rochus and Rose van der Vaard are gifted cheesemakers, and their Oisin goat's milk cheeses and Glenogra cow's milk cheeses are fastidiously fashioned and executed cheeses. The Oisin, in particular, is the result of dazzling, artistically-inspired skilfulness, whether plain or in its smoked version. You will find the cheeses in many wholefoodstores as well as from cheesemongers at farmers' markets. (Kilmallock ☎ 063-91528)

Hospital

Smoothies and Juices

● Wild Orchard

Diarmuid Crowley and John O'Keeffe's company, unlike smoothie media superstars such as Innocent, actually press their own fruit to make their fine, healthful drinks. They produce five smoothies, and three juices, and all are bottles of sheer goodness. (Enterprise Centre, Hospital ☎ 061-383930 ✉ diarmuid@wildorchard.ie 🖱 www.wildorchard.ie)

Kilcornan

Preserves

● Nature's Bounty

'In autumn I can be found foraging in the hedgerows around me for wild fruits and berries for my recipes, most of which are over 100 years old. I want to stay faithful to tradition and to this end I have planted an orchard with heritage apple, plums and damsons", Colette O'Farrell's interpretation of her culinary tradition is shocking: her jams, marmalades and preserves actually shock the system with their purity of fruit, their understanding of texture, their individuality. In an age of mass-production, a taste of Nature's Bounty foods comes like a bolt from the blue. Whether it is the sweetly arresting orchard cottage chutney, the gloriously-textured piccalilli, or the incredible midsummer jam, these are foods for the Gods, with remarkable typicity evident right through the entire range of foods Colette produces. Fabulous. (Cowpark, Kilcornan ☎ 061-393942)

Farmhouse B&B, Rare Breeds Pork Products

Rigney's Farmhouse Bed and Breakfast

Caroline and Joe Rigney's farmhouse B&B is special because – like Pheasant's Hill in Northern Ireland – this is a farm that specialises in rare breeds. Mrs Rigney has a real epicurean's aptitude, so you can expect vivid cooking at breakfast, enjoying her own Curraghchase pork products, which are truly special. As well as running the B&B, Caroline has a farm shop, where she sells the fantastic Curraghchase bacon and sausages made from their happy pigs – these are some of the best pork products we have come across in recent times, and any food lover will drive to Kilcornan on a Sunday, when the shop is open, to buy the wonderful sausages and bacon along with hams, pork fillet stuffed with sausage meat and wrapped in bacon, and white puddings. Ms Rigney is a dynamic woman, and the Curraghchase brand is a sure-fire winner. (Curraghchase, Kilcornan ☎ 061-393988 info@rigneysfarm.com www.rigneysfarm.com)

Limerick City

Restaurant

Brulées

Teresa and Donal Cooper have been looking after the guests who occupy the nine tables in their restaurant for nine years now, quietly and patiently doing a good job. Teresa's cooking is logical and enjoyable – goat's cheese wrapped in pancetta is tangy and oozy; glazed chilli quail is meltingly tender and finger-lickin' tasty. Mains such as pan-seared fillet with spinach and roast polenta cake is soft and melt-in-the-mouth, thanks to properly hung meat and proper cooking, whilst barbary duck with a cassoulet of chickpeas scented with rosemary and with the duck cooked pinky rare, is a winner. Crème brulée, as one might expect, is excellent. The room is calm and quiet, and Brulées is a key address in Limerick city. (Henry Street, Limerick ☎ 061-319931 ✉ brulees@eircom.net – Open 5pm-10pm Tue-Sat, open lunch Thu & Fri)

Restaurant

Café Bar Deli

The Dublin chain heads down to the south-west, so they have obviously figured that the demographic mix is right in Limerick for this keen-value, sharply-served, no-nonsense food. (42 Thomas Street, Limerick ☎ 021-485 1865 ✉ limerick@cafebardeli.ie 🖱 www.cafebardeli.ie – Opening June 2007)

Asian Superstore

Cheong Heng Hong Oriental Supermarket

Cheong Heng Hong is a vast cave of Oriental goodies. Fresh fruit and vegetables are flown in twice a week and fresh tofu, coconuts and Chinese puddings fill the shelves. For the dim sum enthusiast there is a large range of excellent quality, ready-made dim-sum in the freezer. For the budding chef, all sizes of woks, knives cleavers, mortars and pestles line the bulging shelves, at a fraction of the price in a department store. The usual array of sauces in jars is here, giant bottles of soy sauce and vats of curry powder crowd the floor. Rice types vary from Japanese sushi rice to American par-boiled, and if you want to have your own Chinese New Year at home, incense, lanterns and all manner of chintz can be bought here. (95-96 Henry Street, Limerick ☎ 061-316868 – Open 11am-7pm Mon-Sun)

Restaurant

Ciaran's Café

Ciaran O'Callaghan is a man of many theories, one of which holds that we should drink nothing for an hour after eating. Aside from theories, he is a man whose practice, in the form of his work at Ciaran's Café in Limerick's University, has brought excellent vegetarian food to the campus and the city. "Fresh food for a healthier mind" is what they promise, and the cooking drives home this positive message, with fresh grains, pulses, vegetables and herbs cooked with flair and skill. (Drumroe Village, University of Limerick, Castletroy ☎ 061-338787 ✉ info@ciarans.ie 🖱 www.ciarans.ie – Open 9am-5pm Mon-Fri)

Hotel, Bar & Restaurant

Clarion Hotel

A landmark building on the Limerick quays, the Clarion is of course part of the busy hotel group with branches in Cork, Dublin and elsewhere. Locals use the Kudos bar as a meeting place, and the food both there and in the Synergie restaurant likes to add in Asian touches to western ingredients. Staff are very competent.
(Steamboat Quay, Limerick ☎ 061-469555
info@clarionhotellimerick.com
www.clarionhotellimerick.com — Open Synergie Restaurant opens 12.30pm-2.30pm Mon-Fri, 1pm-2.30pm Sun, 7pm-9.45pm Sun-Wed, 5.30pm-9.45pm Thu-Sat; Kudos Bar serves food noon-8.45pm Mon-Sun)

Restaurant

Copper & Spice

Bryan and Seema Conroy have always ploughed a different furrow from other ethnic restaurateurs. Where others soon settle into quotidian repetition, the Conroys remain creative and adaptive. Thanks to Mrs Conroy's formidable skill, they are able to add in dishes from other ethnic cuisines that take the chef's fancy, and those dishes are then every bit as well executed as their core offer of authentic Indian cookery. Any time we are sitting down to a thali plate in Copper & Spice is always a good time.
(2 Cornmarket Row, Limerick ☎ 061-313620
copperandspice@eircom.net
www.copperandspice.com – Open 5pm-10.30pm Tue-Sun)

Deli

La Cucina

Lor and Bru, who run the excellent La Cucina, are so hip that they haven't got a website: instead they have a blog. Is blogging the new black? Anyhow, you can read their adventures, and tales of little Alessia, from the comfort of your desk, then take yourself to the shop for ace Italian goodies and cooked foods, and some very highly-regarded pizza. (5 University Court, Castletroy ☎ 061-333980
http://italianfoodies.blog.com – Open 11am-9pm Mon-Fri, noon-9pm Sat, 5pm-9pm Sun)

Local Specialities

LIMERICK HAM

BACON

Café
Ducarts at the Hunt Museum

A super location, with a terrace with views over the river, means Ducarts is a good choice for simple savouries and salads after a tour of the excellent collection in the museum. (Hunt Museum, Rutland Street, Limerick ☎ 061-312662 ⌘ www.huntmuseum.com – Open 10am-5pm Mon-Sat, 2pm-5pm Sun)

Fishmonger
René Cusack

René Cusack has moved from his original store, and headed around the corner to Alphonsus Street, as well as opening in the Milk Market. Amazingly, the company isn't far off celebrating 100 years in business, an incredible rarity in Ireland, and an incredible history based on sourcing the best fish and serving it well. Now, that centenary will be worth one hell of a big party. (Alphonsus Street, Limerick ☎ 061-440054 – Open 9am-5.30pm Mon-Fri, 9am-3pm Sat; Also Milk Market, Limerick ☎ 061-408011 – Open 9am-5.30pm Tue-Sat)

Wine Shop
Fine Wines

With seven stores in total, including one in Ennis, Fine Wines is a big presence in Limerick. They have a broad popular range of wines, and a huge selection of beers in all the stores. (Vintage House, 48 Roches Street, Limerick ☎ 061-417784 ⌘ www.finewines.ie – Open 10.30am-11pm Mon-Sun)

Butcher
Jim Flavin

A very good butcher's shop, beside the petrol station. (Dublin Road, Castletroy, Limerick ☎ 061-331977 – Open 7am-7pm Mon-Sat)

Artisan producer
Forbidden Food

Connie Devlin began by selling her fab soups in the Limerick Market, and whilst soups continue to form the mainstay of Connie's work – she makes four different ones each week, and has a repertoire of more than 30 that she rotates seasonally – Forbidden Foods has expanded its range. Connie now also makes a red pepper hummus, two varieties of samosa – these are the only Forbidden Foods that contain wheat – and both a mushroom pâté and a chilli, basil and pepper dip. Nothing better than browsing the market with a cup of Caribbean pepperpot, or hot Thai veg soup, to make the fun even better. (6 Reidy Park, Clancy Strand, Limerick ☎ 086-104 4443 ✉ dollydevlin@yahoo.co.uk)

Butcher

● Garrett's Speciality Butchers

Check out this enterprising and ambitious butcher's store for particularly creative sausage making, alongside a host of expertly prepared charcuterie. (Unit 16 Racefield Shopping Centre, Dooradoyle ☎ 061-305734)

Cheese Shop

● Greenacres

Marie Murphy's cheese shop and deli has been the constant mainstay of the Milk Market in Limerick for almost the last decade, and both the stock of good things sold, and the service, are the enormous beneficiaries of Marie's wonderful enthusiasms. On Saturdays the shop opens out to join the lively market. (Limerick Milk Market ☎ 061-400334)

Delicatessen

● Ivan's of Caherdavin

An excellent shop, which today has an enormous businesss in cooked food-to-go – indeed it's so busy one suspects no one in Caherdavin cooks at home any more. Aside from the food-to-go, there are lots of good deli specialities. (Caherdavin, Limerick ☎ 061-455766 ✉ ivanssupermarket@eircom.net – Open 8am-11.30pm Mon-Sun)

Restaurant

● Jasmine Palace

A massive, and massively popular Chinese restaurant in the centre of town, the JP serves Chinese food for western tastes, and does it very well. Recently, however, newer, simpler and more echt ethnic eateries are springing up in Limerick to serve the city's ever-growing immigrant populations. (O'Connell Mall, O'Connell Street, Limerick ☎ 061-412484 ✉ info@jasminepalacerestaurant.com 🖱 www.jasminepalacerestaurant.com – Open 4pm-11.30pm Mon-Thu, 12.30pm-midnight Fri & Sat, 12.30pm-10.30pm Sun)

Market

Limerick Milk Market

Its beautiful location in the city's Milk Market should mean that the Limerick Saturday market is the best farmers' market in the entire country. But, somehow, it waxes and wanes, and never seems to hit its full, enormous, potential. Mind you, there are nevertheless very fine producers here, including the brilliant On the Wild Side, The Gourmet Tart Company, Kilshanny Cheese, The Real Olive Co., Sunflower Bakery, Teresa Storey's preserves, Connie Devlin's excellent Forbidden Foods, Benoit Lorge's chocolates from Kenmare, Frank Krawczyk's salamis from Schull in West Cork, and the dazzling fish filleting skills of the O'Driscoll brothers from Schull. And with Greenacres in situ, and the great fish shop of Rene Cusack, The Market is potentially the jewel in Limerick's culinary crown, and it needs extra support from the authorities to put it at the top of the tree. (Saturdays, Limerick Town Centre)

Butcher's Shop

Brendan Loughnane

A good, creative butcher's shop which has won many awards in competitions for spiced beef, excellent sausages and good puddings. (Upper William Street, Limerick ☎ 061-414213 – Open 8am-7pm Mon-Fri, 8am-5pm Sat)

Restaurant

Moll d'Arby's

Denis Cregan has charge of the kitchen in this atmospheric bar and restaurant. He has talent and technique and it shows in dishes such as a starter plate of James McGeough's charcuterie, including smoked black pudding in filo – very rare, and very good – crubeen ham hock and satay beef, whilst mains such as pan-seared monkfish with crab in ketaifi pastry are exactingly executed. There is a lot of ambition evident here and Moll d'Arby's is a key element of the Limerick culinary renaissance. (George's Quay, Limerick ☎ 061-411511 molldarbys@eircom.net www.molldarbys.com – Open 12.30am-3pm Mon-Fri, 5.30pm-10pm Mon-Wed, 5.30pm-11pm Thur-Sat)

Restaurant

Munchy Munchy

This is the Chinese restaurant where Limerick's Chinese community come to eat. (1-2 Glentworth Street, Limerick ☎ 061-313113 – Open 12.30pm-2.30pm, 5.30pm-11.30pm Mon-Sat, 12.30pm-10.30pm Sun)

Deli

Olio & Farina

Susan Mulvihill opened the first O&F franchise here in a wonderfully pretty store in Limerick in early 2006, selling excellent oils, jars of prepared sauces, potent rum babas, excellent pastas and wines, and a small range of good cookware from the respected Italian company. A second O&F has opened in Galway, with a third destined for Camden Street in Dublin. (2 Little Catherine Street, Limerick ☎ 061-319133 limerick@olioefarina.com www.oliofarina.com – Open 9am-6pm Mon-Sat)

Restaurant

Poppadom

West coast branch of the accomplished Indian restaurant that began in Rathgar in Dublin. (2c Robert Street, Limerick ☎ 061-446644 – Open 5.30pm-11.30pm Mon-Sat)

Fish & Game

John Sadlier

A fresh fish and game shop, right smack in the centre of the city where it belongs. Shops such as Sadlier's are becoming so rare that they should have preservation orders placed on them by the City Council. Food lovers can do their bit to support such specialist shops by spending your money here. (Roches Street, Limerick ☎ 061-414232)

Café

The Sage Café

Former Cranberry Mike Hogan's Sage Café has been "out the door" since it opened in 2006. The clamour for tables is so great that they don't allow you to book, and the grub more than lives up to the hype that surrounds Sage: the food here is excellent. Broccoli, leek and feta cheese samosas with red pepper and mango chutney are light and crispy with a filling full of fresh flavours. Brochette of Tiger Prawns with vanilla-scented rice with light curry cream is flanked by char-grilled courgettes and red onions and is deliciously creamy and delicately spiced. Indian rubbed chicken and dressed potatoes with coriander-flavoured raita is soft and tender, the spices subtle but distinct and the salad varied and crunchy. Desserts, such as baked orange cheesecake, manage the trick of being dense, yet light, with a warm hint of orange: truly excellent baking. The décor makes for a bright, airy and clean-feeling space, and the Sage Café deserves its roaring success. (67-68 Catherine Street, Limerick ☎ 061-409458 info@thesagecafe.com www.thesagecafe.com – Open 9am-5pm Mon-Sat)

Café

The Wild Onion

Bob and Ruth don't change things in The Wild Onion, and why should they? Folk like us are happy to turn up here, year in year out, and re-order the California Reuben, and the Chicago Burger for the boys, and the Tommy Gun for the girl. We scan the papers, enjoy the craic going on in the kitchen, eat our lunch slowly and with pleasure, and feel like regulars, which is what everyone else in here is. Quite, quite delightful. (High Street, Cornmarket, Limerick ☎ 061-440055 eat@wildonioncafe.com www.wildonioncafe.com – Open 8am-4pm Tue-Fri, 9am-3pm Sat)

Wine Shop

The Wine Buff

Mike O'Mara manages the Wine Buff in Limerick, the first of the WB franchises to open in Ireland. Expect the same range of excellent wines sourced largely from France by Paddy O'Flynn, along with the excellent advice and service that distinguishes this very dynamic company. (17 Mallow Street, Limerick ☎ 061-313392 www.thewinebuff.com – Open 10.30am-7pm Mon-Sat, 10.30am-8pm Fri)

Murroe

Coffee Roasters

Ponaire Coffee

Jennifer and Thomas Ryan's Ponaire coffees are full of character, classic artisan products offering great typicity and enjoyment. Such class bespeaks a lot of hard work in the sourcing and the roasting – they source green beans from a dozen different origins, then use a Diedrich IR-series roaster to roast the beans to optimum flavour, before hand-creating each blend. This is meticulous coffee roasting, and the goodness rushes from their Cottage blend, which mixes Indian Malabar beans wth Columbian Excelso. Ponaire belongs in the new generation of coffee roasters who are taking our caffeine consumption to narcotically intoxicating new heights. (Upper Ashroe, Murroe ☎ 061-373434 ponaire@eircom.net)

County Longford

Longford

Longford

Restaurant

Aubergine Gallery Café

There is real energy in Stephen Devlin's cooking in the Aubergine Gallery. Even clichéd dishes, such as a steak sandwich, or a tian of crab with avocado and smoked salmon, come out of the kitchen as if freshly minted, and it's splendid to see a crew – more of the Devlin clan – who seem to get more enthused by their work as time goes by. The upstairs room is modern and lean and, like the food, it is uncluttered by anything unnecessary, so it's a room to return to again and again. And the food has the same merit of never tiring, or seeming tired, so you enjoy direct and timeless flavours, whether it is their confit duck leg with red wine, or sirloin with pepper sauce or a good rhubarb crumble. (1st Floor, The White House, 17 Ballymahon Street ☎ 043-48633 ✉ aubergine@eircom.net – Open noon-5pm Tue-Thur, 6pm-8pm Wed-Thur, noon-4pm, 6pm-9.30pm Fri-Sat, 2pm-8pm Sun)

"The potato has, in the minds of more than half the world, an inalienable and time-honoured association with Ireland."

REDCLIFFE SALAMAN,
THE HISTORY AND SOCIAL INFLUENCE OF THE POTATO

Deli

Clarke's Seafood Deli

The Clarke brothers have made a mighty reputation in Ballina and Westport as being amongst the foremost fish smokers in the west, as well as some of the best seafood retailers. Now in this fine seafood deli, tucked in just off the main street of town, they have a chance to show Longford food lovers what Ballina and Westport have been enjoying. The shop is slick and stylish, has great, informed staff, and offers a supremely useful array of cooked seafood dishes – seafood pies, seafood lasagne; fish cakes – as well as pristine wet fish and shellfish, all of it in optimum condition. A shop like Clarke's can – and will – have a major impact on food lover's shopping in Longford, and it has created a major new destination. (12 Grafton Court, Longford ☎ 043-36832 info@clarkes.ie www.clarkes.ie – Open 9am-6pm Mon-Sat)

Butcher's Shop

Herterich's Butcher's

Herterich's has grown over the years and is now almost a small supermarket. It's a good place for their own sausages and for black and white puddings, and alongside an excellent meat counter there are lots of good deli foods. We like the timeless, intimate feel of the shop, and for two decades we have enjoyed excellent, personable service here. (38 Ballymahon Street, Longford ☎ 043-46597 – Open 9am-6.15pm Mon-Thur, 8am-6.15pm Fri & Sat)

Market

Longford Farmers' Market

Longford's lively Market Square hosts the weekly Farmers' Market. (Market Square, Fridays 9.30am-2pm)

Chocolate Shop and Café

Torc Café and Food Hall

Ruth McGarry-Quinn's Torc Truffles have always seemed to us to define the quiet, creative side of the county of Longford, and her slick, hip shop and café on New Street seems to us to once again express the emerging energy in this often overlooked county and county town. The shop is a beautiful place in which to find gorgeous deli foods, and it is also an excellent place in which to eat, thanks to a bustling atmosphere, switched-on staff, and a tempting array of specials and other modern, good tasting things described on the big blackboards. Of course, the range of Torc Truffles is excellent, but there are now many cracking choices, both sweet and savoury. And how will you find it? Well it's on the road leading into the square as you go east-west, and you only need look for the chocolate fountain in the window, the chocolate lover's red light, burning bright. (New Street, Longford ☎ 043-48277 – Open 9.30am-6pm Mon-Sat www.torcafeandfoodhall.ie)

County Louth

Ardee

Wine and Food Importers

Ardoa Food & Wine

Caran Aiken and Olivier Collin import a range of wines from small estates in France, Germany, Italy and Spain, but for us the stars of their show are the superb vinegars and tapenades they produce. These are truly special foods and should be in every food lover's cupboard, the vinegars in particular demonstrating great finesse and verve: brilliant. (Old Dawson's Demesne, Cappocksgreen, Ardee ☎ 041-685 7931 info@ardoawine.com www.ardoafoodandwine.com)

Local Speciality
RAW MILK FARMHOUSE CHEESE

Butchers and Delicatessen

Callaghan's Butchers and Deli

Peter Callaghan is particularly prized for his award-winning Ardee Gold sausages. (58 Market Street, Ardee ☎ 041-685 3253 – Open 9am-6pm Mon-Thu, 9am-7pm Fri, 9am-6.30pm Sat)

Restaurant

Fuchsia House

Sarah Nic Lochlainn and her husband, Sarajit Chanda, used to manage and cook in various Dublin restaurants before decamping to Fuchsia House. Their previous globetrotting adventures have allowed them to do not just Indian dishes – Mr Chanda is from Bangladesh – but they also feature Thai and Chinese accents in dishes along with some European ideas. Mind you, it is hard not to opt for Indian classics such as rogan josh, tandoori chicken, superb breads such as paratha, their own paneer cheese, Kerala prawns, and pilau rice, when each dish is cooked to such individualistically seasoned and culinarily precise standards as you find in Fuchsia. Serious cooking, great service, excellent value. (Dundalk Road, Ardee ☎ 041-685 8432 – Open noon-3pm, 6pm-11pm Tue-Sat, noon-9pm Sun)

Guesthouse

Beaufort House

Michael Caine, as well as being a restaurateur, is a Yacht-master Instructor, so many of the guests at Beaufort are there for sailing courses or on corporate team-building courses that the Caines run as part of their yacht school and yacht charter. The rooms in the house are extremely comfortable, so even if you don't want to be hauling ropes or navigating the waves and winds, Beaufort is an excellent choice as a guesthouse base in Carlingford. (Ghan Road, Carlingford ☎ 042-937 3879
michaelcaine@beauforthouse.net
www.beauforthouse.net)

Delicatessen

Food For Thought

Both an excellent deli and a very convenient spot in which to grab a simple bite to eat, FFT is a very discriminating deli, with lots of interesting foods that have been sourced and chosen with considerable care. TJ Hayes runs a good operation here, and the shop is a major asset to the village. (Trinity Mews, Dundalk Street, Carlingford ☎ 042-938 3838 pjhayes@iol.ie – Open 9am-7pm Mon-Sat, 10am-7pm Sun)

Tearooms

Georgina's Tearooms

Coffee kisses. Austrian apple pie. Gingerbread men. Rhubarb pie. Feta, leek and cherry tomato tart. Pastrami and gouda on toast with sweet beetroot. A cup of tea. Ah, Georgina's Tearooms. Up the hill in Carlingford. Always someone in there you know. Change? Why change? Small, and perfectly formed, and all too rare. (Castle Hill, Carlingford ☎ 042-937 3346 tedf@eircom.net – Open 10am-6pm Mon-Sun)

Guesthouse with Restaurant

Ghan House

"Sent my parents to Ghan House in Carlingford. They LOVED it and found it extremely relaxing, and they came home with loads of lovely foods." That's a fairly standard response from people who encounter Paul Carroll's lovely country house and restaurant for the first time. LOVED it. Well, yes, and there is lots to love, from careful and creative cooking through to a very relaxed vibe that lets you feel you are both in, and apart from, the lovely village of Carlingford. Hospitable, timeless, easy to love. (Carlingford ☎ 042-937 3682 ✉ ghanhouse@eircom.net 🖱 www.ghanhouse.com – Open 7pm-9.30pm Fri & Sat, midweek & Sun by arrangement only, B&B open all year)

Louth

Bistro

● Kingfisher Bistro

Siblings Mark and Claire Woods run a relaxed, simple little bistro in the Darcy McGee centre and have been doing a good job for almost a decade now. Simple surroundings, and some punchy modern cooking from Mr Woods. (Darcy McGee Grainstore, Dundalk Street, Carlingford ☎ 042-937 3716 ✉ kevinwoods@eircom.net – Open 6.30pm-10pm Tue-Sun. Two sittings on Sat night, 6.30pm and 9pm)

Pub

● Lily Finnegan's

A quintessentially atmospheric wee pub, a few miles out of Carlingford. (Whitestown, Carlingford ☎ 042-937 3730)

Bistro

● The Oystercatcher

Both lodging and bistro, the Kingfisher is a small, comfortable restaurant with a collection of good value rooms upstairs. Local oysters, local lamb and beef, and local seafood are treated with unpretentious care; just the thing after a strenuous day walking the Cooley Way. (Market Square, Carlingford, Accommodation ☎ 042-937 3922 Dining ☎ 042-937 3989 ✉ info@theoystercatcher.com 🖱 www.theoystercatcher.com – Open 6pm-9.30pm Mon-Sun during Jul & Aug, Thur-Sun from Sept-Apr)

Castlebellingham

Farmhouse Cheese

● Bellingham Blue

Louth is becoming the centre of raw milk cheese making in Ireland, for the county can boast two superb and original raw milk cheeses, in Glebe Brethan, and in Peter Thomas's brilliant Bellingham Blue. To echo the words of Cheese Etc supremo Trevor Irvine, "A mature Bellingham Blue knocks spots off most Stiltons". But BB isn't a Stilton clone, for the paste is creamier and more tactile. The milk comes from the family herd of Friesians, and to enjoy it at its best try to get a cheese aged to about three months, when the meld of blue veining and the open-textured cheese are at their most apposite, and most delicious. (Mansfieldtown, Castlebellingham ☎ 042-937 2343 glydefarm@eircom.net)

Farmers' Market

Castlebellingham Farmers' Market

A good farmers' market is held in pretty Castlebellingham on the first Sunday of each month. (1st Sunday in the month, 11am-5pm)

Drogheda

Restaurant

Borzalino Restaurant

The friendliness and consistent standard of cooking in Borzalino's has won them a dedicated audience who enjoy their pasta and pizza specials. "A family-run Italian to which you can quite happily take your family and eat well" is the word on the street. (20 Loughboy, Mell, Drogheda ☎ 041-984 5444 www.borzalinorestaurant.com – Open 6pm-11pm Mon-Sat, 5.30pm-11pm Sun)

Hotel

The D Hotel

Part of the Monogram group that includes the G Hotel and the Hotel Meyrick in Galway, the D has a to-die-for location on the river as part of the Scotch Hall shopping development. The rooms are superb but the cooking has some way to go to catch up with the design hipness. (Scotch Hall, Drogheda ☎ 041-987 7700 thed@monogramhotels.ie www.thedhotel.com)

Wine Bar

D'Vine

Sonia Micallef cooks, drawing on her Franco-Italian parentage, whilst Damien Leddy uncorks the bottles and runs the wine courses in D'Vine, which is enjoying a growing reputation in the town. Don't miss the rustic, trencher man delight of French country dishes such as tartiflette. (Patrickswell Lane, Off Narrow West Street, Drogheda ☎ 041-980 0440 – Open noon-3pm Mon-Fri, 6pm-late Wed-Fri, noon-late Sat, 5pm-late Sun)

Fishmonger

Kirwan's Fish Merchants Ltd

Pat Kirwan's shop is an excellent destination for sparklingly fresh fish and shellfish. (55 Lawrence Street, Drogheda ☎ 041-983 0622 Open 8am-6pm Tue-Sat)

Louth

Off Licence

O'Brien's Wine Off Licence

Drogheda branch of the dynamic wine firm. (Unit 5, The Haymarket, Drogheda ☎ 041-987 6362 sales@obrienswine.ie www.obrienswine.ie – Open 10.30am-11pm Mon-Sat, 12.30pm-11pm Sun)

Delicatessen

Stockwell Artisan Foods

Gwen Fearon and Orlaith Callaghan's Stockwell deli, on Stockwell Street, brings freshly made savoury tarts, pies, soups and stews to the hungry people of Drogheda, and it's a smart and logical extension of the company's food production, which takes place in Termonfeckin. Expect to see more of the good Stockwell foods in and around the town and the county as this company develops. (1 Stockwell Street, Drogheda ☎ 087-637 0436 gwen@dublin.ie)

"Cooking is a question of emotion."
FERRAN ADRIA

Dundalk

Wine Shop

Callan's Wine Shop

There has been a Callan's grocers and spirit merchants on Park Street for 65 years now, and today Mary and Kevin Callan sell excellent wines and a great range of beers. The wines range through the major brands from the vinous world, and the selection is extensive. (Park Street, Dundalk ☎ 042-933 4382 info@callans.ie www.callans.ie – Open 10.30am-11.30pm Mon-Sat, 12.30pm-11pm Sun)

Chocolates

Danucci Chocolates

Mark and Michelle Lowth's chocolate company produce elegant, balanced, superbly packaged chocolates, the flavours of the different varieties always well controlled and modest. You could almost describe Danucci as a bourgeois chocolate company, for everything they produce is like a luxury brand good: discreet, pricey, life-style conscious, controlled, very French, in fact. (5a Blackthorn Business Park, Coes Road, Dundalk ☎ 042-935 6727 info@danucci.com www.danucci.com)

Louth

Farmers' Market

Dundalk Farmers' Market

The Dundalk market takes place in the courtyard of the County museum. Local traders also collaborate with the Friday Newry market just across the border. (Saturday, County Museum www.irelandmarkets.com)

Fishmonger

Johnny Morgan

A really lovely fish shop with a great selection, especially of fish and shellfish landed on the east coast. (7 Eimer Court, Market Square, Dundalk ☎ 042-932 7977 – Open 9.30am-5pm Tue-Fri, 9.30am-3.30pm Sat)

Beer Importer

Noreast Beers

David McIlherron's beer company has recently added the impressive St Peter's organic English ales, and the Aspall Suffolk cider drinks to its portfolio of European beers. These drinks enjoy great typicity, and for ale lovers and serious cider fanciers, they are not to be missed. (Coes Road Industrial Estate, Dundalk ☎ 042-933 9858)

Restaurant

No. 32

Susan Heraghty's restaurant is such a smart, straight-ahead, simple place, with great food. Ms Heraghty understands flavours and textures, and the conjoining and contrasting of these elements, and if the menu looks eclectic in the familiar modern style, then the food is united by a singular signature, whether you have spinach and ricotta roulade with pesto, or home-smoked cod with saffron and herb risotto, or hake tempura with peas and chips. Value for money is exceptional, and this is a clever, modest, local restaurant. (32 Chapel Street, Dundalk ☎ 042-933 1113 info@no32.ie www.no32.ie – Open from 5.30pm Mon-Sat)

Restaurant

Quaglino's at the Century

Pat Kerley is one of the great County Louth veterans, but despite his years at the stove he still cooks with the energy of a young fella, and his up-the-stairs dining room in this fine old Century Bar is deservedly popular. (19 Roden Place, Dundalk ☎ 042-933 4147/933 8567 info@quaglinosrestaurant.com – Open 5.30pm-11pm Mon-Sun)

Restaurant

Rosso

Louisa Gilhooley runs the room whilst head chef Conor Mee rattles the pans in Rosso, and the team here have hit the ground running. A consistently high standard of cooking and artistic flair has made Rosso a welcome newcomer to Dundalk. The dining room is large, and polished wooden tables, comfy chairs, quality cutlery and crockery, along with clever use of lighting, decor and design make Rosso feel special. Mr Mee's cooking gets the balance just right in starters such as Caesar salad with seared tuna or in a cocktail of white crab, salmon and shrimp with avocado guacamole. Crispy fried pork with noodles, pak choi and a little duck confit is fab, really delicious, whilst hake served with a smoked ham and mustard linguine is of equal quality. Hot Valhrona chocolate fondant is perfectly cooked, runny in the middle and cooled with a really good vanilla ice cream. Rosso has got it just right. (5 Roden Place, Dundalk ☎ 042-935 6502 www.rossorestaurant.com – Open 12.15pm-2.30pm, 6pm-9.30pm Tue-Fri, 6pm-9.30pm Sat, 12.30pm-7.30pm Sun)

Dunleer

Farmhouse Cheese

Glebe Brethan Cheese

The Tiernan family's story is one of the great artisan stories of recent times. They imported a herd of Montbeliard cows in order to continue, and to vary, the dairying tradition that the family farm had always been famous for. The cows are pastured on grass during the summer and fed home-grown cereals in the winter. The 45-kilo wheels of raw milk cheese are matured on spruce timbers, and whilst the style is somewhat reminiscent of a French Tomme, the Tiernans do not remove the cream from the milk as the normal Tomme cheese does. Tasted at four months the cheese is mellow and creamy. At eight months it is full, pronounced, stonkingly delicious. Right from the outset they were garnering prizes for a cheese that is wonderfully complete. Glebe Brethan is yet another example of an Irish artisan food hitting the ground running, drawing in influences to make something that emerges as wonderfully individualistic. Try it the way Nick Price cooks it, as a savoury in puff pastry with a red onion relish, and be blown away by a remarkably versatile farmhouse cheese. (Glebe House, Dunleer ☎ 041-685 1157 dtiernan@iol.ie www.glebebrethan.com)

Louth

Termonfeckin

Butcher's Shop and Deli

McEvoy's Farm Shop

David McEvoy is a dedicated farmer, butcher and shopkeeper, a bloke with an endless stream of opinions about modern food, farming and retailing and, in particular, the responsibility of Irish shopkeepers to sell Irish food and the responsibility of Irish shoppers to buy Irish foods. His opinions are not merely theoretical, however, for there are now four McEvoy shops, and three market stalls, at Howth, Malahide and Leopardstown, and the company's most recent innovation has been the introduction of a box delivery service, offering their 3-week aged beef and lamb, 80-day old chickens and the rest of their butchery range, delivered to your door. One of their particular specialities is Xmas turkeys, and they carefully rear their bronze birds – all 3,000 of them each year – for 28 to 30 weeks. "Maturity is everything", insists Mr McEvoy, for this way the flesh develops proper marbling. It works: the McEvoy birds cook superbly and eat superbly well, and for such care in the production they represent excellent value. Aside from the turkeys, the shops are packed with lots of excellent, carefully reared meats and deli foods. (Nunneryland, Termonfeckin ☎ 041-988 1242, Blackrock, Dundalk ☎ 042-932 2680 ☎ Slane Village: 041-988 4938, Wheaton Hall, Drogheda ☎ 041-987 3384 www.mcevoysfarmshop.com – 9am-6pm Mon-Sat)

Restaurant

Triple House Restaurant

A pretty old farmhouse building in pretty Termonfeckin is where Pat Fox has been doing a good job quietly, honestly and successfully for many years now. He cooks local foods with sympathetic grace, and kindly local women serve the dishes with equal grace, creating a distinctive and enduring local restaurant. (Termonfeckin, Drogheda ☎ 041-892 2616 – Open 6.30pm-9pm Tue-Sun)

"Respect for food is one of the most important things to have, even if it's for the humblest of vegetables."

RICHARD CORRIGAN

County Mayo

Achill

Café

The Beehive

Crafts and coffee and nice things to eat: what an ideal mix The Beehive offers, and has been offering ever since Patricia and Michael first opened in 1991. (Keel, Achill Island ☎ 098-43018 joycesbeehive@msn.com – Open 9.30am-6pm Mon-Sun. Closed Nov-Easter)

Mayo

Guesthouse

Bervie

John and Elizabeth Barrett's beach side B&B has the true spirit of Achill – sunshiny, sea sandy, wind washed, out-of-time. This is a house to bring all the family, yet it also perfectly suits some time for yourself. Its secret as a destination is simply the fact that it has that invaluable Get-Away-From-It-All feeling; you arrive here and you feel you have made an escape. It's a place where, if you want to get the sand between your toes, you only have to walk through the garden gate. (Keel, Achill Island ☎ 098-43114 bervie@esatclear.ie www.bervieachill.com)

Restaurant

Calvey's

As seems standard on Achill, the style of Calvey's is old-style, but the food is wickedly tasty. You come here to eat organic Achill lamb, cooked simply and tasting like no other lamb: this is a true pré-sale lamb, and it should have a Slow Food presidia and a PDI certification. There are fish and shellfish dishes, of course, but Calvey's organic lamb is first choice, and when it comes time to leave, you can buy from their butcher's shop and fill up the car. (Keel, Achill Island ☎ 098-43158 www.calveys.com – Open 11.30am-5pm, 5.30pm-9.30pm Mon-Sun)

Restaurant

The Chalet

The room is old-style, and if you are looking for a hip Mediterranean-coast-style experience then you are in the wrong place. But if you just want some nice seafood, then The Chalet does just what you want just the way you want it. Fresh fish and shellfish, not messed about with in anyway, are the best bet. (Keel, Achill Island ☎ 098-43157)

Ballina

Fish Smokery & Delicatessen

Clarke's Salmon Smokery

The Clarke brothers are a dynamic bunch. Their flagship store in Ballina has been followed by new shops in Westport and in Longford, whilst the original shop and smokery remains a benchmark address. The Clarkes represent the new generation of fishmongers, in that a lot of their work is dedicated to prepared fish products, so they are fish traiteurs as much as fishmongers. And they are mighty good cooks, so their dishes are superb examples of the genre, all made with pristine fish. But, for wet fish and for smoked fish, they simply can't be beaten: they understand the culture of the seas, they understand what a gift, a blessing, great fish is, and they show it appropriate respect. That is why they are so special. (O'Rahilly Street, Ballina ☎ 096-21022 info@clarkes.ie www.clarkes.ie – Open Mon-Sat)

Bar and Restaurant

Crockett's on the Quay

Crockett's is a humungously busy bar and restaurant, with some old-fashioned rooms upstairs, just outside the town. The kitchen fires out popular, no-nonsense cooking to huge numbers of people, and during the season the real challenge here is trying to get a table. Extensive menus offer a roll-call of contemporary classics – crispy buffalo wings with blue cheese dressing; crab crème brulée; moules mariniere; fish and chips with mushy peas; darne of salmon; chump of lamb steaks with basil and mint mash; Baileys and coffee parfait. With a holiday party of friends, it's mighty fun. (Ballina ☎ 096-75930 info@crocketsonthequay.ie www.crocketsonthequay.ie – Open for bar food 12.30pm-9pm Mon-Sun. Restaurant opens 6pm-9.30pm Mon-Sun)

Wine Shop

Fahy's

Fahy's is a great wine shop, and one of the best wine destinations in the north west. They have a haul of trophies garnered from competitions, and when you see the selection of wines they stock, and which they sell so ably, you will understand why the critics beat a path to their door. (Teeling Street, Ballina ☎ 096-22143 – Open 11am-11pm Mon-Thu, 11am-11.30pm Fri & Sat, 6pm-11pm Sun)

Ballycastle

Coffee House

● Mary's Bakery

The cooking and baking in Mary's is so fine it lets you enter a little bubble of delight, a little oasis, into which no distractions can deter you. Only mighty. (Main Street, Ballycastle ☎ 096-43361 – Open 10am-6pm Mon-Sun, with more limited hours off season)

Mayo

Shop and Bar

● Polke's

The Bridgestone Guides don't do bars. But, if we did, then they would be bars like Polke's. A wee shop in front, a narrow bar behind, immaculately maintained, an excellent pint of stout. And Mayo gettin' bate by some other county team, played out on the telly in all its aching and longing. Nothing changes in Polke's. But we bet they would love to change that last bit. (Main Street, Ballycastle ☎ 096-43016)

Country House

● Stella Maris

Terence McSweeney and Frances Kelly's lovely converted convent is a place where everything is perfect. Not prissy perfect, just plain perfect. We have noted before that on our most recent stay, everything the five McKennas ate for dinner and the next morning's breakfast was perfect. Everything. Every detail of every dish, from tiramisu to scrambled eggs to fillet of beef, right down to the marmalade. That doesn't happen very often, but Ms Kelly is the kind of cook, and she has the kind of crew, that make it happen. And in a modern Ireland where everything is over-the-top, Stella Maris is wonderfully under-the-top: restrained, calm, genteel, courteous. Ballycastle, by the by, seems to us to be San Sebastian-in-waiting: a most wonderful destination. (Ballycastle ☎ 096-43322 www.stellamarisireland.com – Open for dinner for non-residents, 7pm-9pm Mon-Sun, 'till 10pm weekends)

Castlebar

Café

Café Rua

Cafe Rua may be the friendliest restaurant in the west. It has to be friendly, because it is so busy that it is always necessary to share a table in Colleen and Aran's little, bustling room. But, by the time you have ordered and sat down and said hello, you are suddenly new best friends with the other three people at the table, talking about the weather and the football team (sigh!) and, of course, the food. Because the food in CR is special. Wild salmon salad with boiled potatoes, beetroot and mayo; roast lamb salad with mint mayo, potatoes and greens; lemon and basil chicken with turnip purée, smoked Gubbeen and organic spinach crostini; rhubarb tart; bakewell slice. Joyous grub, packed with flavour, with fresh, herbaceous tastes and the sheen of TLC. There is no greater local hero than this fantastic destination. (New Antrim Street, Castlebar ☎ 094-902 3376 ✉ aran@iol.ie – Open 9.30am-6pm Mon-Sat)

Butter makers

Sheila's

Tom and Sheila Butler's butter-making company was established back in the dark days of 1990, when creating speciality foods was rare as hen's teeth, especially way out west in Mayo. But through hard work and high quality they have prospered, and their four products – a country butter, a farmhouse butter, a unique pro-biotic butter, and some very fine buttermilk, are all distinguished and delicious. You will find them in all good supermarkets throughout the country. (Shraheens, Balla, Castlebar ☎ 094-903 1425 ✉ sheilasmayo1@eircom.net 🖱 www.cuinneog.com)

Claremorris

Tea Shop

Derrymore Farmhouse

Vincent and Manita van Dulmen are best known as makers of very distinctive gouda-style cheeses, though production is temporarily in abeyance. In the meantime they are concentrating on their Tea Shop where you can enjoy their produce ranging from their abundant vegetable garden, their own baking and their own preserves, including honey from their bees. (Derrymore, Partry, Claremorris ☎ 094-9543173 – Open 10.30am-6pm Mon-Sat. Closed Sept to Apr)

Butcher

The Food Store

Niall Heffernan's brilliant butcher's shop, deli and grocery store is only excellent, and food lovers never bother with the by-pass that goes around Claremorris, preferring instead to head to Ballyhaunis Road to get their hands on superb meats and some great food-to-go, as well as some really excellent breads. Mr Heffernan is one of the group of hungry, ambitious creative butchers, the guys who want to win the competitions, the guys who are always improving their stores, always urging on their staff, always working on their offer. This driven, self-critical nature means that the customers win every time, and this is one superb address for fresh meats and pretty much everything you need. (Balllyhaunis Road, Claremorris ☎ 094-936 2091 thefoodstore@eircom.net)

Mayo

Cong

Hotel

Ashford Castle

The Bridgestone Guides don't do castles, but food lovers need to know that Ashford does enjoy the talents of Stefan Matz, a chef whose career we have followed ever since he made a mighty reputation cooking out in Connemara. Mr Matz is a singular talent, and if you don't mind the hoo-haa and blarney of Ashford, then his food is worth anyone's time and money. With the creation of Cullen's Cottage, in the grounds of the hotel, you can now also get a taste of the place without spending a great deal of money. (Cong ☎ 094-954 6003 ashford@ashford.ie www.ashford.ie)

Café

Hungry Monk Café

"Do call in if you are in Cong and see if we are doing the right thing." That's what Robert Devereux wrote to us, so on our big family swoop down the west coast we went to pretty Cong to see if they are doing the right thing. They sure are. They have a lovely, colourful, cottagey room, with Mr Devereux's paintings on the walls. in which to do the good thing, and they deliver it with fresh, clean salads, good soups, and extremely nice puds, all described on the blackboard. The staff are cool, and there are some excellent jars to take away. The right thing, no doubt about it. (Abbey Street, Cong ☎ 094-954 6886 – Open 10am-6pm Tue-Sun. Closed Nov-Mar)

Mulranny

Hotel

● Park Inn Mulranny

Mayo

The resurrection by Tom and Kathleen O'Keefe of the old Great Western Hotel in Mulranny has been the great success story of the West in recent years, and they have managed in just a couple of years to create an hotel that could – and should – become the Kelly's of the West. Their masterstroke has been to recruit Seamus Commons as head chef for their restaurant. A Castlebar man, a L'Ecrivan graduate, his cooking is stonkingly fine, and hits all the pleasure points, with the most dazzling little games played with dishes such as a tasting of fresh water prawns, which has the L'Ecrivain signature of deep-fried prawns in ketafi, along with a prawn and yellow pepper terrine and sautéed prawns with celeriac purée and bisque reduction, or the tasting of lamb which offers seared kidney with black pudding croquette, roasted loin with tomato and mint chutney, and lamb sausage with white onion mousseline. The food is good to think, but even better to eat, and the dining room is a beauty. The hotel rooms are smashing, the apartments which offer families a great-value option are only magnificent, and there is a Blue Flag beach just across the road. The most impressive newcomer in Irish hospitality in yonks, and an unmissable destination. (Mulranny, Westport ☎ 098-36000 www.mulranny.parkinn.ie – Bar lunch served 12.30pm-9pm. Restaurant open 7pm-9pm Mon-Sun)

Guesthouse & Self-catering houses

● Rosturk Woods

Louisa Stoney's B&B and self-catering accommodation enjoy one of the most amazing locations you will find anywhere in Ireland, tucked off into woods as you drive west to Achill. The place has a special feel, almost mystical, somehow ancient, and this unique character is abetted by the hard work of this dynamic woman. The B&B and the two houses – one 2-bed, one 4-bed – are quite delightful, and Mrs Stoney is a mighty cook, and a vital source of info on everything in the region. Rather special. (Mulranny, Westport ☎ 098-36264 stoney@iol.ie www.rosturk-woods.com)

Local Speciality
PUTÓG

Newport

Butcher

Kelly's Butchers

Only one Kelly matters in Newport, and it ain't Grace Kelly. Sean Kelly is the Kelly that counts, for this butcher is one of the most creative charcutiers in the entire country. Just recently, for example, Sean has been winning prizes for his putóg, a black pudding which is cooked inside a sheep's stomach. "People come in and they say, 'Oh, my mother used to make that'", explains Mr Kelly. "It was always the mother that made it, and it was a way of using things up, and they would have very little to use up, so the putóg is only seasoned with salt and pepper because they wouldn't have had any spices." In that quote we can see both culinary creativity, and culinary authenticity. Mr Kelly could spice his putog up with all manner of fireworks, but he doesn't, because they didn't do it in the past. As a statement of Slow Food principles applied to Irish traditional charcuterie, it would be hard to beat. But then, everything in Kelly's is hard to beat, to be honest, though one should on no account miss the puddings and the sausages. Brilliant and inspiring. (Main Street, Newport ☎ 098-41149 – Open 8.30am-7pm Mon-Sat)

Café

Kelly's Kitchen

This is the café run by Kathleen Kelly, of the Kelly family of the celebrated butcher's shop, just a few doors up the main street of Newport. Expect nice domestic cooking, whilst the smart guys get Sean Kelly's fantastic sausages and puddings with brown bread, and maybe some good Mayo lamb cutlets. Sweet. (Main Street, Newport ☎ 098-41647 – Open Daytime)

Mayo

Country House

Newport House

Newport is one of the great country houses. Its secret is to reconcile all the contradictions: it's grand, yet it's not the slightest bit pretentious. It's formal, yet not a bit stuffy. Old folk with money like it, yet so do young ones who are living on the never-never. The cooking is elaborate, yet the flavours are punchy, direct and fresh. Like a Hermes bag, it is an expensive luxury brand, yet it is also profoundly practical, form and function aligned. Reconciling all of these contradictions, and turning them into strengths, helps to create one of the best addresses in the West. (Newport ☎ 098-41222 www.newporthouse.ie)

Westport

Fishmonger and Delicatessen

Clarke's Seafood Delicatessen

The Clarke brothers' second Mayo store is both an excellent wet fish shop and a smart seafood deli. (Peter Street, Westport ☎ 098-24379 info@clarkes.ie www.clarkes.ie – Open 9am-6pm Mon-Sat)

Restaurant

The Lemon Peel at the Asgard

After a decade creating happy food in the Lemon Peel in the Octagon, Robbie McMenamin has moved his restaurant to the Asgard. What won't change is the flavour-filled, fun cooking this chef and his crew put out: baked goat's cheese and red onion tartlet; spare ribs with hoisin dip; roast duck with Grand Marnier; chicken stuffed with chorizo. Both the food and the short list of wines offer good value, and it's easy to see why Mr McMenamin has been the toast of the town for a decade. (The Quay, Westport ☎ 098-26929 robbie@lemonpeel.ie www.lemonpeel.ie – Open 6pm-9.30pm Tue-Sat. Open Sundays in high summer)

Seaweed Products

Lotide Fine Foods

Seamus Moran makes some of the very best sausages we have tasted in recent times: they were pork sausages, flecked through with sea vegetables, and they were to die for. But, it should be no surprise that this man's sea vegetable products are so good: he himself worked as a chef for 20 years, and his family have been in the sea vegetable business since the 1880's. Put the two together and you come up with radical new ideas such as those sausages or dilisk chutney. A dynamic company. (Moyna, Kilmeena, Westport ☎ 098-42616 ✉ info@lo-tide.com 🖱 www.lo-tide.com)

Restaurant

Quay Cottage

A calm and calming ambience and some elegantly simple food have kept the Quay Cottage in business for almost a quarter-of-a-century. Kirstin and Peter McDonagh cook sole on the bone with citrus butter, scallops with saffron sauce and fresh tagliatelle; monkfish kebabs with wild rice; barbary duck with a port and orange glaze, and the food and the setting always seem ageless, if indeed not even timeless. Charming. (The Harbour, Westport ☎ 098-26412 ✉ quaycottage@eircom.net 🖱 www.quaycottage.com – Open 6pm-10pm Mon-Sun from 1st Jun-1st Sept, closed Sun & Mon Sept-May)

Restaurant

Sol Rio

Sinead from Westport and Jose from Portugal have fashioned a local success story in Sol Rio. It's a simple, busy, upstairs room, with menus that offer something for everyone in the family. (Bridge Street, Westport ☎ 098-28944 ✉ solrio@iol.ie 🖱 www.solriowestport.com– Open noon-3pm, 6pm-10pm Tue-Sun)

Hotel

Westport Plaza Hotel

Excellent staff, genuine hospitality, good comfort, and the right sort of customer focus, have shunted the Plaza ahead of the many other hotels in town. (Castlebar Street, Westport ☎ 098-51166 🖱 www.westportplazahotel.ie)

Country Market

Westport Thursday Market

The lovely setting of the Octagon at the top of Westport town is one of the most sublime market locations in the whole country. One of the longest established markets in Ireland. (Town Hall, Westport, Thursday, 8.30am-12.30pm)

County Meath

Ashbourne

Coffee

Ariosa Coffee Roasting Boutique

Michael Kelly's coffee roasting company is one of the very best new food businesses in Ireland. Like other new-generation coffee roasters, he seems to have arrived in the market with his skill base and his signature style fully-formed, his brews complete and completely delicious. Just look at the queue lined up at his Temple Bar stall on Saturday and you will see how brilliant coffee roasting produces a drink that is nothing less than narcotic. We bought a bag of the Achill Blend, brought it home and opened it, and it filled the entire house with the mesmeric scents of roasted coffee beans: narcotic indeed. The Achill blends together six varieties of bean, showing the level of complexity at which Mr Kelly works, and his complexity produces coffee that reveal the true art of coffee roasting. (Racehill, Ashbourne ☎ 01-835 3078
info@ariosacoffee.com www.ariosacoffee.com)

Chocolate Shop

Chez Emily

The second chocolate shop from the resplendently talented Helena Hemeryck and Ferdinand Vandaele is part of the blossoming culinary culture of Ashbourne. The chocs are superb in both taste and presentation, and our advice is to work your way through all the flavours, slowly. (Main Street, Ashbourne 01-835 2252
info@chezemily.ie www.chezemily.ie)

Fusion Restaurant

EatZen

We have been waiting a long time for Chinese restaurants with contemporary design to open in Ireland and then, of course, two of them come along in double-quick time. There are two EatZens – the address here in the town centre and the first in Clonee – and their wild modern design is matched by a fun fusion food offer: black cod in champagne sauce is sort-of-Nobu; chicken wings stuffed with prawns is one of the funkiest forms of a modern cheffy obsession with chicken wings, XO sauce with fried rice, and these are typical of quixotic cooking from Simon Tsang that is really pushing the envelope. And how nice to see a Chinese restaurant with proper wine glasses. (Ashbourne Town Centre ☎ 01-835 2110 info@eatzen.ie www.eatzen.ie – Open 5.30pm-11.30pm Mon-Sat, 1pm-10.30pm Sun)

Fishmonger

Nick's Fish

A veteran of the wholesale fish business, Nicholas Lynch has brought his expertise to this pristine and professionally run fishmonger's shop, a vital addition to burgeoning Ashbourne. (9 Town Centre, Ashbourne ☎ 01-835 3555 – Open 10am-6pm Tue-Fri, 10am-5pm Sat)

Meath

Athboy

Butcher

Brogan's Butchers

Niall Brogan is a brilliant butcher. He won't use charolais cattle for his beef because "they are too lean", so he has his own blackhead and whitehead cattle. He has his own lamb – superb lamb – and makes his own puddings. It's a small shop, but everything in here is precise, expert and, for the cook, winningly delicious. So, if you find yourself dragged out to Athboy because your sister or your Mum needs a wedding outfit, you know where to go to rescue the day with a good dinner back home. (Main Street, Athboy ☎ 046-943 2122 brogansbutchers@hotmail.com – Open 9am-6pm Mon-Sat)

Bakery

Doreen's Bakery

"Rhubarb wanted". That's what the sign in the window of Doreen's said one day. Doesn't that just say everything that needs to be said about this sublimely cute bakery? It says: we make our own rhubarb tarts. We don't use stuff from jars. We use local products. Walk in, then, and feast your eyes on apple squares, meringues, blueberry muffins, white sodas, all the staples of a great local bakery. Pure darling. (Main Street, Athboy ☎ 046-943 2054 – Open 9am-6pm Mon-Sat)

Cheese Warehouse

Sheridan Cheesemongers Ltd

The Sheridan's crew are planning to move from their Athboy site to The Old Railway Store on the Virginia Road in Meath, and to develop a new cheese complex which will become a show-case for Irish artisan cheeses. There will be a retail section, tasting areas and the maturing cheese will be visible through glass. It all sounds typically audacious and thrilling. Planned opening is early 2008. (Athboy ☎ 046-943 0373 www.sheridanscheesemongers.com)

Ballivor

Fudge

Man of Aran Fudge

Meath

Tomás Póil is an Aran Islander, and transplanted to the mainland he has set about making a wildly colourful range of fudges which he sells in a small number of shops and at many markets. Banana chocolate delight; peppermint chocolate chip; Granny's nutty fudge – these are just some of the wild, wickedly colourful fudges Tomás creates. (Station House, Ballivor ☎ 086-256 6542 info@manofaranfudge.ie www.manofaranfudge.ie)

Clonee

Fusion Restaurant

EatZen

The first EatZen, of the two opened by a trio of Chinese restaurateurs from Dublin and London, offers fusion coking from various Asian cuisines in a hip, modern room with lots of style. (Unit 1 Clonee Village, Main Street ☎ 01-801 3738 info@eatzen.ie www.eatzen.ie – Open 5.30pm-11.30pm Mon-Sat, 1pm-10.30pm Sun)

Garden Centre Cafe

Garden Works

The second store of the garden centres that are also places of pilgrimage for food lovers, GW is a great place for plants, and a great place to eat. (Piercetown, Dunboyne, Clonee ☎ 01-825 5375 info@gardenworks.ie www.gardenworks.ie – Cafe open 9.30am-5pm Mon-Fri, 9.30am-5.30pm Sat, noon-5.30pm Sun. Late opening Thur, 'till 8pm Apr-June and Oct-Dec)

Enfield

Craft Brewery

The Celtic Brewing Co

The Celtic Brewing Company is one of the pioneers of craft brewing in Ireland, having opened in 1997. Today, under the Finian's brand name, they produce a stout, a red ale, an organic lager and the premium Shiva lager, which you can find in Monty's Restaurant in Dublin's Temple Bar. (Enfield ☎ 046-954 1558 📫 celticbrew@eircom.net)

Kells

Farmhouse Cheese and Yogurt

Glenboy Goat Products

Gordon and Ann Hugh make two goat's milk yogurts from the pasteurised milk of their own herd of almost 200 goats, who graze on organic pastures, and they also produce goat's milk and some goat's cheese and very fine smoothies. (Balgeeth, Kells ☎ 046-924 9624)

Farmers' Market

Kells Farmers' Market

Kells has both a country market, on Fridays, and a weekly farmers' market, on Saturday. (Saturday, 10am-2pm, FBD Insurance Ground, Kells)

Soft cheese, buttermilk, cream, cheesecakes

Kilbeg Dairy Delights

Kieran and Jane Cassidy's company is a bespoke producer of cheesecakes, buttermilk, soft cheeses and yogurts, and is another shining example of dairy producers – they have a herd of Holsteins – taking their destiny in hand and allowing their creativity to produce fine artisan foods. Along with Glenilen in Cork and Moonshine Dairy in Westmeath, Kilbeg represents a brilliant new generation of Irish artisan dairy foods. (Horoath, Carlanstown, Kells ☎ 046-924 4687 📫 info@kilbegdairydelights.ie 🖱 www.kilbegdairydelights.ie)

Restaurant

Vanilla Pod Restaurant

A stand-alone feature of the Headfort Arms Hotel, the VP is a bistro-style room with straight-ahead, no-nonsense modern cooking – Thai chicken salad, chowder of mussels, prawns and salmon; sirloin with roasted tomato and balsamic onions – and they are serious about their cooking, and serious about their wines. The list is extremely well-written and presented, with wines that are both good to drink, and good to think. (Kells ☎ 046-924 0084 info@headfortarms.ie www.headfortarms.ie – Open 5.30pm-10pm Mon-Thu & Sun, 5.30pm-11pm Fri & Sat, noon-3pm Sun)

Laytown

Farmers' Market and Ecology Centre

Sonairte National Ecology Centre

The ecology centre hosts a market on the 3rd Sunday of each month, and in between times their produce is sold each Saturday at the Dublin Food Co-Op. (The Ninch, Laytown ☎ 041-982 7572 info@sonairte.org www.sonairte.org)

Meath

Navan

Hotel & Restaurant

Bellinter House

Jay Bourke's country house has been the focus of so much media attention that he could paper the walls with clippings and quotes. But, two factors single the house out as a place of great promise. Firstly, the house has been restored, not renovated. A huge amount of money has been spent to put Bellinter back to what it was. Others would have made it blandly contemporary, but Mr Bourke is smarter than that. Secondly, Eleanor Walsh, the woman who created the original culinary signature for the Bourke and Foyle group in the original Eden in Temple Bar, is heading up the kitchen, and has met with immediate success, especially from locals who want to enjoy Ms Walsh's signature dishes, such as smokies, bangers and mash, pork belly with pea champ, and berry sponge pudding. This is good grub, and it has no pretensions: you can go to the Drawing Room restaurant upstairs and have a mug of soup, or chips with garlic mayonnaise. Bellinter is, then, a radical destination, for all the right reasons. (Navan ☎ 046-903 0900 info@bellinterhouse.com www.bellinterhouse.com – Eden Restaurant open 6pm-9.30pm Mon-Sun, noon-3pm Sat & Sun. Drawing Room open 11am-11pm)

Fish Shop

Connolly's Seafood

Connolly's is a smashing seafood shop, right in the heart of busy Navan, and Kieran and Noleen always have a smashing range of fish and shellfish in ace condition. Service is delightful. (Navan Shopping Centre, Navan, ☎ 046-907 2233 – Open 8.30am-5.30pm Tue-Fri, 8.30am-1pm Sat)

Bakery and Delicatessen

L'Artisan & Spicer's Bakery

Local bakery champions, the Spicer family, run an excellent store with great foods for sale in the shopping centre. Home-made croissants and loaves are sold alongside cheeses in mint condition. (Navan Shopping Centre, Navan ☎ 046-907 5588 – Open 9.30am-6pm Mon-Sat, 'till 7pm Thu & 9pm Fri, 2pm-6pm Sun)

Meath

Patisserie and Café

George's Pastisserie and Café

The lucky folk of Navan are the beneficiaries of George Heise's expansion plans, as this brilliant patissier and baker brings his baking to the centre of town. The smart café has teas and coffees and artisan foods, but it is those sweet delights that will see a permanent queue out the door. (Navan Shopping Centre, Navan ☎ 041-982 4493 www.georgespatisserie.com – Open 9am-6pm Tue-Sat)

Butcher

Hugh Maguire

Hugh Maguire is one of the leaders of the younger generation of Irish charcutiers, butchers who exhibit huge creative skill, and wild culinary imagination. Like the best butchers, he doesn't waste time with all the sauces and stuffings others think customers want. Instead, he goes back to basics, asking how you produce the best sausages, the best bacon, the best black pudding. And, having asked the question, he gives the answer, for the Maguire bangers, rashers and puds are brilliant creations, utterly distinctive, foods which define the cutting-edge of charcuterie. There is no challenge Mr Maguire won't rise to, whether it is creating the perfect Polish paprika sausage for a competition – and, of course, taking top prize – or fashioning the most brilliant Lincolnshire sausage you ever did eat. Outstanding. (13 Trimgate Street ☎ 046-902 1697 hughmaguirebutchers@eircom.net)

Gastro Pub

O'Brien's Good Food and Drink House

Tim O'Brien is partner in another successful restaurant in Meath – Franzini O'Brien's in Trim – and has enjoyed speedy success with this new venture in Johnstown, a few minutes from Navan. The menu is as people-pleasing as can be, there is an early bird for those tired commuters, and it is supremely family-friendly, as any restaurant needs to be in the suburban hinterlands. No surprise then that O'Brien's has scooped popular awards for best newcomer. (Johnstown Village, Navan ☎ 046-902 0555 – Open 5.30pm-10pm Mon-Sat, 1pm-9pm Sun)

Wine Merchant

O'Brien's Wine Shop

A Midlands outpost for the dynamic Dublin wine chain. (Kennedy Road, Navan ☎ 046-907 3206 sales@obrienswine.ie www.obrienswine.ie - Open 10.30am-11pm Mon-Sat, 12.30pm-11pm Sun)

Bar

Ryan's Bar

Ryan's is a hugely popular bar, both for drinks and for its food offer, with hot soups, wraps and toasted sandwiches pulling in the crowds. There is also a little coffee shop which opens daily. (22 Trimgate Street, Navan ☎ 046-902 1154 enquiries@ryansbar.ie www.ryansbar.ie – Bar food served noon-7.45pm Mon-Sat)

Cafe Wine Bar

Ryan's Vine Wine Bar

The excellent wine shop and cafe of Ryan's bar has great wines distributed over its two floors, and very friendly service. The adjacent cafe is a great spot for indulging in fresh croissants and pain au chocolat. (22 Trimgate Street, Navan ☎ 046-902 1154 enquiries@ryansbar.ie www.ryansbar.ie – Open 9am-8pm Mon-Sat)

Oldcastle

Chocolate Shop

Aine's Chocolates

Ann Rudden is a fine chocolatier, who made her name as a producer of handmade chocolates, and who most recently has branched into chocolate retailing in her own shop on

Oliver Plunkett Street. The chocolates have deservedly won a raft of awards over recent years, and the impressive thing about Aine's is the level of consistency through the entire range, whether you choose truffles, pralines, chocolate bars or a jar of caramel fudge sauce. Very fine indeed. (Oliver Plunkett Street, Oldcastle ☎ 049-854 2769 www.aineschocolates.com – Open 10am-5pm Mon-Fri)

Ratoath

Cookery School

Fairyhouse Food & Wine School

Billie O'Shea trained originally as a nurse, before finding her true vocation as a food lover and cookery teacher. In the purpose-built Fairyhouse School she runs courses that offer both practical tuition – in one- and two-day courses – as well as a fine range of demonstration classes. There is also a cook club for children between the ages of eight and 12, and everything is permeated with energy, enthusiasm and a lack of pretension. The small cookery schools opening in Ireland have the potential to contribute enormously to our culinary culture, and it is great to see people like Billie taking up – and rising to – the challenge. (Ratoath ☎ 086-883 1124 www.fairyhousecookery.com)

Slane

Patisserie and Delicatessen

George's Pastisserie and Delicatessen

George Heise has carved out a mighty reputation ever since opening up in Slane in 2001. His baking is precise, expert and is of a standard that is rare in Ireland: this is patisserie of an exacting Continental standard and, to be honest, it can blow you away with its stunning appearance and even more stunning tastes. Aside from the patisserie, a range of breads and health breads are produced, and these are sold at the Sonairte Centre and at the Dublin Food Co-Op on Saturdays where George mans a mighty busy stall. The shop also has a good small menu to accompany teas and coffees, and has a smartly chosen range of artisan foods. Only terrific. (Chapel Street, Slane ☎ 041-982 4493 georgheise@eircom.net www.georgespatisserie.com – Open 9am-6pm Tue-Sat)

Restaurant

George's Restaurant at The Poets Rest

You see him here, there and everywhere: George Heise made his name with his baking in Slane, but has now three ventures, including this old pub which has been converted into a restaurant. Though he is known in Ireland as a baker, Mr Heise is first and foremost a chef – indeed he is a Master of Culinary Arts – and in that role has worked all over the world. This is a very promising venture from a man with huge energy, ambition and ability. (Chapel Street, Slane ☎ 041-982 4493 georgheise@eircom.net www.georgespatisserie.com – Open noon-10pm Tue-Sun)

"There is an holistic sense of well-being we enjoy when our hunger is truly satisfied that can only be had from eating good food cooked with great care."

DENIS COTTER

Meath

Tara

Ice Cream

Burke's Farm Ice Cream

Bernadette Burke's ice cream company makes some fantastically imaginative ice creams – apple pie ice cream is typical of their whacky and excellent experiments. But they are sensible enough to anchor everything with some excellent plain dairy ices, and the vanilla is dreamy, thanks in no small part to the richness of milk from a herd of Jersey cows. You will find them at various fairs and events and at the Red Stables Market at St Anne's Park in Dublin. (Corbalton, Tara ☎ 087-953 2656 burkefarmicecream@eircom.net)

Mushrooms

The Gourmet Mushroom Company

Mark and Garrett O'Connor's mushroom company has been a dynamic presence in the speciality mushroom market since beginning production near Tara in 1998, and they now own the organic Haymes Farm mushroom company in the UK As well as standard white mushrooms, their crème de la crème is shiitake, oyster, Paris brown, girolles, and a selection of wild mushrooms that includes girolles and pied de mouton. Brilliant fungi. (Rathfeigh Farm, Tara ☎ 041-982 5026 www.gourmetmushrooms.ie)

Trim

Restaurant

● Franzini O'Brien's

Chicken wings; bbq ribs; teriaki beef; good oaky chardonnays and raspingly-fruited red wines – the international roll-call of finger lickin' foods and big wines seems to ensure success in County Meath, and Franzini O'Brien's formula has worked and they aren't about to change it. The laws of demographics dictate what restaurants can achieve in the rapidly-morphing boom towns such as Trim, and the value-service-family-friendly focus of F O'Bs is right on the money. (French's Lane, Trim ☎ 046-943 1002 www.franziniobriens.com – Open 6.30pm-10pm Mon-Sat 1pm-9pm Sun)

Meath

Bakery and Coffee Shop

● Kerr's Kitchen

Phil and Paul Kerr produce excellent brown soda breads, carefully using fine local ingredients, such as the rare Martry Mills stoneground flour, and then substituting sunflower oil for either butter or eggs. The result is a very healthy loaf, but not one that flags its healthfulness: the Kerrs are determined first and foremost to make the best loaf they can. Look out for the breads in Trim and in shops in the surrounding area. (Haggart Street, Trim ☎ 046-943 7144 – Open 10am-6pm Mon-Sat)

Organic Market

● Trim Visitor Centre Organic Market

Trim has a monthly farmers' market – re-launched in 2006 – as well as the weekly Friday afternoon market that takes place at the Visitor centre. The centre coffee shop also has some good handmade foods of its own, so culinary needs as well as cultural needs can be satisfied.
(Trim Visitor Centre 3pm-6pm Fri
✉ trimvisitorcentre@eircom.net)

County Monaghan

Ballybay

Farmers' Market

Ballybay Farmer's Market

A hugely promising new market for a county that has heretofore missed out on the delights of marketeering. The Ballybay market takes place on the first and third Fridays of the month and a dozen or more stall holders have organics, home baking, shrubs and plants, the produce of the local Camphill community, and lots more. Contact Carol on ☎ 086-157 9551 if you would like to take part. (Riverdale Car Park, Ballybay 9.30am-1.30pm)

Carrickmacross

Monaghan

Hotel & Restaurant

Nuremore Hotel

With interests in both Rosso restaurant in Dundalk and his own restaurant, 23, in Warrenpoint, Ray McArdle is every bit as busy as his old boss, Michael Deane, is up in Belfast, where he also has three restaurants to shepherd, as well as a shop. Mr McArdle continues to cook in the Nuremore, and seems to thrive on the challenges of so many tasks, for his food is superb. In fact, it is worth mentioning that we went to a wedding party in the hotel, and the food at the reception, the severest test of any kitchen, was also superb. He favours a rich, classical style of European food, and he makes it seem wonderfully logical and, even, not indulgent. Julie Gilhooley's hotel is extremely popular, and it is a very comfortable place, thanks in no small way to excellent staff. (Carrickmacross ☎ 042-966 1438 ✉ nuremore@eircom.net 🖱 www.nuremore.com – Restaurant open 12.30pm-2.30pm, 6.30pm-9.30pm Mon-Sun, no lunch on Sat)

Castleblayney

Cured Meats

Malone Foods

Malones produce a very fine range of salamis – whiskey;

pepper; garlic – a stout-cured beef (using the bench-mark O'Hara's stout from Carlow), and a very excellent pastrami. Superb packaging makes for indispensably useful products. (Lough Egish, Castleblayney ☎ 042-974 5102 info@malonefoods.ie www.malonefoods.ie)

Clones

Country House

Hilton Park

Having worked with Rowley Leigh in London's Kensington Place, Fred Madden has returned home to cook alongside his Mum, Lucy, in the gargantuan and magnificent Hilton Park. Johnny Madden, meantime, has been busy restoring an old bedroom to its former pristine glory, so Hilton now has "three grand bedrooms and three cosy bedrooms", along with its extraordinary public rooms. There is nowhere else quite like Hilton, and the high costs of staying here are worth it for a genuinely unforgettable country house experience, with exceptional cooking. (Scotshouse, Clones ☎ 047-56007 mail@hiltonpark.ie www.hiltonpark.ie – Open Apr-Sept. Groups only outside those months)

Monaghan

Emyvale

Butcher

McGee's Foods

In a little shop in Emyvale is where Joe McGee's meat empire all began. Today, he has four shops – the others are in Letterkenny, Dungannon and Belfast – and he is a man moving fast, whilst respecting the vital slowness that lies behind great meat. To this end, McGee's raise their own Angus and Hereford stock at the farm at Gortnagran, on pastures washed by the "soft, mizzly rain" of County Tyrone. "This is not just British or Irish beef. It's not even just beef from County Tyrone. It's beef from McGee's farm, made to a very particular process, and sold exclusively at McGee's by skilled and experienced butchers." Well, hang that manifesto high as the way forward for beef and for butcher's shops, and fair play to Joe McGee for understanding that "eating is an agricultural act". Bet you can taste that "mizzly rain". You can, can't you? Soft rain, and slow food: that's the way. (Main Street, Emyvale ☎ 047-86645 – Open 9am-6pm Mon-Thur, 9am-6.30pm Fri & Sat)

Local Speciality
BOXTY PANCAKES

Glaslough

Country House, Cookery School and Hunting Lodge Hotel

Castle Leslie

There are so many developments in train in Castle Leslie, Sammy Leslie's massive family estate at the edge of Glaslough village, that it needs DVDs and a 50-page press dossier just to describe them. The equestrian centre is being restored to a state-of-the-art adventure. The castle itself is reverting to a member's club, where one can go to stay and eat, and then decide that you would like to take out a membership. Houses and cottages are being built which one can rent, and some which one can buy. The Hunting Lodge has been transformed into a thirty bedroom hotel, with a bistro restaurant and a cellar bar and wood burning stoves to specialise in pizza. There is a cookery school and, of course, there is a spa. All of this is an extraordinary achievement on the part of Sammy Leslie, who always wanted the estate unified, and working as a successful business enterprise. For the purposes of Bridgestone readers, the most significant element, of course, will be the food in the Hunting Lodge Hotel, where one expects most ordinary punters to go to stay and to eat. And, also, the cookery school, where Noel McMeel is the culinary guide. McMeel's ambition is modest and immense: "I want to teach people to taste again", he says, and there is no more genial, temperate or talented man to take you down the Taste Path than this gifted chef and teacher. Mind you, with courses such as Food & Erotica, and Valentine's Aphrodisiacs, Mr McMeel may lead some students down a different path altogether. Mr McMeel will hopefully have the benefits of the produce of the estate's 25-acre walled garden, which Dessie Clements is restoring. We reckon they didn't work as hard as this when building the pyramids, and what is astonishing is the speed with which Castle Leslie has emerged from its dormancy into an explosively energised present and future. (Glaslough ☎ 047-88109 info@castleleslie.com www.castleleslie.com – Food served all day and evening in the Hunting Lodge Hotel)

County Offaly

Ballinahown

Honey

Meadowsweet Apiaries

Andrew McGuinness has become the most celebrated honey maker in Ireland over the last couple of years. Like his county companions such as Ralph Haslam or Prue and Simon Rudd or Cathal O'Donoghue or Florrie Smye, he has become synonymous with a cabal of gifted artisans working in County Offaly who have propelled the county into the first league of specialist food production in Ireland. Mr McGuinness has done this by taking honey back to its terroir: he has a heather honey from hives in the Clara bog that is "dark and viscous: not a honey for the faint-hearted". A Clara Bog claret, you might say. He has a summer honey where the bees have fed on white clover, blackberry and rosebay willow herbs. A Cote d'Or honey. His unfiltered honey, because it hasn't been heat filtered, will cure your hay fever. And, a trained chemist, he also makes bees wax beauty and furniture products. Superb stuff, so search out your favourite terroir, your own personal cuvée, of the busy bee, and never forget Einstein: "No bees, no food for mankind. The bee is the basis of life on earth."
(Doon, Ballinahown ☎ 086-884 4938
andrewmcguinness@hotmail.com)

Birr

Pub

The Chestnut

A lovely bar, just off the square in the centre of town.
(Green Street, Birr ☎ 057-912 2011)

Tea Room

Emma's Cafe & Deli

Emma Ward's café and deli is not just a beautiful shop, it is also a beautiful shop-front, a little design jewel. Inside, Ms Ward has kept things similarly classic and unalloyed, with neat tables, good shelves with food, and a nice counter. So, we sat at the counter and had organic vegetable soup with brown bread, and a toasted ciabatta with ham and cheese, then a very good espresso. The music was great, and the people of Birr moved around the room in a way that said, "Aren't we lucky to have Emma's, right here, just for us?" You sure are. A real star. (31 Main Street, Birr ☎ 057-912 5678 – Open 9.30am-6pm Mon-Fri, 10am-6pm Sat)

Organic Farm

Mossfield Organic Farm

Ralph Haslam won the supreme award at the first Bord Bia great taste awards in 2006, and his success confirmed the remarkable rise of a new generation of artisans in Ireland. For what is astonishing about Mr Haslam is the fact that only a few years ago he was a dairy farmer, who had never made cheese. Then, in the space of a few years, he is all over the media as the newest award-winning cheese maker, an artisan poster boy for our age. What an extraordinary tale, told in such a short span of time. And what amazing cheeses, the fruit of the finest organic milk and patient care, as well as the skills of Marian Roeleveld. For us, the matured, plain Mossfield cheese is a definition of contemporary Irish agriculture: innovative, idiosyncratic, world-class, touched by and expressing its terroir, and only just beginning in terms of how experience wil shape the cheese's flavour profile in the future. Look out in the future for ice creams, farmhouse butter, and lots of dynamic new Mossfield foods. Mr Haslam has only just begun. (Clareen, Birr ☎ 057-913 1002 organicsstore@eircom.net www.mossfieldorganicfarm.ie)

Organic Store

The Organic Store

Jonathan Haslam's store is a statement of just how bounteous a place County Offaly has become in terms of superb foods. Of course, he has his Dad's cheese from Mossfield Farm to trumpet, but just look at the range of organic vegetables from producers within the county, produce of the most impeccable gourmet and gastronomic standards, and you can see why Offaly is a cult place for food lovers. Organic poultry can be found here, along with everything a good wholefood shop also sells, and Mr Haslam's shop is an organic retail mecca in the midst of a food lover's mecca. (Main Street, Birr ☎ 057-912 5881 – Open 9.30am-6.30pm Mon-Fri, 10am-6.30pm Sat)

Charcuterie, Preserves and Baking

Prue & Simon's

Wonderful sausages. Rashers with terrific sweet natural flavours. Funky relishes such as rhubarb and carrot conserve. The Rudd family seem to be endlessly inventive when it comes to food, spinning off brilliant products, selling them with tireless energy at farmers' markets – and in their shop in the Blackrock market in Dublin. The Prue & Simon's products improve the quality of your life, simple as that, and we hope soon to see an Xmas pudding from Prue Rudd as part of the range, for her Xmas puds are a legend in County Offaly. (Busherstown, Moneygall, Birr ☎ 0505-45206 ✉ prue@prueandsimons.com 🖱 www.prueandsimons.com)

Market Stall

Rudd's Fine Foods

Andrew Rudd is a scion of the great Offaly food-loving family, and aside from his stall in the Blackrock market in Dublin he also imports high-end speciality food from Europe. The foods are sold in the market alongside the family foods, and you will also find them in good delis. (Syngefield, Birr ☎ 057-912 5646 🖱 www.rudds.ie)

Preserves

Slieve Bloom Foods

Ciara Morris is yet another of those distinguished food producers in County Offaly whose products are of bench-mark status. Preserves such as tomato marmalade, plum and brandy jam, or ruby breakfast marmalade are ace foods, and belong on every table. (Clareen, Birr ☎ 057-913 1372)

Townhouse and Bistro

Spinners Town House and Bistro

Clare O'Sullivan has taken over the very stylish Spinners, a complex of thirteen fine rooms with a 50-seater bistro, where Rory Dunne is head chef. Spinners is a most handsome complex with a gorgeous courtyard and has always been a key address in town, so it bodes well for the future that Ms O'Sullivan and her crew have such drive and energy. (Castle Street, Birr ☎ 057-912 1673 🖱 www.spinnerstownhouse.com – Open 6.30pm-9pm Sun-Mon, Wed-Thu, 6.30pm-10pm Fri-Sat, 12.30pm-2.30pm Sun. Early bird 4pm-6pm Mon, Wed-Fri & Sat)

Country House

Whigsborough House

Anna Heagney's house is a beauty, and this hostess, with her calm, unflustered grace, is also a superb cook. She operates a system whereby menus are fixed for a couple of months, which means that you choose in advance what you would like for dinner, and she gets time to perfect the dishes. The system allows Anna the maximum time to get everything right, and she does get everything right: tomato, saffron, ricotta and olive tart is fresh and light, elderflower marinated chicken is fab, whilst meringue mess is a kid's dream dessert, so grown men love it. It's a lovely house, dating from 1740, and it hasn't been boutiq-uised, so it's the real country house thing. (Fivealley, Birr ☎ 057-9133318 whigsborough@eircom.net)

Cloghan

Soup

Clanwood Farm

Orla Clancy makes super soups, using organic ingredients, and sells them under the Clanwood Farm label. Carrot and parsnip; country vegetable; carrot and roasted red pepper; potato and leek, and tomato and basil are the distinguished line up, and they offer the bonus of conven-ience alongside superb freshness and wholesomeness. (Cush, Cloghan ☎ 087-649 4477 www.clanwoodfarm.com)

Offaly

Organic Farm

Lough Boora Farm

Tony Garahy operates an awesomely successful box-delivery system which brings the produce of Lough Boora farm to the Midlands. Lucky them, for this is a superb organic farm, with top-notch produce. To get some idea of just how original they are, you should note that LB create a superb calendar each year, with photographs of their produce, their animals, their seasonal work, and for a decade now they have been doing the good thing, quietly, holistically, successfully, and celebrating it as it should be celebrated. Touring the farm with Tony one freezing March day, John McKenna tripped whilst climbing over a barbed wire fence and bashed the bejasus out of himself. No matter: even minor trauma can't wipe the smile off your face when you see this pioneering farm at work. (Cloghan ☎ 057-934 5005)

Coolnagrower

Organic Farm

● Philip Dreaper

You will find Philip's superb organic produce not just in Offaly's excellent local stores, but in some of the country's multiple grocers. As a producer who has produce throughout the entire year, his box delivery scheme is a vital one to know about. (Coolnagrower, Fortal, Birr ☎ 057-912 1562 coolnagrower@eircom.net)

Fernbane

Tea Rooms

● Maidin Ghael

On the road between Athlone and Birr, MG is Sharon and Laura Spollen's nice little bakery and café in the centre of Fernbane, just across from the school. A cup of tea, an excellent almond slice chosen from their tasty range of baking, and a valuable port of refuge for the schoolteachers. (Main Street, Fernbane ☎ 090-645 4665 – Open 9am-6pm Mon-Sat)

Offaly

Killeigh

Organic Dairy

● Glenisk Organic Dairy

The Cleary brothers organic dairy company powers ever onwards. From mid-2007 the company will be carbon neutral, including their packaging, and they are preparing new dairy products and revamping their existing brands to signal their gentle eco-footprint. The quality level is superlative, and their ascent to brand status and nationwide distribution has been seamless and wildly successful. Can good Irish dairy companies save the world whilst saving Irish dairy farming and agriculture. Of course they can! (Newtown, Killeigh ☎ 057-934 4259 info@glenisk.com www.glenisk.com)

Local Speciality
BLUEBERRIES

Portarlington

Blueberries

Derryvilla Farm

John and Belinda Seager celebrate 30 years in business this year, having kicked off their visionary blueberry-growing venture back in the dark days of 1977. They make a blueberry tonic with their fruit that could raise the dead from their graves, so potently delicious and life-affirming a drink is it, so packed with the goodness of blueberries and all their vitamins B and C. Just for the record, blueberries act as an anti-depressant, an anti-insomniac, are anti-ulcer, anti-diabetic, anti-inflamatory, anti-allergic, and they furthermore work as a detoxicant and as a laxative. Super foods? Wonder foods, more like it. (Derryvilla, Portarlington ☎ 057-934 3945 info@derryvillablueberries.com www.derryvillablueberries.com)

Sugarcraft

Sweet Creations

Miriam Chadwick is one of those sugarcraft wizards whose work fair makes your eyes pop out of your head. There doesn't appear to be any living thing that Ms Chadwick cannot render into representational sugar work for a wedding, birthday, anniversary or special occasion cake: she is the Frank Gehry of the trio-tower, the Rembrandt of the wedding cake. Stunning. (Pinewood, Cushina, Portarlington ☎ 086-405 1555 sweetcreations@eircom.net www.sweetcreationsireland.com)

Offaly

Tullamore

Relishes

Annaharvey Farm Foods

"Good, simple, traditional, wholesome farmhouse cooking" was how Rachael Deverell described her work in Annaharvey Farm Foods to Michelle O'Brien, the brilliant co-ordinator of the ground-breaking Offaly Delicious compendium of producers. Rachael's food kitchen, shop and cookery school have grown out of the family's farm, equestrian complex and guest house, and now has a very distinct identity, not to mention a culinary signature that embodies those "good, simple, traditional, wholesome" qualities. Cakes, tarts, jams, cookies, relishes, chutneys, desserts, savoury dishes, Xmas hampers and more can all be found here at the farm shop, another example of dynamic food practice in Offaly creating another signature destination. (Tullamore ☎ 057-934 3544 ✉ foods@annaharveyfarm.ie 🖱 www.annaharveyfarm.ie)

Café & Deli

Delicious Caffé

"Delicious has made eating in town a whole lot more fun" is how one local food producer described the slick Delicious Caffé. It's a hip operation, with a shop at the front with some very interesting wines and good jars, a counter packed with good savoury things to choose from, and to take away, and then the caffé itself at the rear. Very clever, very funky. (Harbour Street, Tullamore ☎ 057-932 5943 ✉ anne.williams@deliciouscaffe.com – Open 8am-7pm Mon-Sat)

Beef and Lamb

Farm Factory Direct

Robert, Margaret and Ivor Deverell's FFD sell the meat of the superb Hereford cattle that were once such a feature of Irish agriculture, before higher-yielding and inferior-tasting breeds took over in the agri-business world. But the Deverells, working with Hereford Prime, a breeders group established back in 1997, sell the real thing, along with Offaly lamb, and you can order direct from them. That way, you get better meat at better prices and the farmers get more money. What, no slice for the beef barons? Oh dear. So, order today. And make a beef baron miserable. Are you sure it's only the sweetness of the beef you're tasting? (Kilcruttin Business Park, Tullamore ☎ 057-932 9405 ✉ deverellivor@hotmail.com 🖱 www.farmfactorydirect.ie)

Farmhouse Cheese

Mill House Sheep's Cheese

Elfie and Bennie Gerber are amongst the best cheese makers in the Midlands, and they remain the least known. Their sheep's milk cheeses, the plain Mill House and the flavoured Pastorello, as well as the 12 month-old Hobelkase, are a statement of simplicity and goodness, pure flavours beautifully captured by the cheese making process. Their herd of east Friesian sheep are mollycoddled like wee babies,

Offaly

for the Gerber philosophy is simply that happy sheep produce happy milk, and happy milk, we might add, makes for excellent cheese. The flavouring of the Pastorello cheeses is very imaginative – saffron and basil; coriander, caraway and fennel; green peppercorn – are made along with the plain, and the flavouring is done very subtly and well. Superb products that deserve much greater prominence. (Killeenmore, Tullamore ☎ 057-934 4334
info@millhouseireland.com
www.millhouseireland.com)

Craft Bakery

O'Donoghue's Bakery

"Use your loaf – keep the dough in town." Cathal O'Donoghue is one smart guy, as you can see from the slogan of this marvellous bakery. He not only understands baking, he understands local food economics. He knows that everyone who goes into a supermarket and who buys a loaf from mass-market bakers is, to put it bluntly, a mug, someone who is paying for "water standing upright" as real bakers call mass-production bread, and someone who is also betraying their local economy. So, do the smart thing: buy Cathal's bread, support your local baker, and support your local economy. (Kilcruttin Centre, Tullamore ☎ 057-932 1411 odonoghuesbakery@eircom.net – Office Open 9am-5pm Mon-Fri)

Offaly

Relishes

The Scullery

We have just enjoyed a lunch of superlative corned beef – from luminary butcher George McCartney of Moira – with some bread, and with Florrie Smye's brand-new apple and cinnamon compote. The compote was as superb as the beef, its texture runny and tactile, the cinnamon notes beautifully judged. Ace. Later on today we will have some of Florrie's other brand-new compote, mixed berry, with some yogurt, and the compote will add its graceful, balanced fruit flavours to another quotidian piece of eating, making the commonplace something special. That's what the Scullery foods do: they make the ordinary extraordinary, and Florrie keeps finding new ingredients with which she manages to do just that, from Tom Thai sauce to the brilliant chilli sauce to the prize-winning roasted corn relish. A good company that keeps on getting better. (Sycamore Lodge, Geashill, Tullamore,
☎ 086-174 4402 sculleryfinefoods@eircom.net)

Butcher

Tormey's Butchers

The Tullamore branch of the celebrated Midland's butchering dynasty is as pristine as all their other shops, and is blessed with their own superlative beef, and with charcuterie standards of the highest order. (Bridge Street, Tullamore ☎ 057-932 1426 crtormeyshop@yahoo.com – Open 9am-6pm Tue-Sat)

Market

Tullamore County Fair

Tommy Corrigan organises the lively Tullamore fair, so expect good chocolates and cheeses, herbs and spices, organic vegetables and home baking, chutneys and olives, fish and horticulture. (Millennium Square, Tullamore, Sat, 9am-3pm ☎ 087-02792615 tullamorecountryfair@eircom.net)

Shop

Wild Harvest

Fergus Dunne's shop is a beauty, and one of the stars of the town. He has produce from Lough Boora farm – look out for those sandy-soil carrots – he has Moonshine Dairy products, he has Soul Bakery bread, he has Philip Dreaper's produce, the freezer has good things, there are Mill House cheeses, and local preserves. In fact, anything good and local is here. (O'Connor Square ☎ 057-936 0333)

Bar & Restaurant

The Wolftrap

You can get some idea of the funkiness of Gina Murphy, Padraig McLoughlin and their crew from the fact that they call their company Meet & Veg (ho, ho) and that on their site the location map for Tullamore shows it as the heartbeat central of Ireland. Ms Murphy and Mr McLoughlin made a huge reputation in Mayo at Crockett's on the Quay, and they and the crew are clearly determined to bring the same chutzpah to Tullamore, as part of a newly emerging and already confident County Offaly food culture. Punchy, modern flavourful cooking is the signature of the stylish restaurant where Stephen Johnston masterminds the food. (William Street, Tullamore ☎ 057-932 3374 www.thewolftrap.ie – Open for bar food noon-8.30pm Tue-Sat, 'till 8pm Sat. Restaurant open 6pm-10.30pm Tue-Sat)

County Roscommon

Boyle

Farmers' Market

Boyle Farmers' Market

The Boyle Farmers' Market is held every Saturday in the lovely courtyard grounds of King House, and it has proven to be one of the big food success stories of the North-West. That alluring scent you have just picked up is Myra Irvine's fresh soups, and Myra, of course, also has the range of Cheese Etc cheeses. Brid Tiernan has organic eggs for sale – get there early! – whilst Peter has a great variety of fish and a great variety of advice as to what to do with it. The Kearns family have organic vegetables and very fine spuds, Marion Norris has juices and jams whilst Leitrim Organic farmers' stall has sidled over the border to supply excellent organic meats. Another interloper from Leitrim is Ann-Marie Hetherton's Stonehouse Dairy with their freshly made ice creams – bring on the sunshine – and Maureen Kelleher-McNally is selling beautiful porter cakes and tarts and fruit cakes and brown breads. Patricia and Violet Feeney have more excellent baking, whilst Siobhan and John Quinn have lovely chutneys and cakes and buns and breads. As well as her usual jams, Louise Cole has homespun, hand-knitted knitwear from her herd of alpacas. As the seasons change, more seasonal producers arrive to join this happy jamboree. (King House, Main Street, Boyle, unabhan2@eircom.net, Saturday 10am-2pm)

Roscommon

Craft Brewery

The Hooker Brewery

The easiest question you can ask us about this new *Bridgestone Irish Food Guide* is: "What was the best new drink you discovered during three years of research?" The answer is: "Galway Hooker". No question about it. Aidan Murphy and Ronan Brennan's beer is a masterpiece of brewing, a pale ale that is quite the most moreish drink we have encountered in years. Everything about

GH is the antithesis of mass-produced beers: it is subtle, graceful, has superb texture and mouth-feel, the fruit and hop notes are poised and tantalising, it is refreshing rather than gaseous, and it is fresh rather than flat and dull. An amazing feat of brewing, and a future star that already outsells Guinness at weekend nights in pubs such as Sheridan's on the Docks in Galway. (Racecourse Road, Roscommon ☎ 087-776 2823 www.nameyourbeer.net)

Local Speciality
PALE ALE

Organic Shop
● Tattie Hoaker

Tattie Hoaker is a wonderful destination address for local organic produce and for excellent wholefoods, and you will also find them selling at markets in Sligo, Carrick-on-Shannon, Roscommon and Manorhamilton. Lucky locals can also enjoy the services of the Tattie Hoaker box delivery scheme, which operates in parts of Leitrim, Roscommon, Sligo, Donegal and Mayo. This seemingly-modest venture is actually utterly visionary in its ability to market and sell local organic produce in the North West. (14 Goff Street, Roscommon ☎ 090-663 0492 www.thetattiehoaker@eircom.net – Open 10am-6pm Mon-Sat)

Shannonbridge

Restaurant
● The Old Fort

Right beside the River Shannon, The Old Fort restaurant is, believe it or not, sited in an attractively restored fort. The owner, Fergal Moran, grew up here and has worked patiently with Duchas, the heritage service, to make sure the restoration has been done sympathetically. There is a very wide-ranging menu served in the upstairs dining room, and whilst they have acquired a reputation for cooking and serving a good steak, cooked exactly as ordered, they also show with more elaborate dishes such as roast chicken with Moroccan figs that they can go well beyond the quotidian things. Food, service and value all sync happily together. (Shannonbridge ☎ 090-9674973 info@theoldfortrestaurant.com www.theoldfortrestaurant.com – Open 4pm-9.30pm Wed-Sat, noon-4pm Sun)

Strokestown

Organic Pigs

● Ted & Kay Mole

If you are lucky enough you can sometimes find the Brittle Blue pigs reared by Ted and Kay for sale at the Leitrim Organic Butchers shop in Ballinasloe, and at their market stalls in the west and in Dublin. For the most part, though, the pork is sold from the farm, mainly by the half side, with bacon available in one kg packs and sausages in one-and-a-half kg packs from them. This is superb pork, a product which is slowly becoming more available at artisan quality level, but which still takes some hunting down. (Strokestown, Roscommon ☎ 071-963 3775)

"I have no doubt that the appreciation of food and wine has a civilising influence. There is a direct relationship between care for what we eat and drink and our attitude to land, livestock and environment. Put simply, if you value the purity and richness of a free-range egg, you are less likely to approve of mass production and intensive farming."

GERRY GALVIN

County Sligo

Ballintogher

Country House

Kingsfort Country House

A brilliant new arrival on the Sligo hospitality scene, Corine Ledanois' gorgeous house in wee Ballintogher is a dream. Pull into the drive and you are transported from Sligo to Provence, and the bricolage style of the house is purest chic. The curious interplay of design gives the house a great away-from-it-all vibe, and the food is very fine also. (Ballintogher ☎ 071-911 5111
www.kingsfortcountryhouse.com)

Ballymote

Country House

Temple House

Roderick and Helena are the latest generation of Percevals to take up the reins of the resplendent Temple House, succeeding the legendary Sandy and Deb, who established the house as one of Ireland's greatest destinations. Early days yet, but the couple have energy and plans, and the many devotees of the house will wish them well. (Ballymote, Sligo ☎ 071-918 3329
mail2007@templehouse.ie www.templehouse.ie)

Castlebaldwin

Guesthouse & Restaurant

Clevery Mill

A smart mix of guestrooms and restaurant has made Clevery very much a local hero in west Sligo. The dining room is comfortable, the food is straight-ahead tasty cooking, and it's easy to see why locals love this astute combination of informality, good value, and good cooking. There is comfort here, and there is also ambition, not to mention the wit to name their local sources of produce, which turns the cooking into a celebration of place. (Castlebaldwin ☎ 071-912 7424 cleverymill@eircom.net
www.cleverymill.com – Open 6.30pm-9.30pm Tue-Sat, 12.30pm-3.30pm Sun)

Guesthouse & Restaurant

Cromleach Lodge

The restaurant in Cromleach has been completely made-over and is now a fine room called Moira's. With a crowd it's a grand place for a big night out. Locals also like to eat in the bar at Cromleach, which has proven itself to be popular for lunch. (Ballindoon, Castlebaldwin, Boyle ☎ 071-916 5155 www.cromleach.com – Open for bar food 11am-9pm, 'till 6pm at weekends, Mon-Sun. Restaurant open 6pm-9pm Mon-Sun, & 2pm-5pm Sun lunch)

Local Specialities

ATLANTIC SEA VEGETABLES
ARCTIC CHAR
WILD MUSSELS

Cliffoney

Restaurant

The Old Post House

Recently taken over by Shane McGonigle and Kay Ryan, this pretty old house hard by the main Sligo-Donegal road enjoys extraordinary views out across the bay, and enjoys a promising new team who have the hunger to create a major new destination in north Sligo. (Cliffoney ☎ 071-917 6777 – Open noon-4.30pm Wed-Sat, noon-6pm Sun, 6pm-10pm Wed-Sun. More limited hours off season)

Curry

Organic Pasta

Noodle House Pasta

Ingrid Basler's organic pasta company make one of the most useful store-cupboard ingredients that you can find in Ireland. Superb organic quality allied to a 4-minute cooking time means that any number of ravenous McKenna children can be taken care of in not much more than five minutes, those frenetic teenage appetites quelled by dishes created around superb pasta. Only brilliant. (Rathmagurry, Curry ☎ 071-918 5589)

Enniscrone

Victorian Seaweed bathhouse

● Kilcullen's Hot Sea Water Health Baths

Hot sea water is the ultimate relaxant, and the wonderfully whacky out-of-time Victorian primness of the Kilcullen's baths just accentuates the sensuality of the experience. Sublime. (Enniscrone ☎ 096-36238 www.kilcullenseaweedbaths.com – Open 10am-9pm Mon-Sun in summer, noon-8pm Mon-Sun in winter)

Rathlee

Sea Vegetables

● Carraig Fhada Seaweed

Other sea vegetable collectors are now beginning to make waves in the market for marine products, but Frank Melvin was there first, creating the finest quality, air-dried, sun-bleached sea vegetables you can buy. Look out for the top-notch Carraig Fhada products in wholefood shops and, in case no one has ever told you, do remember that adding a piece of kombu to the water in which you are cooking pulses means that they will not break up and turn mushy. There is a magic to sea vegetables. (Cabra, Rathlee, Easky ☎ 096-49042)

Rosses Point

Restaurant

● The Waterfront

Joe Grogan's successful restaurant now also has a shop and bakery, and the locals all head in here to buy the excellent brown bread, as well as good croissants, flapjacks, shortbread, bacon and onion rolls and lots of other good things. In the bar and restaurant, the cooking is rock-solid and reliable, with particularly fine fish cookery. Mr Grogan has run a great operation in Rosses Point over the years, and he and his team deserve credit – and your custom – for maintaining high standards and for offering an invaluable service to the people of Sligo with good cheer and professional inspiration. (Rosses Point ☎ 071-917 7122 jgrogan@eircom.net – Open 9.30am-9.45pm, Bar open 5pm-9.45pm, Restaurant open 6pm-9.45pm Mon-Sat & Sun lunch)

Sligo

Restaurant

● Café Society

Anita Patil's restaurant has a broad and busy menu, but the dishes to choose are the ethnic specialities, such as the combination platters, or the very fine lamb curry, for it is here that you best see the signature style of the restaurant. There is a lot of promise here to create a very distinctive new ethnic cuisine. (3 Teeling Street, Sligo ☎ 071-914 2712 – Open 8.30am-9.30pm Mon-Sat)

Country Grocer

● Cosgrove's

In the perfect world of the future, all shops will be like Cosgrove's. Unchanged, unchanging, and the very definition of what a grocer's shop should be, it is a shop where charming people sell superb foods with charming grace, and every time you shop in here it enriches not only your culinary life, but also your cultural life. Bliss. (Market Street, Sligo ☎ 071-914 2809 – Open 9.30am-8pm Mon-Sat)

Coffee Shop & Restaurant

● Eurobar

Gerry Kenny's excellent eaterie and coffee bar has just the sort of left-field, Italianesque, laid-back ambience we like, and it's an ace place for good drinks and well-concocted, simple foods. (Stephen St. car park, Sligo ☎ 071-916 1788 ✉ eurobar@eircom.net 🖱 www.eurobar.ie – Open 9am-5pm Mon-Fri, 10am-5pm Sat)

Food-To-Go

● The Gourmet Parlour

We got our Sligo beach picnic from Catherine and Annette's GP one fine summer's day before heading off to Rosses Point to swim and soak up some sun. Lovely sausage rolls, thick, wobbly slices of quiche, nice sandwiches, excellent carrot cake. It was a classic Irish picnic from the classic Irish traiteur, and if you are holidaying in Sligo we heartily recommend it. But there is more to the GP than just picnic food, for since 1990 Catherine and Annette have sustained a standard of consistent excellence with everything they make – from breads to meringues, from simnel cake to scones – that has established them as one of the most important food resources in Sligo, whether you just want to buy lunch, or have them cater for a big, blow-out party. (Bridge Street, Sligo ☎ 071-914 4617 – Open 9am-6pm Mon-Sat)

Pub

Hargadon's

One of the great atmospheric pubs of the west, and one of the best known, thanks to a legendary photograph taken in the bar by Mike Bunn for his ground-breaking book, *Ireland – The Taste & The Country*, published way back in 1991. The book is worth hunting down not just for the brilliant photography but also for J.P. Donleavy's surreal introduction, in which he declares, "For every Irishman is a king". Monarchs of the republic, then, especially after several pints in Hargadon's. (4 O'Connell Street, Sligo ☎ 071-917 0933)

Delicatessen

Kate's Kitchen

Kate and Frank's kitchen is a legend, a genuine trove of culinary treasures. You can find the rarest things in here – look out for the splendiferous organic tapenades and hummus made by Clair "The Hummus Queen of Mayo" O'Connor near Killala Bay, for example – alongside everyday necessities, and beautiful wines. This year Kate and Frank will celebrate 25 years in business, and that should be a celebration for the whole town of Sligo, for this shop has been a focal point for producers and public through all that time, a port of call that unites producer and punter via the nexus of service and selectivity orchestrated by Kate and Frank. Best of all, Kate's has gotten better and better ever since we first wrote about it in the first Bridgestone Guide, when we quoted a customer in the shop as saying "This is just the shop I was looking for!" Kate's is the shop we have all been looking for. (3 Castle Street, Sligo ☎ 071-914 3022 www.kateskitchensligo.com – Open 9am-6.30pm Mon-Sat)

Wine Merchant

Octavius Wines

Michael Gramsch has been doing sound wine business in Ireland for a decade now, orchestrating a fine list of European and New World wines, serving them with advice and

Sligo

assistance, and a decade of hard work has built a devoted customer base who enjoy Mr Gramsch's discrimination concerning what he puts on his shelves. (Ballast Quay, Sligo ☎ 071-915 3555 info@octavius.ie www.octavius.ie – Open 10am-6.30pm Mon-Sat)

Restaurant

Ósta Café & Wine Bar

"I don't like complicated, fussy food. Just a few fresh ingredients, handled as little as possible." Brid Torrades said that in an interview recently, and it has been her life's work to put it into practice right from when she started cooking in Sligo – in The Glebe House, near Collooney – and right to the present day, where she orchestrates wonderfully simple food in Osta, and into the future, for she is about to open a big, buzzy brasserie in Tobergal Lane, where there will be a bakery, micro brews and lots more on offer. Ms Torrades has been one of the most significant figures in the North West's culinary ferment for many years now, yet her enthusiasm remains undimmed, and her abilities are greater than ever. Every place she has cooked in has been characterised by caring, sharing hospitality and great food, and Osta continues that tradition. We can still recall a dish of puréed parsnips, eaten in Glebe House in 1992, as one of the greatest things we ever did eat in Ireland. That's the gift Ms Torrades enjoys – the simple made monumental. (Unit 2, Weir View House, Stephen Street, Sligo ☎ 071-914 4639 info@osta.ie www.osta.ie – Open 8am-8.30pm Mon-Wed, 8am-10pm Thu-Sat, open Sun high season)

Restaurant

Poppadom

A polished and professional Indian restaurant which is sister to the long-established Dublin branch, with another restaurant in Limerick city. (O'Connell Street, Sligo ☎ 071-914 7171 www.poppadomsligo.com – Open 5.30pm-11pm Sun-Thur, 5.30pm-midnight Fri & Sat)

Farmers' Market

Sligo Farmers' Market

One of the Origin markets which have established themselves so successfully in locations in and around the border, the Sligo market doesn't have the greatest location – it should be down by the river, in an ideal world – but it has loads of great producers selling great produce.

Tattie Hoaker foods are here, and Kearns' organics, there is baking from Bluebell Farm and from the Marsden sisters and from Morning Star Bakery. Gerry Blain has fresh fish, John Stygall has cheeses, Leitrim Organic Growers have meats, and there are fresh eggs, juices, soups, zesty lemon flavoured oils, cakes, quiches, organic chickens and lots, lots more. In short, there is everything you could possibly want. (Sligo IT Sports Field Car Park, Saturday 9am-1pm)

Wine Merchant

● Patrick Stewart

Patrick Stewart's wine shop is small, but it's packed with lots of good bottles, and the boss has an inspiringly good eye for quaffers and special occasion treats. (Sligo Shopping Centre, Wine Street, Sligo ☎ 071-915 1811 – Open 11am-6pm Mon-Wed, 10.30am-7pm Thur-Sat)

Wholefood Shop

● Tir na nOg

Mary and Norah's wholefood shop has been a Sligo flagship since whenever, and today it remains one of the town's best-loved destinations for great local foods and for vital wholefoods. (Grattan Street, Sligo ☎ 071-916 2752 – Open 9am-6pm Mon-Sat)

"One is only if and because one eats."

LEON R. KASS *THE HUNGRY SOUL*

Strandhill

Sligo

Restaurant & Gourmet Takeaways

● Triskell

We first wrote about Catherine Byrne's cooking back in the first *Bridgestone Guide* in 1991, when she was cooking at Laura's in Carney, near to Lissadell House. Now, with Marie-Claire Danguy, she is back in the food business, this time cooking nice food above the Strand Bar, in Strandhill. The girls describe their cooking as "uncomplicated and full of flavour", so expect North Western cuisine grand-mere flavours in dishes with fresh fish and tender local meats. (The Strand Bar, Strandhill ☎ 071-912 8402 ✉ triskellrestaurant@eircom.net – Open from 6pm Mon-Sat, 1pm-3pm Sun)

Tubbercurry

Farmed Arctic Char

● Cool Springs Arctic Char

Ten or twelve thousand years ago, Arctic char got trapped in the lakes of Sligo when the glaciers retreated, converting themselves into fresh water fish in the process. Ten or twelve thousand years later, Bill Carty and Mari Johnston's company, Cloonacool artic char, is farming the fish, and hoping to bring a new – yet ancient – taste back to our tables. Mr Carty comes out of an environmental science background, and tried dairying and suckler herds on the family farm before switching to this inspired idea. The fish get organic feed and fresh water – "Clean, cold water", says Mr Carty – and take two years to grow to maturity. The slowness of the growth, and the coldness of the water in Lough Talt, gives the flesh density and flavour, and already restaurateurs and fish wholesalers are beginning to beat a path to Cloonacool. (Ballyglass, Cloonacool, Tubbercurry ☎ 071-918 4393 ✉ billcarty@eircom.net 🖱 www.cloonacoolarcticchar.ie)

Sligo

County Tipperary

Ardfinnan

Restaurant

The Riverside

Dianne and Rodolphe's little restaurant is in the middle of nearly nowhere, and it isn't the world's greatest room. But, there is some really fine cooking going on here: cod with a herb crust, warm haricots and a chorizo dressing is spot on; sirloin with champ and garlic butter is a real winner, ace country cooking. Desserts are to-die-for: chocolate gateau is a star, and lemon tart has some of the best pastry eaten in these parts. Value is outstanding, service by Dianne is brilliant, and The Riverside deserves your appetite and your money. (Main Street, Ardfinnan ☎ 052-66998 rodway@eircom.net – Open 6pm-9.30pm Thu-Sat, 5pm-9.30pm Sun)

Local Speciality

TEA BRACK

Ballybrado

Specialist Meat Producers

Ladybird Organic

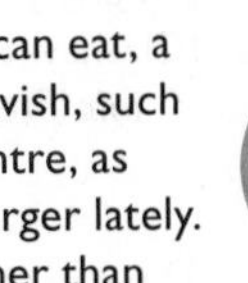

Richard Auler and Stella Coffey make Ladybird beef burgers using all of the meat of organic Angus animals. All the meat, all the good stuff, to produce Sirloin-Plus Beefburgers. The result is the best beef burger you can eat, a burger so good that it calls out for something lavish, such as a little sliver of foie gras inserted into the centre, as some chefs have been doing to the quotidian burger lately. But, actually, Ladybird burgers need nothing other than the very best bread, a good grill, some relish, and your very best bottle of artisan ale or a classsy claret. Thinking out of the box has gifted Richard and Stella with one of the most exceptional new food products in Ireland, and one that any parent with ravenous kids thanks their lucky stars for. Superb. At local farmers' markets you will also be able to buy their rashers and sausages and ham and shoulder fillets. (Ballybrado ☎ 052-42816)

Tipperary

Ballymacarbry

B&B with Dinner

Glasha Farmhouse

"The breakfasts were a feast, the dinners in the evening were another feast. Paddy & Olive made us feel so welcome. We will certainly return again, can't wait." Isn't it wonderful all the positive energy that a great B&B can generate amongst its happy customers, people who dash off a note to the Bridgestone guides the minute they get back home from Olive and Paddy O'Gorman's celebrated Glasha farmhouse. It's fantastic, and the praise is well deserved. Walkers who love the rolling hills tend to comprise many guests at Glasha, but you can be determined to do no more than walk from bedroom to dining room and you will still have a great time here. (Ballymacarbry ☎ 052-36108 glasha@eircom.net www.glashafarmhouse.com)

Beef

Omega Beef Direct

Joe and Eileen Condon's beef business is a taste of the future. They slowly, organically mature traditional Galloway animals at a density of one cow to 20 acres, giving beef whose essential omega 3 and 6 are high and in balance. They sell their meat through a delivery system and via farmers' markets. They orchestrate a superb web site, from which you order a box of beef which is delivered the next day. Along with other specialists such as Maurice Kettyle, Ladybird Organics and others, this is becoming the way in which concerned consumers now access their meat. The great thing about the taste of the future, of course, is that you can enjoy it right now. The meat is a taste sensation. (Clashavaugha, Ballymacarbry ☎ 087-2735447 info@omegabeefdirect.ie www.omegabeefdirect.ie)

Tipperary

Borrisokane

Organic Farmer

Michael Seymour

"A contented farmer is a scarce commodity these days", wrote Cait Curran in *Organic Matters* magazine, "but Michael Seymour is as close to that description as you are likely to find."

Why so contented? Well, Mr Seymour converted his farm to organics back in 1997, and in the intervening decade he has taken to selling his Angus beef and Belclare/Texel cross sheep direct to the consumer. "I'd much rather be master of my own destiny and have my own market", he told Ms Curran. To that end, he sells at the weekly Nenagh market, "You can stand over what you produce and the customer likes to meet the producer", he says. It all seems so simple when done by smart farmers and marketeers like Mr Seymour: "I'm very happy with what I'm doing. I have control of the business at every stage and that is what I set out to do." Mission accomplished, deliciously. (Finnoe Road, Borrisokane ☎ 067-27182)

Cahir

Orchard

● The Apple Farm

Here is the maths: Con Traas has sixty acres of a farm. Standard economics says 60 acres equals half a miserable income. Listen to the man from the ministry and he will tell you to sell up, because there simply isn't enough land to make a living. And yet, Con Traas has ten full-time employees, and he has up to a dozen part-time employees during the height of the season. How? Because he is the outstanding specialist in apples and apple juices, and fresh fruit, he is the luxury brand of fruit and drink, and he sells almost all of this produce from his barn at the farm, and because artisan economics makes a nonsense of conventional farm economics. And when he isn't employing people and making juice, he is experimenting: most recently he has been growing a new variety of apple called Wellant, and he has been making a new apple and blackcurrant juice, with the blackcurrants grown by Simon and Tina Mosse near Callan, a simply outstanding new concoction. So, do the maths, but above all, try the world-class produce of this visionary, iconoclastic, wizard of the orchard. (Moorstown, Cahir ☎ 052-41459 con@theapplefarm.com www.theapplefarm.com)

Organic Meat

● Ballybrado Direct

John Purcell and Josef Finke's company has expanded beyond its organic meat processing function – under the Good Herdsman label they supply organic meat to

Ireland's multiple retailers – to include a web shopping centre which sources breads from baker Kevin Drohan, vegetables from Paul Dreaper of Offaly, and the selection of foods is quite amazing. If you seek the living alternative to the banality of industrial food, it is really only a click away, and next thing you know it's been delivered to your door. (Cahir ☎ 052-45500 www.ballybrado.com)

Farmers' Market

● Cahir Farmers' Market

The O'Brien family. Keith and Jim. The Traas family. Little Farm. Clover Field. Fish from Pat, beef from Joe. Bakes and cakes from Ann and Mary. Pâtés from Maria. Cahir Market: shopping as it should be. Sure where else would you be on a Saturday morning? (Craft Granary near the Square, Cahir www.claneire.com, Saturday 9am-1pm)

Local Specialities
APPLE JUICE
FRESH-WATER CRAYFISH

Farm Shop

● O'Brien's Farm Shop

The O'Brien family sell not only at the weekly Cahir farmers' market, but also have a darling farm shop, just at the side of the N7 Cork Dublin road a mile or so south of New Inn, and clearly signposted. Here you can buy their fab floury spuds, local hen and duck eggs from John and Brid Landy, root vegetables from John and Marie Hartness, local cheeses, as well as the family's own farm produce of apples, apple juices, fruit, vegetables and an array of chutneys, pickles and whathaveyou. Every farm should have a shop like O'Brien's. (Outrath, Cahir ☎ 052-62282 info@obriens.com www.obriensfarmshop.com – Open weekdays. Telephone first if you are travelling far. O'Brien's produce is also available in the Cahir Farmers' Market)

Tipperary

Café & Deli

● The River House

Sheena Buttimer is doing a good job in this attractive room at the bridge in Cahir, a fine mix of café and deli which is just what the town has needed. (1 Castle Street, Cahir ☎ 052-41951 info@riverhouse.ie www.riverhouse.ie – Open 9am-5pm Mon-Sun)

Carrick-on-Suir

Wine Merchant

Approach Trade

Rafael Alvarez's wine company is the cutting-edge importer of Spanish wines into Ireland. He has the wines of superstar producers such as Alvaro Palacios, from the stunning Les Terrasses to the billionaire's choice L'Ermita. He has the wines of the Guitian family from Galicia, and the rare wines of Emilio Rojo, and wines from the legendary Mariano Garcia of Bodegas Mauro. The San Leon manzanilla from Herederos de Argueso is the finest we have ever enjoyed. There isn't a weak link in the entire chain of wines imported by this meticulous merchant, and levels of service are every bit as stellar as the selection of wines. A model modern wine importer. (Mill River Pk, Carrick-on-Suir ☎ 051-640164 info@approachwines.com www.approachwines.com)

Farmers' Market

Carrick-on-Suir Farmers' Market

With one of the best sites for a market you will find – under a canopy of trees in front of the church, just a dander off the main street, the Carrick market is a beauty. Here is what we bought: a huge rake of Ladybird burgers from Richard Auler; fresh seafood from Pat Hartley; lamb and buttermilk from John of Tinnock Farm as well as some superb free-range chicken; vegetables from Paddy Stokes and Julia Foran; lots of superb ices for the kids from Cramers Grove; brilliant red pepper ketchup from Ffrench's fine foods, and a basket or two of produce from the Camphill community. And how much did we spend on this whirlygig tour on a Friday morning, in the space of 15 minutes? 143 euro. Money was never so well spent. (Heritage Centre, Friday 10am-2pm)

Cashel

Guesthouse & Restaurant

Bailey's Guesthouse

With stylish rooms, a stylish bar and bar food, a stylish restaurant – 41 – and a stylish leisure centre, Bailey's has slowly, purposefully, and quietly become a key address in Cashel, and the place of choice for anyone visiting the town. The original townhouse has been abetted by a discreet extension which has allowed all the new development, and there is real ambition here, making Bailey's a hot new address. (Cashel ☎ 062-61937 info@baileys-ireland.com www.baileys-ireland.com – Food served 10.30am-noon (coffee), 12.30pm-3pm (lunch), 3pm-6pm (bar food), 6pm-9.30pm (bar food and à la carte restaurant menu), Mon-Sun, no bar food on Sat night)

Café

Café Hans

"If you haven't arrived in Cafe Hans by 12.40 you might as well go off and have a guided tour of The Rock and come back after 2pm because by 12.40 this place is totally full and by 1pm there are about 10 people STANDING in the restaurant waiting for a table. And they are STANDING there quite happily because they know that it will be worth the wait." That's what Eamon Barrett experienced on his first trip to CH, and it's what everyone experiences in this most brilliant restaurant. What has all those people STANDING? Superb food from Steffi and Hansi Matthiae, that's what. Thank heavens all these food lovers are such polite people. "Quite possibly the best lunchtime restaurant in the country", says Mr Barrett. Quite. (Moor Lane, Cashel ☎ 062-63660 – Open noon-5.30pm Tue-Sat)

Restaurant

Chez Hans

Jason Matthiae's restaurant is a legend in its own lifetime, a lifetime that began as long ago as 1968, when Jason's dad, Hans-Peter, first began to do the good thing, inventing a cuisine bourgeois-style that treated West Cork scallops with due respect, which sought out the best local meats, and which served everything in this glorious old deconsecrated church in a full, fine style. Little has changed in CH since the early days, save that they manage always to remain contemporary – no mean feat after almost 40 years, but helped of course by Jason's experience and his own strong contemporary style of cooking – and save that many people would nominate Chez Hans as their favourite restaurant in the whole of Ireland. It's easy to see why: every evening here seems special, and on a busy night the energy level in the room, stoked by glorious food and great wines, is thunderous. A great institution, growing stronger than ever after forty years. (Moor Lane, Cashel ☎ 062-61177 – Open 6pm-10pm Tue-Sat)

Tipperary

Sheep's Milk Cheese

Crozier Dairy Products

Harry Clifton-Browne is making a very fine sheep's milk cheese these days. In its best condition, Crozier Blue now ranks as one of the most interesting artisan cheeses in Ireland, its flavours limpid and mineral, clean and distinct, supremely pleasing and tactile. We are also big fans of the exceptional sheep's milk yogurt that Crozier make, which is one of the very best things, reminiscent of the supreme yogurts of Turkey and the Middle East, and a vital accompaniment to all your Claudia Roden and Diana Henry dishes. (Ballinamona, Cashel ☎ 062-61120 cliftonbrowne@eircom.net)

Bakery and Café

The Spearman

The Spearman family's sweet bakery and café is the sort of essential address every town needs. In its quiet, modest competence and charm, the Spearman is reminiscent of great old Tipperary tea rooms and bakeries such as Gleeson's of Nenagh, and it serves the same vital function as that much-missed bakery of both facilitating a community and focusing a community. Charming. (97 Main Street, Cashel ☎ 062-61143 – Open 9am-5.45pm Mon-Fri, 9am-5pm Sat)

Clonmel

Restaurant

Angela's Coffee Emporium & Restaurant

Angela Ryan's brilliant café does the simple things, superbly. Her cooking never wavers from optimum flavour savour, whether you are enjoying Chicken chardonnay, with its wafting winey aromas, or sweet lamb moussaka with its auberginey calmness. Like many Australian cooks of her generation – Ms Ryan is from Tasmania – she has such a firm grasp on ethnic cuisines that everything seems echt, and nothing ever tastes ersatz: supreme of chicken with black olives, basil and tomato is quintessentially Mediterranean, whilst salmon with chilli and mango is Ireland meets Asia in the sweetest embrace. The room has awesome energy, a lot of it emanating from this charming hostess, and Angela's is a great destination.
(14 Abbey Street, Clonmel ☎ 052-26899
ryanseamus@eircom.net – Open 8am-5.30pm Tue-Sat)

Restaurant

Befani's Mediterranean & Tapas Restaurant

"One of the most exciting places I've eaten in all year", reported Claire Goodwillie after a trip from Kilkenny to Clonmel to try Mr Befani's tapas bar and restaurant. "Worth every bit of the 40-minute drive from Kilkenny." The calamari is outstanding; fish fritters are light as a feather; fritto misto is "a lovely hot pile of seafood, crispy and piquant with freshly squeezed lemon". Cassoulet is correctly made and bowl-scrapingly delicious, hake with salsa verde and mussels gets "ten out of ten". Crema Catalana, and cherry and custard tart conclude things fortissimo, and the place is packed out with happy punters everywhichway. No surprise there. (6 Sarsfield Street, Clonmel ☎ 052-77893 ✉ info@befani.com 🖱 www.befani.com – Open 9am-11am Mon-Sat, noon-3pm Mon-Sun, 6pm-10pm Mon-Sun. Tapas served noon-10pm Mon-Sun)

Farmers' Market

Clonmel Farmers' Market

Get to school early on Saturdays in Clonmel to get the freshest produce at the Clonmel Market, just beside the shopping centre. (St Peter & Paul's Primary School, beside Oakville Shopping Centre. Saturdays, 10am-2pm)

Bakery

The Griddle Bakery

Kevin Drohan's interesting bakery also has a branch at 30 New Street in Carrick-on-Suir, and as well as an excellent range of craft breads for sale in the shops he bakes for the Ballybrado Direct webshop. (Irishtown, Clonmel ☎ 052-22583)

Wholefood Shop

The Honeypot

Next-door neighbour to Angela's restaurant, this is a fine, busy wholefood shop with lots of good things to discover. (The Honey Pot, 14 Abbey Street, Clonmel ☎ 052-21457 – Open 9.30am-6pm Mon-Sat)

Ice Cream

Tipperary Organic Ice Cream

Paddy and Joyce's lovely organic ice creams come in four flavours – vanilla; strawberries and cream; lemon zest, and chocolate and hazelnut. You will find them in good delis and look out for their ice cream stand at the summer farmers' markets in Dublin: with the sun beating down on you, a big, cold ice is just what you need. (Carrigeen Business Park, Clonmel ☎ 052-81905 joyce@tipperaryorganic.ie www.tipperaryorganic.ie)

Craft Butcher

● James Whelan Butchers

Pat Whelan's butcher's shop is the taste of the future. For one, you don't have to go to Clonmel to get their superb meats: they will deliver their products to you via courier, with ordering made simple via their web site. For another, Mr Whelan has updated and revised the traditional Irish butcher's shop, so that when you do visit the shop, it looks and feels more like a meat boutique than anything else. Bringing style, and superlative levels of service to the charcuterie business, is a radical step, but Pat Whelan manages to take it all in his ambitious stride, and one senses that the James Whelan story is really only beginning. Don't miss their dry-aged Tipperary beef, which is their particular signature, but in truth everything sold in JWB is of bench-mark quality. (Oakville Shopping Centre, Clonmel ☎ 052-22927 www.jameswhelanbutchers.com – Open 7.30am-6pm Mon-Wed, 7.30am-6.30pm Thu, 7.30am-7pm Fri, 7.30am-6pm Sat)

Wine Shop

● The Wine Buff

The Clonmel arm of the fast-growing WB franchise has the lovely wines that have made the group's reputation so speedily and successfully. (2 The Westgate, Clonmel ☎ 052-80494 www.thewinebuff.com – Open 11am-7pm Mon-Sat, 'till 8pm Fri)

Tipperary

Clogheen

Farmhouse Cheese

● Bay Lough Farmhouse Cheese

Dick and Anne Keating have long been keepers of the flame of the good food revolution in Tipp. As farmers – with more than a century of family farming in the county – as cider makers, and especially as cheese makers, their work is supremely individual and vital. The raw milk Baylough is a territorial-style cheese, and there are a number of flavoured varieties and also a smoked cheese which they smoke themselves using oak. But it is the plain cheese, for us, that best shows the quality of the Baylough milk and the skill of the cheese makers, especially when it has been well kept and allowed to develop its rich floral aperture and the paste has developed a fudgy, sweet richness. Darling work. (Clogheen ☎ 052-65275)

Restaurant and Accommodation

The Old Convent

Dermot and Christine Gannon's restaurant with rooms has been the runaway success story of 2007. It was always going to be. Ever since we first met him years ago when he was working alongside Paddy Foyle in Clifden, Mr Gannon was always a man waiting for the right chance, and biding his time. He worked here, there and everywhere, met and married Christine, and then found the Old Convent or, as they say, "it found us". Within a few weeks of opening their doors, and with their tasting menu offer polished and primped, it was difficult to get a table here. But what is significant about TOC is not just that what Dermot and Christine achieve is better, it's the fact that it is different. Everything has the most distinct signature, especially the cooking, which is simply stunning: rum-baked brill with crab, pea and pistachio risotto; Tipperary lamb fillet with Baylough croquette; Ballybrado organic pork salad with Crozier Blue cheese; rump of Tipperary beef with shiitake mushroom batter; Tipperary organic ice cream martini; organic chocolate fondue, stunning tastes, stunning textures. As a showcase of culinary skill, as a showcase of the foods of the county, The Old Convent cannot be bettered. And, the rooms are superb. A new star. (Clogheen ☎ 052-65565 info@theoldconvent.ie www.theoldconvent.ie – Open 7pm-9pm Thu-Sun)

Tipperary

Dundrum

Meat Processor

TJ Crowe

TJ Crowe is the smileiest pork butcher in the business. He not only processes his own animals, he does so for lots of other artisans, so local rare-breed pigs from locals such as

Tom and Sharon Shore – Gloucester Old Spot pigs, just amazing – are prepared here, or the superlative pork of the Crowe family of Newmarket. TJ has been rearing pigs since he was five years old. Today he slaughters 15 pigs each second week, and then processes them. His methods are traditional, ancient, truly Slow, which may be why he smiles so much. Beautiful brawns, lovely sausages, dry-cured bacon, all the glory of the most glorious animal, treated with respect. (Dundrum ☎ 062-71137 ☎ 087-824 7394)

Fethard

Farmhouse Cheese

● Cashel Blue Cheese

Jane and Louis Grubb's pioneering blue cheese is perhaps Ireland's best-known artisan brand, retailed here, there and everywhere, in Ireland and overseas. Brought to a 10-week-old maturity, the cheese is sublimely moreish, the blue veining counterpointing the creamy paste just so. Perfect with red wine, sublime with smoked salmon in a pasta sauce, the way the Italians like to do it. (Beechmount, Fethard ☎ 052-31151 jlgrubb@eircom.net www.cashelblue.com)

Kilgarvan Quay

Restaurant

● Brocka-on-the-Water

"Like nothing anywhere else" is how *Food & Wine* magazine summed up Anne, Anthony and Nancy's Brocka-on-the-Water. And it's true. Brocka isn't like a conventional restaurant. It's more like something you might find in the Tuscan foothills, or a waterfront place in Galicia – someone's house that also serves food to the public, but which doesn't do so in an overtly commercial way. It is the most captivating place, but its secret is not just the magic of the house and the experience. No, its real secret is the fact that Anne, Anthony and Nancy are cool as all get out: this trio are as hip as it gets. So, settle in for the rollmop herrings, the lamb with mint, aubergine and red onion, the brilliant vegetables grown in the garden by Nancy, and do not – under any circumstances – miss Anne's legendary meringues. (Kilgarvan Quay, Ballinderry ☎ 067-22038 – Open 7pm-10pm Mon-Sat. Reservations only.)

Kilsheelan

Bakery and Preserves

● Ffrench's Fine Foods

There is real assurance and polish to the breads and the imaginative relishes and ketchups that Michael and Claire bake and make: we are big fans of the Cajun red pepper ketchup. Find them at the Naas, Carrick and other local markets.(Gurteen, Kilsheelan ☎ 052-33731
✉ info@ffrenchs.com)

Nenagh

Café

● Café Q

This modern, comfortable room in the centre of town is an offshoot of the O'Connor family's Quigley's bakery, whose bread and cake shop is just across from Café Q. Their bakery and kitchen on the edge of town produces all the foods, breads and cakes they sell, which makes Café Q quite a different proposition from the majority of day-time eateries who buy in their produce from industrialised manufacturing and franchise operators. "We stand over everything", says Margaret O'Connor, who has developed the cafés into a successful chain, with branches in Roscrea, Thurles, and Tullamore, as well as three outlets in Limerick. With meat from the Hanlon brothers, locally roasted coffees, vegetables prepared from scratch and good Belgian chocolate in the chocolate cakes, Café Q is a real alternative to the bland franchises taking over every main street. (62 Pearse Street, Nenagh ☎ 067-36445
✉ quigleysbakery@eircom)

Country Shop

● Country Choice

Peter Ward can walk it – he runs the best shop in the country, and does so in an inimitable style – but just as importantly, he can talk it. Talking it was what first brought Mr Ward to national fame – at the Kinsale Food Conference in 2002 he declared, to ringing applause, that anyone in an Irish B&B or hotel who gave a customer a pot of imported jam at breakfast was "guilty of treason". Since then, he has become the leading face of Irish artisan food. He is chairman of the TASTE Council. He is a major Slow Food activist. He has become a poster boy for the food media both in Ireland and abroad. He has, in short, taken up the intellectual mantle of food advocacy carried for so long by Myrtle Allen. And, like Mrs Allen, Mr Ward almost pretends not to be an intellectual, yet you need only listen to him for two minutes to be blown away by the force of his arguments on behalf of farming, food production and food economies. And, like Mrs Allen, talking about it doesn't displace walking it: six days a week his shop, Country Choice, is a shrine to what he preaches. It is jam-packed with the best Irish foods. It serves gorgeous country cooking. It supports local cheese makers and many other producers by selling their foods at peak condition – if you seek something rare then look for Barbara Harding's Ballymass summer pasture butter, made from the milk of three cows and only sold here. Culture enshrined, and culture politicised, and culture to eat, Country Choice has it all. (25 Kenyon Street, Nenagh ☎ 067-32596 ✉ info@countrychoice.ie 🖱 www.countrychoice.ie – Open 9am-6pm Mon-Sat, coffee shop closes at 5pm)

"Good honest food produced with passion and attention to detail."

SIMON PRATT

Craft Butcher

● Hackett's

Michael Hackett's butcher's shop is the butcher's shop of your dreams. Simple, clean, with only a small amount of meat on display, it is a shop the way butcher's shops used to be, and it is home to magnificent Tipperary beef, as good as you can get. (94 Silver Street, Nenagh ☎ 067-31340 – Open 9am-6pm Mon-Sat, closed Wed)

Craft Butcher

● Hanlon's

Gregory and Michael Hanlon's shop is a benchmark country butcher's shop. In its modern style, and with its extensive offer aimed as much at the time-starved as at the true gourmet, it is a counterpoint to Hackett's just around the corner. The beauty of Nenagh, of course, is that it is a town that gives you all you need, and it gives you real choice. And that choice is amongst practitioners who have real class, who are on top of their game, so your choice is a real choice. And Hanlon's is a superb example of a butcher's shop on top of their game. (14 Kenyon Street, Nenagh ☎ 067-41299 – Open 8am-6pm Mon-Sat, 8am-7pm Fri)

Farmers' Market

Nenagh Farmers' Market

With great producers such as Tom and Sharon Shore and Michael Seymour, to name but two committed local food specialists, the NFM is a little jewel waiting for you to discover it. Don't delay, and tell them we sent you. (Teach and Leinn, Kenyon Street, Nenagh, Sat 10am-2pm)

Bakery

Quigley's Bakery

The Quigley's bakery has been firing up the ovens in Nenagh since 1850, and today the bakery services the shop and café on Kenyon Street. They make 10 varieties of bread, including an understandably popular Polish bread, and their confectionery is all hand made, and has that lovely element of domestic baking that makes Irish patisserie so charming. The café in the rere of the bakery shop has just been restyled, and is a sweet little spot to take tea and lunches. (9 Kenyon Street ☎ 067-31454 quigleysbakery@eircom.ie www.quigleys.ie)

Roscrea

Farmhouse Cheese

Boulabane Cheese

Michael Cantwell's Boulabane Cheese is a semi-soft farmhouse cheese, and is the newest arrival into Ireland's cheese culture. Michael is a prominent Slow Food participant, so expect to see Boulabane marching forth into our culinary consciousness, but Slowly. (Boulabane, Roscrea ☎ 0505-43111)

Terryglass

Tipperary

Gastropub

The Derg Inn

Here's what a local food lover said to us about Mick and Joyce Soden's gastro-pub: "The Derg Inn is really worth a mention. They are very caring people when it comes to food and hospitality. They are good on poetry, art, and music. They use good meat including lamb. They always have some nice fish. They use lots of local vegetables in the summer, and their soda bread is great". Well quite an encomium, eh? And last time here we really enjoyed the crab on brown bread, the good fresh fish with chips and tartare sauce, some nice slices of pizza and a good bowl of chowder. (Terryglass ☎ 067-22037 ✉ derginn@eircom.net 🖱 www.derginn.ie – Food served noon-9.30pm Mon-Sun)

"Produce is the backbone of my cooking and around here I have the best produce. I like to show the ingredients off."

NEVEN MAGUIRE

Thurles

Artisan Cheese maker

● Cooleeney Cheese

Breda and Jim Maher get the key to the cheese maker's door in 2007, after 21 years of creating some of Ireland's greatest farmhouse cheeses. To be honest, they had possession of that key right from the start of their enterprise, for the original Cooleeney camembert has always been one of those cheeses that defined Irish farmhouse cheese making. Its richness, its smooth-textured paste, its development as the cheese matured, are all signs of how the best Irish milk from the best Irish pastures is, in the hands of a gifted cheese maker, the key to unlocking the potential of a magic liquid. And that is what Cooleeney does: it reveals the magic of milk, the magic of raw milk. As the company has developed they have added the Maighean raw cow's milk cheese, the goat's milk Gortnamona, made with pasteurised goat's milk, and recent additions include Chulchoill, a pasteurised goat's milk log, and Daru, a semi-hard pasteurised cow's milk cheese. The company also makes the flavoured Dunbarra cheeses. But it is in the Cooleeney camembert and the refulgent, agrestic Maighean that we best see the formidable power and poise of this great cheese making endeavour, cheeses that are, in truth, definitions of what Irish agriculture and artisan skills can achieve. (Moyne, Thurles ☎ 0504-45112 ✉ info@cooleeney.com 🖱 www.cooleeney.com)

Tipperary

Preserves

Crossogue Preserves

Veronica Molloy's preserves are especially fine relishes and chutneys, and have a well-deserved reputation for distinctive culinary excellence. (Ballycahill, Thurles ☎ 0504-54416 info@crossoguepreserves.com www.crossoguepreserves.com)

Country House & Restaurant

Inch House

A sweet, demure country house with a sweet, demure restaurant that is the toast of all the locals for miles around, the Egan family's lovely house is a taste of gentler, more civilised, less frenetic Ireland, and all the more welcome for that. The great hospitality and fine country cooking of Inch make it a great destination. (Thurles ☎ 0504-51261 mairin@inchhouse.ie www.inchhouse.ie – Restaurant open 7pm-9.30pm Tue-Sat)

Farmers' Market

Thurles Farmers' Market

Saturday mornings at the greyhound track is where you need to be to get the best local produce. (Saturday 9.30am-1pm)

County Waterford

Ardmore

Restaurant

White Horses

Caring is sharing. And so, if you have a loved one who hasn't managed to make it to White Horses to have lunch or dinner with you in Geraldine Flavin and Christine Power's sweet restaurant, then do not leave without bringing them home at least a couple of slices of the superlative sweet pies, cakes, bombes, bakes, trifles and other delights that this talented kitchen manages to conjure up from the magic of eggs, flour and butter. Everything else the girls cook has the same depth of skill and generosity, which explains why WH is such a cult success. Delightful. (Main Street, Ardmore ☎ 024-94040 whitehorses@eircom.net – Open 11am-11pm Tue-Sun)

"Irish stew is the common denominator of all the meat and potato daubes and, by virtue of its purity, it may be the best."

RICHARD OLNEY

Ballymacarbry

Country House & Restaurant

Hanora's Cottage

The Wall family's mountain-top house and restaurant exudes a chalet-like feel, tucked into the trees and snuggled by an adjacent river, and its warm welcome is just the ticket after a day's exhilarating, exhausting trek in the beauty of the Comeragh Mountains. The breakfasts created by Mary Wall are amongst the finest served in the entire country. (Nire Valley, Ballymacarbry ☎ 052-36134 www.hanorascottage.com)

Cappoquin

Bakery and Cafe

Barron's Bakery

This lovely local bakery dates all the way back to 1887, and still uses the traditional Scotch Brick ovens, where bread is baked on the falling heat of the oven that has been fired up before. Joe and Esther Barron and their multi-ethnic crew of bakers still do things the old way, the correct way, and their breads are treasurable, delicious staples. (Cappoquin ☎ 058-54045 – Open 9am-5.30pm Mon-Sat)

Apple Juice

Crinnaghtaun Apple Juice

Julie Keane makes a terrific apple juice from the apples grown by her husband, David. Bramleys and Cox's Pippins are the mainstays of the juice, which is made only from the free-flowing juice as it comes from the press. This is a serious, considered, expert drink with great typicity and character, and not something that should be reserved for the kids. You need the goodness of Crinnaghtaun in your life because, let's face it, you're worth it. (Cappoquin ☎ 058-54258 www.irishapplejuice.com)

Farmhouse Cheese

Knockalara Farmhouse Cheese

Sheep's milk cheeses are still a rarity in Ireland, but for many years now Wolfgang and Agnes Schliebitz's brilliant Knockalara range has shown just how splendid cheeses made with sheep's milk can be. Their Dromana range of fresh and flavoured cheeses in oil are a must-have kitchen staple, but the more mature Knockalara remains the benchmark cheese, with subtle, flinty, complex and expertly conjoined flavours all in happy evidence. You will find the smiling cheesemakers selling at local markets. (Knockalara, Cappoquin ☎ 024-96326 wschliebitz@eircom.net)

Butcher

Murphy's Meat Centre

A fine local butcher's shop, in the centre of town, particularly noted for good pork sausages. (Main Street, Cappoquin ☎ 058-54539 – Open 9am-5.30pm)

Country House

Richmond House

"Wonderful, friendly, timeless, elegant and ever so slightly frayed around the edges, which gives the house tremendous character." Eamon Barrett's summation of the charms of Richmond is right on the money, and it shows what an archetype of the country house this splendid place is. Paul Deevy cooks superbly – contemporary country cooking, if that isn't a contradiction in terms – Claire Deevy is one of the best hostesses, and when you wrap that combination into a cosy old friend of a house then you have one of the best experiences Irish hospitality can offer. A star of the county, and a star of the country. (Cappoquin ☎ 058-54278 ✉ info@richmondhouse.net
🖱 www.richmondhouse.net – Open for Dinner for non-residents)

Cheekpoint

Bistro

McAlpin's Cottage Bistro

Aidan and Marian McAlpin are enjoying continued success with The Cottage Bistro in Cheekpoint. They put out some really tasty food and people absolutely love it. Mussels in garlic butter are ace, and the chicken curry is just super. Sirloin of Irish beef, cooked rare with some chips and garlic or pepper sauce is another great dish, and Marian continues to make many of the desserts herself, so finish with some great domestic-style baking to cap a great dinner in lovely Cheekpoint. (Cheekpoint ☎ 051-380854
✉ mcalpinscottagebistro@eircom.net – Open Dinner)

Dungarvan

B&B

An Bohreen

It is Ann Mulligan's brilliant cooking that sets An Bohreen apart from the mass of B&B's. Skilful, delicious, and delivered with true professional aplomb, her cooking raises the bar in terms of what we consider B&B cooking, and her expertise makes this pretty and engagingly modest house into a true destination for travellers.
(Killineen West, Dungarvan ☎ 051-291010
🖱 www.anbohreen.com)

Bagel Bakers

Broadway Bagels

Des and Rosie Sheehan established their bagel company because Mrs Sheehan couldn't get the quality of bagel she was used to when growing up in New York. Since 2002 they have successfully grown their business on the back of bagels that have true quality and typicity, that are "munchy with a malty taste" as Mrs Sheehan likes 'em. Look out for the poppy seed and "The Works" – poppy seed, sesame, red onion and toasted garlic – in stores and supermarkets. (Dungarvan Business Pk, Dungarvan ☎ 058 23999)

Farmers' Market

Dungarvan Farmers' Market

Dungarvan Farmers' Market trades in Gratton Square on Thursday mornings, with everything from organic wines to sheep's milk cheeses to local apple juices. Many of the great Waterford artisans are here: Barron's bakery; Condon's beef; Knockalara Cheese; Clashganny apple juices; organic vegetables from Siobhan La Touche and organic salad bags from Glenribben Farm of Lismore; jams, bakes and other treats from Michelle Dwane of Barnawee Foods (who also runs a local guesthouse); free-range eggs from Ballinamult; chewy bagels filled with good things from Naked Lunch – Condon's grilled organic omega beef in a Broadway Bagel for us, please – bakes and cakes from Indulge Bakery, and there are chocolate stalls with wickedly fine hot chocolate, plant stalls, craft stalls, handmade wooden toys, and much more. A market that sums up the zeitgeist of the town itself. (Gratton Square, Thursday mornings. Contact Síobhan La Touche, ☎ 086-394 0564
✉ contact@dungarvanfarmersmarket.com
🖱 www.dungarvanfarmersmarket.com)

B&B

Gortnadiha House

Seasoned travellers will tell you that Eileen Harty's breakfasts are the very best you can find. Certainly, the hostess has energy and fizzle, and she pours everything into her lovely house and the care of her guests, making Gortnadiha the quintessential B&B&B: great beds, sublime breakfasts, brilliant banter. It can be difficult to get out of here to go on your travels before 11am or noon, such is the craic, so don't plan too much. (Ring, Dungarvan
☎ 058-46142 ✉ gortnadihalodge@eircom.net
🖱 www.waterfordfarms.com/gortnadiha)

Butcher

John David Power

Waterford's butchers are skilful, proud charcutiers, and none is more skilful or more proud of his craft than the ebullient JD Power. Let this chap take care of your meat requirements and life becomes a whole lot better. (57 Main Street, Dungarvan ☎ 058-42339 – Open 9am-5.50pm)

Country House

Powersfield House

Eunice Power is one of those meticulous, multi-talented, multi-tasking women who can seemingly turn her hand to anything. As well as running a lovely B&B, she has a catering company, and a cookery school, and everything she does is accomplished with flair and fastidious attention to detail, and with an enviable, genuine human warmth that makes every element of Powersfield something special. (Ballinamuck West, Dungarvan ☎ 058-45594 eunice@powersfield.com www.powersfield.com)

Restaurant

Q82

Andrew Quealy's restaurant is above his eponymous pub, and it's a modern, stylish room where modern, stylish food has succeeded in winning a local audience. Veal with tuna mayo; rabbit and ham hock terrine; nicely cooked main courses of fish such as roast sea bass or red emperor with broad beans and asparagus, and nice puds such as hot chocolate pudding or a good pecan pie add up to an impressive totality, though the bill can also mount up. One senses Q82 is still striving towards its signature style, so there is much to expect to enjoy in the future. (82 O'Connell Street, Dungarvan West, Dungarvan ☎ 058-24555 – Quealy's Bar open noon-3pm, 5pm-8pm. Q82 restaurant open 6pm-9.30pm info@quealys.com)

Restaurant & Townhouse

The Tannery

Chef, author, television presenter, restaurateur, consultant restaurateur, Paul Flynn has made himself into a true renaissance figure amongst Irish cooks. The funny thing is that Mr Flynn is gifted at all of these things – his writing style, for instance, is as witty, accomplished and original as his cooking, and he has already proven on other consulting jobs that he knows better than the public what the public want, so his redrafting of the new Balzac restaurant, in Dublin, is freighted with promise. And yet, one senses that the true thrill for Flynn remains the same: improvising with ingredients in a kitchen with a good crew, taking Irish culinary ideas apart and rebirthing them. Intellectually he may be a ringmaster, but temperamentally he remains a performer, and that sense of performance is what gives his work such relish. He is one of the great Irish cooks, and he and Maire Flynn have made The Tannery – and its beautiful Townhouse rooms – into one of the great Irish destinations, and have done so entirely on their own terms. Like other mavericks, Mr Flynn marches to the beat of a different drum, but he knows both the tempo and the tempi of his time. All that remains is to establish a cookery school, and we're sure he'll get to that soon. (10 Quay Street, Dungarvan ☎ 058-45420 info@tannery.ie www.tannery.ie – Open 12.30pm-2.15pm Tue-Fri & Sun, 6.30pm-9.30pm Tue-Sat, 6pm-9pm Sun Jul-Aug and bank holidays)

Local Specialities

BLAS
TURNOVERS
WHITE BRACKS
VIENNAS
BLOOMERS
RINGPAN
CURRANT SODA
BOSSES
RICH BRACKS
HEALTH PANS

Cakes and Cookies

Tara's

Waterford

Tara Breen's company produces fab cookies, bakes, cakes and sweet whatnots that are a terrific tea-time treat and a boon for school lunchboxes. There is a real flair to everything this company produces, from the hip, colourful packaging to the zesty, up-for-it flavours that distinguish the entire range of cakes and good things. (57 O'Connell Street, Dungarvan ☎ 058-23159 www.tarascookies.com)

Dunmore East

Organic Chickens

Born Free Organic Chickens

Paul Crotty and JJ Ahern's organic birds lead the ideal life – lots of space, a good diet, fresh green grass and lots of tasty clover – and that makes for an ideal bird which has true flavour and texture, and whose bones will make the most droolsome stock when all else has been eaten. (Ballymabin, Dunmore East ☎ 087-279 2613 paul_crotty@eircom.net)

Traiteur

The Lemon Tree

Joan Boland's neat food operation is just humming along. Great baking, good breads, real homemade savouries and now a small selection of wines to complement the food. Recent tastings included a miniature Christmas cake, fully iced and decorated, just about bite size and absolutely delicious. Value is very strong. (Dunmore East ☎ 051-383164 lemontreecatering@eircom.net – Open 11am-7pm Mon-Sat)

Bar

The Spinnaker Bar

Sister to the popular Chez K's in Waterford city, Niall Edmondson's pretty pub in this prettiest of villages has some nice simple food, and lively entertainment to while away those holiday evenings. (Dunmore East ☎ 051-383133 info@thespinnakerbar.com www.thespinnakerbar.com – Open 12.30pm-10pm summer, 5pm-9.30pm Wed-Sat, 12.30pm-10pm Sat & Sun winter)

Ferrybank

Chocolatier

Gallwey's

Ciara Power's Gallwey's range of whiskey truffles, coffee truffles and pralines are unashamedly, richly, spiritedly luxurious. Abandon restraint, and plunge into the chocolate indulgence that these gloriously old-style chocs offer with every bite. (Abbeylands Business Park, Ferrybank ☎ 051-830860 gallweyschocolates@eircom.net www.gallweys.com)

Knockanore

Farmhouse Cheese

● Knockanore Cheese

Eamonn and Patricia Lonergan's cheeses have been made, using milk from their own Friesian herd, since 1987, and that long experience shows in these subtle-flavoured cheeses, which you will find in plain, smoked and flavoured versions. (Ballyneety, Knockanore ☎ 024-97275 www.knockanorecheese.com)

Lismore

Wine Shop & Deli

● Hand Made Wines

A new wine shop and deli, owned by the wine and food writer Tom Doorley. Mr Doorley's long experience as a wine writer is shown in the 350-bottle range of wines that traverses all price points, and which focuses in particular on the Rhone Valley, Spain and Italy. Helpful, hand-written notes on all the bottles makes choosing simple and take the pressure out of selecting a special bottle as a gift. There are also nice deli items from Ireland and further afield to pack alongside the bottle that sports your name. (Main Street, Lismore ☎ 058-53688 www.tomdoorley.com)

Butcher

● Michael McGrath

Step in the door, step back in time to the era of the classic butcher's shop, the time of sawdust, sage culinary advice, and meticulously reared and processed meat. McGrath's is a legend in the south-east, and one taste of this beef and you will understand exactly why they are legendary. (Main Street, Lismore ☎ 058-54350 – Open 7am-6pm Mon-Sat)

Passage East

B&B

● Parkswood House

Roger and Terrie Pooley's beautiful house enjoys the most dazzling location, high above the River Suir and with views out towards Dunbrody Abbey and Cheekpoint. There are five fine rooms in the house and a self-catering cottage, and its location makes for the most splendid base for exploring all of the sunny south-east. (Passage East ☎ 051-380863 ✉ info@parkswood.com 🖱 www.parkswood.com)

Portlaw

Organic Apple Juice

● Clashganny Apple Juice

An organic orchard established by Richard Galvin and Philip Little in 1999, Clashganny now boasts 10,000 organic apple trees, producing both fresh eating apples and a wizard apple juice. Look for these fine juices and apples at local farmers' markets in Dungarvan and Ardkeen. (Portlaw ☎ 051-387041)

Craft Bakery

● Portlaw Bakery

Waterford has been fortunate – and prudent – in supporting and thereby preserving its traditional bakeries such as Barron's and Michael Madder's excellent Portlaw Bakery. Look out for the breads in local shops, and you will find them in Ardkeen stores in Waterford. (Portlaw ☎ 051-387221)

Tramore

Chipper

● Cunningham's Chipper

Sixty years young in 2007, Cunningham's is a local legend for crisp chips, and chipper staff who do a superb job with the fryers. (Main Street, Tramore ☎ 051-381529 4pm-12.30am Mon-Sun)

"We are all connected in the web of life and it is food that spins that web."

VANDANA SHIVA

Waterford

Waterford

Shop

Ardkeen Stores

Owned and run by the Jephson family since 1967, Ardkeen Stores is as important a foodstore to Waterford as Field's is to Skibbereen in West Cork. Over recent years the family have focused very strongly on sourcing food locally, and have championed products like Paul Crotty's Born Free organic chickens, Portlaw bakery breads, Grantstown tomatoes, Crinnaghtaun Apple Juice from Cappoquin and Coolfin organic goat's milk from Portlaw. Chef Martin Dwyer acts as food consultant to the store and a wide array of his dependable recipes can be picked up in store. Another demonstration of the Jephson's commitment to good food is the family's generous gesture in allowing the local Farmers' Market set up stall in the supermarket car park on the second Sunday of each month. A fabulous enterprise, proof of a dedicated local food philosophy that is life-affirming. (Ardkeen Shopping Centre, Dunmore Road, Waterford City ☎ 051-874620
✉ QualityFood@ardkeen.com 🖰 www.ardkeen.com)

Producers' market

Ardkeen Producers' Market

David and Sinead Galvin organise the monthly market at Ardkeen Stores, featuring a great array of local producers and artisans. (Contact Sinead on ☎ 087-939 8813)

Restaurant

L'Atmosphere

"Fantastic food, and amazing value." That's pretty much what you hear about Arnaud Mary's restaurant from happy locals. The cooking is smart, modern French-European: fried foie gras with coco beans and duck jus; rare tuna (presented with a little jug of sesame sauce, tall bread and lovely peas with a mother of pearl spoon!); whole lobster roasted; pigeon breast with the remainder of the pigeon meat minced and served underneath the breast on a Grand Marnier soaked piece of toasted bread. The flavours are as amazing as the value, and small wonder Arnaud's Atmosphere is the toast of the town. (19 Henrietta Street, Waterford ☎ 051-858426
🖰 www.restaurant-latmosphere.com)

Restaurant

Bodega!

Bodega! is one of the great restaurants. Hugely atmospheric at all times of the day and night, it's a dream vision of talented, artistic owners – Cormac and Donagh – who stamp their left-field imprimatur on the excellent food and the fine drinks that make folk flock here in their droves. Bohemian, blissful, and an attraction for all ages, this is one of the great Waterford city addresses. They have recently begun to host music evenings, and once again the carefully chosen musicians seem to fit into the Bodega! fabric extremely well, another good complement to a great institution. (54 John Street, Waterford ☎ 051-844177 info@bodegawaterford.com www.bodegawaterford.com – Open Lunch & Dinner)

Bakery

La Boulangerie

An excellent craft bakery run by Arnaud Mary, who also masterminds the hugely successful L'Atmosphere restaurant on Henrietta Street. (John Street, Waterford ☎ 051-843767 latmosphererestaurant@hotmail.com – Open 8am-6pm Mon-Sat)

Restaurant

Chez K's

Chez K's has really come into its own over the last year or so, and the consistency of the kitchen now is such that they can produce food that is without fault. Roast fig, Parma ham and Cashel Blue salad is spot on, salt & pepper squid with vermicelli and a mild chilli dipping sauce is very tasty. Mains of salmon and a fine sirloin steak with Crozier sauce are pleasing, accessible food, dishes where ambition and execution coincide. The menu suits the room and it suits the punters, and expect a lot more to come from CK over the next while. (20 William Street, Waterford ☎ 051-844180 info@chez-ks.com www.chez-ks.com – Open 5.30pm-9.30pm Mon-Sat)

Restaurant

Espresso

The sister restaurant to La Palma on The Mall, Espresso concentrates on pasta and pizzas. (4 Parnell Street, Waterford ☎ 051-879823 www.lapalma.ie – Open Lunch & Dinner)

Café

The Granary Café

Peter Fowler's café is part of the Waterford Treasures Museum, and it is right where it needs to be, because this operation is a Waterford treasure. Everything they serve is made on board, and it means that old standards like chicken and mushroom pie, or lemon meringue pie (lemon meringue pie!) are amazing. The staff are as sharp as the cooking, the coffee is ace, and the good citizens of Waterford won't be able to keep this a secret for very long. (The Granary Cafe @ Waterford Treasures Museum, The Quay, Waterford ☎ 051-854428 – Open 8.30pm-5pm, 6pm Summer, Mon-Sun)

Shop

Jay Bees

Ask us where do the best chocolate brownies we have ever eaten come from, and the answer is Jay Bees. This community of Mennonite Amish are bakers to their fingertips, and everything they grow and bake and make has the stamp of sure goodness, rising to a crescendo of pleasure with those incredible brownies. (Campus Stn, Ballinakina, Woodstown ☎ 051-382305 – Open 8am-7pm Mon-Fri, 8.30am-7pm Sat)

Country Market

Jenkin's Lane Food & Craft Market

Local crafts and local foods mingle happily in the Jenkin's Lane Market, so it's a valuable source not merely for local foods but also for nice gift items for someone special. That's you. (Jenkin's Lane, off Georges Street. Saturday 10am-4pm)

Butcher

Kearney's

Tom Kearney is a classy butcher, and the beef fillet from his own animals – hung for three weeks – or a couple of T-bones for Friday night will blow you away with their fineness. The butcher of choice for Waterford food lovers. (27a John Street, Waterford ☎ 051-874434 – Open 8.30am-6pm Mon-Sat)

Restaurant

La Boheme

Eric and Christine Theze have established a beautiful basement room in Waterford's Chamber of Commerce as the site for M. Theze's formal, technique-led French cooking. Lobster is the house speciality, and they cook and present it very well indeed, in fact the fish cookery is a strength. Prices are high, though choosing the early bird menus allows you to find some good value for money. (2 George's Street, Waterford ☎ 051-875645 – Open Dinner)

Restaurant

La Palma Restaurant

Sandro Cavaliere's restaurant has moved to a sumptuous new home on The Mall, which looks and feels, especially in its slick cocktail bar, like somewhere in the centre of London. The cooking is reliable and ever-enjoyable Italian food, and it's massively popular with Waterford locals. (20 The Mall, Waterford. ☎ 051-879823
enquiries@lapalma.ie www.lapalma.ie)

Country House & Restaurant

Waterford Castle

Michael Quinn's cooking at the Castle just gets better and better. This cook understands food so well that his dishes have a sense of the purest culinary instinct about them, but then when the chef smokes his own mackerel for his mackerel pâté, you get some idea of what he is aiming to achieve, and having venison from the estate means that venison here is for the gods. Roast partidge is masterly game cookery, a white truffle oil soup and an oxtail pithivier are perfection, Sally Barnes' smoked haddock risotto with a hen's egg on top, and wild sea bass don't put a step wrong. Finish with pannacotta with a lime and chilli syrup and a Shock vodka granita and you get the sublime and the original, and that is what Mr Quinn offers. (The Island, Ballinakill, Waterford ☎ 051-878203
www.waterfordcastle.com - Open Dinner)

Wine Shop & Restaurant

The Wine Vault

Davis Dennison's wine shop and restaurant is a great fixture of Waterford's culinary life. Mr Dennison keeps the cooking nice and simple, all the better to showcase a marvellous range of wines, which he sources and selects with perspicacious care from all over the world.
(High Street, Waterford ☎ 051-853 444
www.waterfordwinevault.com – Open 12.30pm-2.30pm, 5.30pm-10.30pm Mon-Sat)

Wine Shop

World Wide Wines

Think of any stellar wine shop you know anywhere, and its excellence is matched, bottle for bottle, by the wonder that is World Wide Wines. Claire and Declan Brady's shop is an outstanding destination for any lover of liquor. Top end wines, value wines, boutique wines and a collection of rare and old whiskeys that gives you enough scope to do a bit of damage to a lottery win. Of course, there's also a stellar selection of vintage champagne, and every conceivable amount of gins, vodkas, beers, Reidl glasses, good cheeses and chocolates. An amazing shop. (Cove Centre, Dunmore Road, Waterford ☎ 051-878798
worldwidewines@eircom.net)

"The motives are important: you must believe in the food, it simply will not work for a small business if you do not believe in it as a high-quality food that will win respect."

NORMAN STEELE, MILLEENS CHEESE

County Westmeath

Athlone

Farmers' Market

Athlone Farmers' Market

Legendary local honey producer Andrew McGuinness heads up the team who organise the excellent Athlone Market every Saturday. (Market Square, Athlone, Saturday 10am-3pm)

Restaurant

Kin Khao

Adam and Janya do some nice things in the little Kin Khao, and what is really pleasing is their willingness to serve the real thing, rather than the ersatz westernised offer that Thai restaurants compromise with. So, try a dish such as Lao curry, made without coconut, or Ho Mok Gai, which they have adapted into a chicken dish from its original version which featured fish, or a rare salad such as Yum Phed Yan, duck with tomatoes. Such regional authenticity is valuable for a cuisine which is frequently presented in Ireland as a homogenous entity, but which is in fact intensely regional. Super-friendly staff, and excellent value for money. (Abbey Lane ☎ 090-649 8805 info@thaikinkhao.com www.kinkhaothai.ie – Open 12.30pm-5.30pm Wed-Sun, 5.30pm-10.30pm Mon-Sun)

Restaurant

The Left Bank Bistro

Ask Annie or Mary how things are going in their classic bistro on the left bank, and all they will do is to say how lucky they are to have such superb staff – so loyal, so hard-working, so dedicated. Well, the superb staff are lucky to have such superb bosses, and the synergy between them has kept the LBB in top position in the Midlands for many years now. They don't try to reinvent the wheel in here, they just do savoury food with an Asiatic spin, and they do it very well: Mediterranean hake with olive crust, warm potato salad; goujons of hoki deep-fried with tartare and sautéed potatoes; chilli-marinated beef with egg noodles and spring onions. Michael Durr's cooking is as crisp and clean as the style of the room itself, and the LBB is a classic. (Fry Place, Athlone ☎ 090-649 4446 ✉ info@leftbankbistro.com 🖱 www.leftbankbistro.com – Open 10.30am-9.30pm. Lunch served noon-5pm, dinner served 5.30pm-close Tue-Sat)

Fishmonger

Rene Cusack

Good news for Athlone as Rene Cusack's expanding fresh fish empire moves eastwards from Limerick to conquer the Midlands. Great fish, great service, and a great tradition of knowledgeable fish selling is a major assset to the town. (8 Belhavel, Golden Island, Athlone ☎ 090-642 0355 – Open 9am-6pm Mon-Sat)

Indian Restaurant

Saagar

Saagar began back in 1992 when Sunil and Meera Kumar first opened in Mullingar. The riverside Athlone branch continues their dedicated service of classic Indian cooking. (Lloyd's Lane, Athlone ☎ 090-270011
✉ info@saagarindianrestaurants.com
🖱 www.saagarindianrestaurants.com – Open 5.30pm-11.30pm Mon-Sun)

Organic Farm

Terryglass Organics

By the size of the queue shall you know the scale of the quality. On Sunday in Dun Laoghaire market, for instance, the queue lined up waiting to be served at Jens Krumpe's Terryglass Organics stall is only massive. It's lengthy, but people are patient: they want Terryglass produce, and who minds the wait? These smart folk want superb, well-hung Angus beef, and they want Tamworth and Saddleback pork – some of the very best – and they want healthy chickens and well-hung lamb, all produced to organic standards. The Dun Laoghaire queue is repeated across Dublin over the weekends, at Dalkey on Friday, at Marlay Park, Rathfarnham and Bray on Saturday, and at Dundrum on Sundays. Somehow, Mr Krumpe also finds time to bring his amazing produce to Farmleigh during the summer season, and he has a flourishing box delivery scheme. He is an exemplary artisan, and the Terryglass meats simply have to be tried. (Portanenna, Ballykeeran, Athlone ☎ 087-6597313
✉ terryglassorganics@eircom.net)

Glasson

Pub and Restaurant

Farrell's of Glasson

Kathleen and Joe Farrell's pub is beginning to make quite a name for itself as a pub with some interesting cooking. (Glasson ☎ 090-648 5208 – Food served 6pm-9.30pm Tue, 1pm-9.30pm Wed-Sat, 1pm-8pm Sun)

Bar & Restaurant

Grogan's of Glasson

A pretty and hugely popular gastropub in a pretty and hugely popular village, Grogan's draws the crowds for tasty food such as deep-fried haddock with potato wedges with tartare and salad, all competently delivered by busy staff. (Glasson ☎ 090-648 5158 – Open noon-5pm Mon-Sat, 12.30pm-3.30pm Sun, 5pm-9pm Mon-Sat, 4pm-8pm Sun)

Restaurant with Rooms

Wineport Lodge

Wineport is the waterside retreat of your dreams. Hard by the shore of Lough Ree, Ray Byrne and Jane English's bespoke hotel is an enchantment, a place where the magic of food, wine, location and service can seem almost to play a spell on you. Breakfast on the balcony overlooking the lake. A drink before dinner on the deck as boats pull in and passengers disembark for dinner. Delicious dishes from chef Fergal O'Donnell as the sun sets over the water. Utterly glorious bedrooms with superb walnut furniture. It is common to hear people talk about Wineport in an almost reverential way, but it isn't a place to be revered, it is a place to be enjoyed, thanks to the exceptional crew who create this pleasure every day of the year. (Glasson, Athlone ☎ 090-643 9010 lodge@wineport.ie www.wineport.ie – Open 6pm-9.30pm Mon-Sat, 3pm-9.30pm Sun)

Horseleap

Country House and Restaurant

Temple

Okay, so here are some extracts from our notebook on our first visit to Temple after Declan and Bernadette Fagan had opened their spa and hotel – Initial impression of the room is – wow! Such assured glamour. The most wonderful breakfast. A place in harmony with its surroundings and with itself. Brilliant pigeon and rabbit with potato rösti. The most holistic of spas in the quintessential Irish pastoral – on and on it goes. But, there is one note we made at breakfast which gives the real secret of this outstanding address: They have, somehow, managed to keep the atmosphere of the old house. For those who knew Temple as a small country house, that will be all you need to know to come here. Temple remains the gentlest, most spiritual of places, a tribute to its owners, the gentlest, most spiritual of people. (Horseleap, Moate ☎ 0506-35118 ✉ relax@templespa.ie 🖱 www.templespa.ie – Open 10.30am-9.30pm Tue-Sat. Lunch served noon-5pm, dinner served 5.30pm-close)

Local Specialities
WESTMEATH BEEF
BALLINAGORE POTATOES

Mullingar

Wine Shop
● Cana

A few doors up from the junction in the centre of Town, Cana is a very good wine shop, with an excellent range and most helpful service. (6 Castle Street, Mullingar ☎ 044-934 2742 – Open 10.30am-11pm Sun-Thur, 'till 11.30pm Fri & Sat)

Café
● Gallery 29

The Gray sisters, Emily and Ann, do a great job here in Gallery 29. They are hard-working, dedicated cooks and practitioners, and it is the happy customer who benefits from their application. Their menus read conventional and modern – a mix of soups, sandwiches, savouries, sweet things and a couple of daily specials – but what makes their food different is the care and attention, the TLC, which this kitchen bestows on everything that is sent out to the customers. It is gratifying to see this care, and even more gratifying to eat and enjoy it. (29 Oliver Plunkett Street, Mullingar ☎ 044-934 9449 – Open 9am-5.30pm Tue-Sat)

Coffee Shop

iLiA

Since the last Bridgestone Food Guide, Julie Kenny has opened ilia Gourmet to complement ilia, a coffee experience, her original café and restaurant. We have a feeling this dynamic lady is still nowhere near hitting capacity, and that future years will see future ilia plans and projects brought to realisation. Which is just fine by us, and even more fine as far as the residents of Mullingar are concerned. ILiA does everything well – good cooking, a lovely ambience, nice service, great foods in the shop, two places you return to again and again for a piece of that magic. Excellent. (28 Oliver Plunkett Street, Mullingar ☎ 044-40300; iLiA Gourmet, 25 Oliver Plunkett Street, Mullingar ☎ 044 47182 info@ilia.ie www.ilia.ie – Open 9am-6pm Mon-Sat)

Dairy Products

Moon Shine Dairy Farm

Mary and Gerry Kelly's Moonshine Dairy is a comet. A brilliant new blaze of culinary light from the deepest Midlands, Moonshine is an organic farm that has embraced bio-dynamic principles, and has begun to make a range of products that are stellar in their taste, their elegance, their completeness. They have a range of fresh cow's milk cheeses which are flavoured with various herbs, and they have yogurts and smoothies which are the most superlative dairy products. The presentation and packaging is as distinguished as the flavours these mighty products enjoy. Moonshine is a light you need in your life. (Lough Ennel, Ladestown, Mullingar ☎ 044-934 4631 www.kellysorganic.com)

Farmers' Market

Mullingar Farmers' Market

For some time now, we have been arguing that Westmeath needs to have two big food festivals each year. One is a Beef Festival, because there is no beef like the Westmeath beef. And the other is a Potato Festival, which should be held in Ballinagore, where wonderfully fine Record potatoes are grown. Well, maybe it will happen, for there are now farmer's markets enjoying great success in Mullingar and Athlone, and the recent formation of a Westmeath Food Group will surely be the final catalyst, for what else should food groups do except plan parties, festivals and all round fun? Imagine being able to taste twenty different dishes of Ballinagore potatoes, from

champ to Hassleback to gnocchi to colcannon? Or Mullingar beef cooked thirty different ways, from barbecued to Thai beef salad to rib roast on the bone to beef and Guinness pie? And the great champions of Westmeath food, folk such as Ann Hammill who sells her superlative produce at the markets, or folk like Paddy Keogh of Wines Direct who have quietly championed Westmeath for years, would be honorary patrons, and active participants. And when Roger and Pat O'Brien bring the Ballinagore spuds to the market after the harvest, that will be the time to let the celebrations begin. (The Fairgreen, Mullingar 10.30am-2.30pm, Sun)

Restaurant

Oscar's

Oscar's is an enormously popular local restaurant, which serves popular dishes but makes sure to cook them with lots of care and lots of flair, so it's no wonder its such a local hero. (21 Oliver Plunkett Street, Mullingar ☎ 044-934 4909 – Open 6pm-9.30pm Mon-Thu, 6pm-10pm Fri & Sat, 12.30pm-2.15pm, 6pm-8.15pm Sun)

Restaurant

Saagar Indian Restaurant

The original of the small chain of Saagar Indian restaurants, established in 1992 and going as strong as ever. (2 Dublin Bridge, Mullingar ☎ 044-40911
info@saagarindianrestaurants.com
www.saagarindianrestaurants.com – Open 5.30pm-11.30pm Mon-Sun)

Butcher

C. R. Tormey & Sons

If you want to understand what the expression "Beef to the heel, like a Mullingar heifer" means, you need only go to James Tormey's butcher's shop and ask for a rib of beef on the bone. Now, take it home and cook it, which is easy as this meat and this cut requires almost no intervention from the cook. Now, taste that sweetness, that herbaceous sweetness, that grassy sweetness. So, now you understand the phrase, and now you understand that there is no other beef quite like this. By the way, everything Mr Tormey sells at this sparkling shop is just as good. (Harbour Place, Mullingar ☎ 044-45433 – Open 8am-6pm Mon-Sat, 'till 8.30pm on Thur & Fri)

Wine Importer

Wines Direct

Paddy Keogh's wine shop at his wine warehouse has been open for nigh-on three years now, retailing the excellent wines which this hugely energetic merchant criss-crosses the global wine world to discover and bring back home. We like all the home-made pictures of the wine producers with whom Paddy deals, the little producers, the curious families, the odds and sods of the specialist wine world whose vintages and bottles have wound up here in Irish-town, and who have helped to make the reputation of this excellent wine business. When he isn't championing his wine makers, Mr Keogh is also one of the best champions Westmeath's food culture ever had, something he does quietly and effectively. (Irishtown, Mullingar ☎ 1890-579 579 shop@winesdirect.ie www.winesdirect.ie)

Rathowen

Fish Smoker

Corry Lane

John Rogan catches his own eels in Lough Owel before he smokes them. His salmon comes from Clare Island, and he uses beech wood for the smoking. He also smokes trout and mack-erel. He is a countryman character, very attuned to his ingredients, and there is an air of woodsmanship to the Corry Lane fish, which may come from its utterly splendid remoteness. We have visited the smokehouse, but we would be hard pressed to tell you where on earth it is. This rustic, wild element is the grace note of this fine range of smoked fish. (Rathowen ☎ 043-76264 corrylanesmoked@eircom.net)

County Wexford

Bridgestown

Apple Juice

● Ballycross Apple Farm

The Von Englebrechten family make some very fine juices indeed. Hand-picked, traditionally pressed, with a range of single varietal juices at the fore of the range – the sweet Elstar, the dry Bramley, the balanced Jonagold – these are pure, invigorating juices. We also like the richness of the apple and blackcurrant, and the healthful charge of the apple and carrot. Classic drinks that embody good health and good eating and drinking. (Bridgestown ☎ 053-35160 Farmshop open Aug-Feb, 2pm-6pm Sat & Sun)

Bunclody

Home Bakery

● Sugar and Spice

Mary Murphy's sweet little home bakery, up at the top end of the town past all the pharmacies, is of a type which has become all-too-rare in modern Ireland. It's simple and compact, and rather fine. (Main Street, Bunclody ☎ 053-937 6388 sugar_spice@eircom.net - Open 8.15am-6pm Mon-Fri, 8.15am-5pm Sat)

Campile

Farmers' Market

● Dunbrody Abbey Market

The Sunday market at Dunbrody operates in conjunction with the cookery school. (Dunbrody Abbey Cooking and Visitor Centre, Sunday noon-2.30pm)

Cooking Centre

● Dunbrody Cooking Centre

Pierce McAuliffe's cookery school pre-dated the current rush of private, chef-driven, hands-on tuition centres, and has been teaching happy skills to happy pupils from all walks of life for a happy number of years. (Dunbrody, Campile ☎ 051-388933 www.cookingireland.com)

Carne

Seafood Bar

The Lobster Pot Seafood Bar

The Lobster Pot is just about as atmospheric a bar and restaurant as you will find in Ireland. Even if you arrive here on a day when the sun of the sunny south-east isn't shining – okay, so it was blowing a gale when we were last here – you soon forget about the outside storms from the second you walk into this warren of cosily lit rooms, bedecked with memorabilia, and settle into a cosy settle. The day's specials – pan-fried prawn tails in their shells; deep-fried whitebait with tartare – are often great choices, but the standard menu items such as an excellent chowder are delivered with sharp attention to detail. The gleam factor is exemplary, and getting a table during the season is the only hassle in this fab pub. (Carne ☎ 053-31110 – Bar open noon-8.45pm Mon-Sun. À la Carte Restaurant menu 6pm-9pm Tue-Sat & 12.30pm-8.30pm Sun. In winter closes 7.30pm on Sun)

Duncannon

Restaurant and Accommodation

Aldridge Lodge

Aldridge Lodge has attracted lots of attention since opening, but it is still early days yet in terms of this ambitious operation acquiring a distinct culinary signature. Service is friendly, the room is pleasant and value for money is very keen. (Duncannon ☎ 051-389116 info@aldridgelodge.com www.aldridgelodge.com – Open 6.30pm-9.30pm Tue-Sat, 5pm-9.30pm Sun)

Restaurant

Sqigl

Cindy Roche's bistro is consistent, and charming. The restaurant is in a barn behind her folks' bar, and it's a bright, feminine space, which has been putting out happy food for several years now. The fish cookery is always a particular signature, but the modern influences that the kitchen is drawing in from Asia and the Middle East work very well with local foods. Value for money is extremely keen and this is one of those friendly, local places every town and village needs. (Quay Road, Duncannon ☎ 051-389700 sqigl2003@eircom.net – Open 7pm-9pm Tue-Sat)

Enniscorthy

Country House

● Ballinkeele House

John and Margaret Maher's fine old country house enjoys stellar standards of housekeeping and some very apt country cooking, so your base for the opera festival is in the bag. (Enniscorthy ☎ 053-913 8105 ✉ john@ballinkeele.ie 🖱 www.ballinkeele.ie – Open Feb-end Oct)

Farmhouse Cheese

● Carrigbyrne Farmhouse Cheese

Paddy Berridge and his family have been making the popular Carrigbyrne cheeses for nearly a quarter of a century now, but even with such a well-established range – St Killian; St Brendan; Emerald Irish brie – they are still experimenting with new ideas, working on a vacherin-style cheese, testing a mini St Killian. It is wonderful to see this spirit of adventure and endeavour alive and well in such a classic cheese company. (Adamstown, Enniscorthy ☎ 053-924 0560 ✉ info@carrigbyrne.ie 🖱 www.carrigbyrne.ie)

Farmers' Market

● Enniscorthy Farmers' Market

In a delightful article in *The Irish Times* on how local producer Denis Shannon had navigated through his life, Mr Shannon was quoted as saying of his work in the local farmers' markets, "Things are improving all the time. If I could grow more I could sell it". That's the story of the Enniscorthy market after three years in existence, as it is for so many other markets. And it also shows how alternative folk such as Mr Shannon have thrived with these markets – he also sells at Wexford market on Fridays – attracted by their alternative way of doing things. Synergy, we think they call it. (Saturday 9am-2pm)

Restaurant

● Galo Chargrill

David Conroy's Galo Grill is pleasingly rough at the edges. A big menu lists the food in both English and Portuguese, the grilled fish dishes are the best bet, and they can turn out some really nice puds, Unpretentious, good value, great with a crowd. (19 Main Street, Enniscorthy ☎ 053-923 8077 – Open noon-3.15pm, 5.30pm-10pm Tue-Sat, noon-9pm Sun)

Yogurt

Killowen Yogurts

Nicholas Dunne's company makes very fine yogurts. They have a sherbetty sharpness that places them apart from mainstream dairy products, and the blending and integration of fruits into the yogurts is extremely well achieved. Their sharpness makes them a very good foil for savoury and Middle Eastern dishes. (The Beeches, Courtnacuddy, Enniscorthy ☎ 053-924 4819 ✉ killowenfoods@eircom.net)

Hotel and Spa

Monart

Liam Griffin's super-funky hotel and spa is the most significant arrival in Irish hospitality in yonks. Other spas in Ireland are getting it wrong, but here they are getting it right – the ambience, the pitch, the tenor of this luxurious adventure is just right, in terms of style, design, service and food. Monart makes you feel good – the ambition surely of every spa – but it actually manages to do that from the moment you drive in the gates to the moment you leave. The food is healthful, but only in the sense that it is based on good ingredients, and that such good cooking makes everyone happy, and happiness is healthfulness. A real winner, a true spa for the soul. (The Still, Enniscorthy ☎ 053-923 0999 🖱 www.monart.ie)

Country House

Salville House

A demure and pleasingly simple country house, which is home to some of the best country house cooking you will find, thanks to Gordon Parker's assured culinary skills. (Enniscorthy ☎ 053-923 5252 🖱 www.salvillehouse.com)

Restaurant

Via Veneto

Paolo Fresilli is President of the Italian Chef's Federation, and his own restaurant just off the main square is nondescript in the true Italian trattoria style, with a cute, authentic interior. Some of the cooking is rather generous with the cream – panzerotti with a porcini cream; veal a la dragoncello – but for the most part this is accessible Italian cooking, albeit a long way from the River Cafe, with a nice atmospheric room with staff who are genuinely friendly. (58 Weafer Street, Enniscorthy ☎ 053-923 6929 – Open 5.30pm-10pm Tue-Sat, 12.30pm-10pm Sun)

Gorey

Farmers' Market
Gorey Farmers' Market

The Gorey market takes place on Saturdays from 9am. (Gorey Community School, 9am, Sat)

Butcher
Tomas Kinsella

Down the town and in the midst of all the frock shops – Gorey has frock shops as other towns have pharmacies or hairdressers – Kinsella's is an impressive, classy butcher's shop, with expertly prepared and presented meats in a swish store. (4 Esmonde Street, Gorey ☎ 053-948 1863 – Open 8am-6pm Mon-Sat)

Butcher
Terry Redmond Butchers

Alan Redmond's prize-winning sausages are the main attraction in the simple, but always busy Redmond's butcher's shop. (John Street, Gorey ☎ 053-942 1344 – Open 9am-6pm Mon-Sat)

Kerlogue

Cookery School & Catering Service
Phelim Byrne

A new cookery school from local man Phelim Byrne is good news for Wexford. Mr Byrne offers a broad range of classes, and abets this new enterprise with a catering service, and with a range of prepared sauces and other foods. This is an ambitious project from a chap with lots of energy, experience and determination, and it deserves to become part of the south east's culinary culture. (Wexford Enterprise Centre, Strandfield Business Park, Kerlogue, Rosslare Road, Wexford ☎ 053-918 4995 info@phelimbyrne.ie www.phelimbyrne.ie)

Killinnick

Farm Shop
Karoo Farm Shop

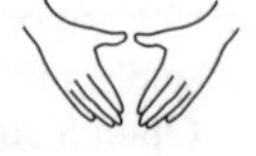

Mignon Fochessati's brilliant shop, in a lovely old mill building just behind the busy

Texaco station on the main Rosslare road, is a little jewel. Everything for sale here is well chosen, and an expert eye has both made the space and selected the contents – Ditty's biscuits, Stable Diet cereals and bars, Wicklow fine foods; Java Republic coffees; excellent local vegetables. The shop has something of the feel of a French country store – it's smart but relaxed, the notes detailing the sources of the foods are very hip, and with plans to introduce a range of South African wines from Mignon's homeland, it is clear that Karoo is just beginning. (Killinick ☎ 053-915 8585 info@karoo.ie – Open 9am-6pm Mon-Sat 11am-5pm Sun)

New Ross

Café & Wholefood Shop

● In A Nutshell

"If only every town could have somewhere like this". Visitors to New Ross who encounter the sparkling IAN tend to sigh like this when they discover this peach of a shop and café. The shop at the front of the store can only be described as an URRU for the South East, whilst Patsey Roger's food in the café attracts food lovers from the entire hinterland who cannot find anything to match the quality of food on offer here. This entire operation is pristine, and positively glows with energy. It doesn't matter what you choose, for everything in the café is blessed with care and professionalism, and In A Nutshell is a diamond. (18 South Street, New Ross ☎ 051-422777 inanutshell8@gmail.com – Cafe open 9am-5pm, Deli/ shop open 9am-6pm Tue-Sat)

Farmers' Market

● New Ross Farmers' Market

The New Ross market takes place in Conduit Lane on Saturdays from 9am.

Farm Produce

● Tinnock Farm Produce

Peggy Gaffney and John Murphy are the hardest working farmers in the south east. As well as farming, they sell their products – country butter; buttermilk; lamb; beef; eggs, and the magnificent chickens reared by their neighbour Mary Regan – at an incredible number of markets each week:

Enniscorthy; Carrick-on-Suir; New Ross; Wexford; Kilkenny and Dun Laoghaire are each serviced each week, a daunting work rate. Mr Murphy seems to take it all in his stride; every time we join the queue to buy produce he is smiling and helpful, and we love the fact that he has cuts like breast of lamb and boned and rolled shoulder of lamb for sale at keen prices. Fantastic stuff. (Tinnock, Campile, New Ross ☎ 087-417 0506/087-220 3300)

Rosslare

Resort Hotel

Kelly's Resort Hotel

In a newspaper interview recently, just after he had picked up yet another gong for his hotelier's skills in running the family hotel, Bill Kelly noted that "The globalisation of the hotel business means a lot of the hotel products, whether you go to New York or Dublin, end up looking the same. That offers us the opportunity to give a unique product and service to customers". That's the Kelly's mantra: uniqueness, and service. Mr Kelly has been at the helm of the hotel for twenty years now, the fourth-generation of his family to head this shrine to relaxation, aesthetics and good taste. Twenty years on, and he seems keener than ever for new challenges, constantly tweaking the design, liaising with architects and artists on the new spa, all with a view to improving, improving, improving. There is no other hotel like Kelly's, and Bill Kelly's personal achievement over two decades of success is deserving of a book. (Rosslare ☎ 053-913 2114 info@kellys.ie www.kellys.ie – Closed mid Dec-late Feb)

Restaurant

La Marine

Eugene Callaghan is one of Ireland's greatest chefs, and for ten years now he has been showing in La Marine what a mature, relaxed cook at the peak of his game can achieve. Of all the chefs who came out of the great Roscoff diaspora in the early 1990's, Mr Callaghan was always the most understated and, reading his menus, you get little or no suggestion of the magic he can place on a plate. If there is a signature to his work, it is a love of sweetness, the sun-kissed Mediterranean style seen in dishes such as tomato and fennel soup, or duck confit with orange, or rack of lamb with courgettes and mint, or cod marseillaise with garlic aïoli. Superb food, a thunderously lively room, and one of the great wine lists. (Rosslare ☎ 053-913 2114 ✉ info@kellys.ie 🖱 www.kellys.ie – Open 12.30pm-2.15pm, 6.30pm-9.30pm Mon-Sun. Closed mid Dec-late Feb)

Wexford

Restaurant

● La Dolce Vita

Agreement is rare amongst Ireland's food lovers, but no one will bet against the fact that Roberto Pons produces the best Italian cooking in the country. He does it in the most logical way: a series of dishes are made ready for noon each day when the punters turn up to grab a table. Menus are handed out ten minutes later, when the early birds order and the latecomers start a queue, and then the food arrives – antipasto of cured meats with courgettes; squid stew with tomatoes, peas and herbs; tuna with fagioli, great tiramisu, expert coffees. "I'd queue up to eat this food any time" is what the locals and visitors say, and La Dolce Vita showcases a chef who is right in his element, and on top of his game. (6-7 Trimmer's Lane, Selskar, Wexford ☎ 053-917 0806 – Open 9am-5.30pm Mon-Sat, lunch served noon-4pm)

Restaurant

● Forde's Restaurant

Liam Forde is a Wexford veteran at this stage of his career, but he remains one heck of a good cook, and if his culinary style isn't contemporary, it is nevertheless classic and ageless. The really sharp fish and shellfish cookery best shows a kitchen that knows how to handle ingredients – lobster is perfectly cooked; a trio of monkfish, scallops and tiger prawns is perfection, two dishes that go perfectly with their signature spring roll of potato. The room gleams, staff are friendly and value for money is very keen. A great local restaurant. (The Crescent, Wexford ☎ 053-23832 – Open 6pm-9.45pm Mon-Sun, 12.30pm-5pm Sun)

Butcher

● T Furlong & Sons

"Est. 1621" it says on the wall of Furlong's, which might sound like a joke, except it isn't. The family have been in the town for almost four centuries, and moved to the Bull Ring as long ago as 1993. It is a modern butchers shop, with excellent meats and a large deli-counter section with a great range of prepared foods including many varieties of their own cooked meats. (The Bullring ☎ 053-912 2885 – Open 9am-6pm Mon-Thu, 9am-6.30pm Fri)

Wine Merchant & Delicatessen

● Greenacres

"An amazing achievement", "Jawdropping". "Mies van der Rohe comes to town". It's no mean feat to take an old solicitor's office and transform it into a state-of-the-art wine shop with an art gallery, but that is just what James and Paula O'Connor have done in Selskar. Greenacres is glam, a gorgeous space for contemporary art, both in the bottles and on the walls. Mr O'Connor is rare in offering a serious en primeur offer each year through the shop, en primeur usually being the reserve of the bigger wine merchants, and he supplements these blockbuster wines with lots of good quaffers and a strong mid-price range. Should your boat come in, then you will find that bottle of Chateau Petrus here, and there are lots of good paintings calling out for your generosity. (Selskar, Wexford ☎ 053-912 2975 info@greenacres.ie www.greenacres.ie – Open 9.30am-6pm Mon-Sat)

Local Speciality
CRAB

Townhouse

● McMenamin's Townhouse

Seamus and Kay McMenamin have a new address on Glena Terrace, and have spent months primping and perfecting their four rooms. Great housekeeping, great hospitality, and one of the very best breakfasts you can enjoy anywhere in Ireland. (6 Glena Terrace, Spawell Road, Wexford ☎ 053-924 6442
info@wexford-bedandbreakfast.com
www.wexford-bedandbreakfast.com)

Farmers' Market

● Wexford Farmers' Market

The Friday Wexford farmers' market is held at the Mailin Street Car Park. (Mailin Street Car Park, from 9am, Fri)

Yoletown

Food Producer

● Stable Diet Foods

Katherine Carroll and Vincent Power's company began by accident, when Ms Carroll first made a few malt house scones and some carrot cakes for a local wholefood shop, Only Natural. News of the goodness and trueness of her baking spread, and Stable Diet was quietly born. Today, the company has more than 25 employees, and their baking products and biscuits, their cereals and crumbles, their fab porridge, are in stores all over the country. Yet the ethos remains the same, even if the scale has changed. Stable Diet make wholesome products, and they make them carefully – they mind them. They are a medium-sized company, but they think like artisans, quietly innovating, keeping in contact with customers from the early days, meticulously attending to quality. Everything has changed: nothing has changed, and that's the way it should be. (Yoletown, Broadway ☎ 053-913 1287)

"By the second half of the nineteenth century soda bread had gained widespread popularity throughout the country. This may in part be attributed to the fact that when soda is combined with sour milk or buttermilk it produces a very light and palatable leavened wheat bread that could be successfully produced in a domestic setting."

REGINA SEXTON AND CATHAL COWAN
IRELAND'S TRADITIONAL FOODS

County Wicklow

Arklow

Bakery

The Stone Oven Bakery

It's been more than twenty years now since Egon and Liane Friedrich moved to Arklow from Cologne, transforming their hobby of baking into a profession and, in the process, creating one of the first artisan bakeries in the entire country. The Friedrichs don't get enough kudos for their pioneering baking, but then their metier has always been just to get on with it, and to make great breads, many of which are utterly distinctive, such as Sailor's Bribe – a spelt bread with cranberries, prunes, dates, figs, brazil nuts, seeds, almonds, hazelnuts and a rye dough starter – and the unique Fisherman's Brunch, which uses dilisk on a rye sourdough and organic spelt base. What's with all these sailors and fisherman? Yes, Mr Friedrich is a very keen sailor. (65 Main Street, Lr, Arklow ☎ 0402-39418 bakery@stoneoven.com www.stoneoven.com – Open 10am-4pm Mon-Sat. Closed Wed)

Farmhouse Cheese

Wicklow Farmhouse Cheese

John Hempenstall's Wicklow Blue brie-style farmhouse cheese has given birth to a sister cheese, the blue-free Wicklow Baun. They pasteurise the milk of their own herd to make these deliciously creamy, seductive cheeses, and have recently begun to make goat's milk cheeses using a local goat's milk. The cheeses are beautifully consistent and pleasing. (Curranstown, Arklow ☎ 0402-91713 wfcheese@eircom.net)

Ashford

Country House & Cookery School

Ballyknocken House

Catherine Fulvio is the star of County Wicklow cooking and hospitality. Like the best people in the business, she walks it and she talks it, and does both brilliantly. Vitally for her county, she thinks first and foremost about her own neck of the woods, something that the Cork food establishment have always done, and which has made them so successful. But, Mrs Fulvio's true importance still lies mainly in her work as teacher and hostess in Ballyknocken House, where she puts into action what she preaches: the best local foods, cooked with skill and TLC, served with simplicity and warmth – the memory of a bowl of turnip and brown bread soup eaten here years ago has never faded, such was its potent deliciousness. And in her cookery classes, she proves herself to be a masterly communicator – give this woman a television series! (Glenealy, Ashford ☎ 0404-44627 info@ballyknocken.com www.ballyknocken.com)

Wicklow

Wine Shop

Caprani

Most folk bypass Ashford nowadays, but if you are searching for a good bottle of wine, then the smart Caprani wine shop in the hotel is well worth the detour into the village to pick up something nice. (Ashford ☎ 0404-40682 – Open 10.30am-10pm Mon-Sat, 12.30pm-10pm Sun)

Cafe and Gardens

Mount Usher Garden Cafe

"There will be no radical change", says Simon Pratt of the Avoca empire, as he takes charge at the celebrated Mount Usher gardens, taking over from Madelaine Jay, who has brought Mount Usher to fame over the last twenty five years, preserving these fabulous gardens where the Walpole brothers created an ode to the gardening theories of William Robinson. Mr Pratt will be refurbishing the tea rooms to create a garden café, and there are plans for a bakery and an organic vegetable shop, practical complements to this idyllic oasis. (☎ 0404-40116 info@mountushergardens.ie www.mountushergardens.ie – Open 10am-6pm Mon-Sun)

Aughrim

Farmers' Market

Aughrim Farmers' Market

Beautiful Aughrim plays host to a busy market each Saturday, and look out especially for the produce of Gold River farm, normally the preserve of chefs, but available here to ordinary decent food lovers, and get yourself a big strawberry sorbet from Three Wells Ice Cream. (The Pavilion, Aughrim, Saturday 11am-2pm)

Organic Farm

Gold River Farm

The organic farming families of Wicklow are legendary – the Healys, the Langes, the Johnstons, the Crockers – and the Pierce and Winterbotham families of Gold River Farm are key practitioners of this organic aristocracy. Basically, they have revolutionised the way in which Dublin's leading chefs source and use organic vegetables and salads. Chefs call Gold River in the evening, vegetables and salads are dug in the morning, and delivered straight away. This short supply-chain, from farm to fork in less than one day, has given leading Dublin restaurants a new attitude towards – and a new respect for – vegetables and salad leaves. And what Alan Pierce and Mark Winterbotham produce is jaw-droppingly brilliant: the vigour, the beauty, the sheer aesthetic and organoleptic delight of their produce is stunning: every simple carrot or leaf calls out to be immortalised in a still life painting. Quiet revolutionaries. (The Sycamores, Tinakilly, Aughrim ☎ 0402-36426 goldriver@eircom.net)

Ice Cream

Three Wells Farmhouse Ice Cream

Enda and Tracey Byrne's farmhouse ice cream operation uses the milk and cream of their own herd. The Byrnes have taken advantage of the know-how of the Dutch company Farm House Ice Cream to create and develop their recipes, and this is a hugely promising dairy venture. (Three Wells, Aughrim ☎ 0402-36570
info@threewellsdairy.com
www.threewellsdairy.com)

Baltinglass

Baking

Ballyhubbock Home Foods

Olive Finlay bakes bread and scones, makes tarts and cakes, and sells these lovely foods in local shops as well as at the Athy farmer's market. (Stratford-on-Slaney, Baltinglass ☎ 045-404706)

Confectionery

Wicklow Fine Foods

Jim and Mary Healy's WFF company produces chocolates – sold under the Chocolate Garden of Ireland label – very fine chocolate spreads, as well as some particularly delicious waffles and biscuits. You can buy on-line and at their store in Baltinglass, whilst the products are also stocked by good delis. (Lathaleere, Baltinglass ☎ 059-648 1999 info@wicklowfinefoods.com www.wicklowfinefoods.com)

Wicklow

Blessington

Ice Cream

Goldenhill Fresh Farmhouse Ice Cream

"We know where our cows go at night and we know each one by name." Well, that is quite a marketing slogan for an ice cream company, and its the promise of their own milk and cream from their own cows that gives Damien and Aoife Clarke's Goldenhill ice cream its artisan character. (Goldenhill Farm, Golden Hill, Manor Kilbride, Blessington ☎ 01-458 2017/086-364 0135 info@goldenhill.ie www.goldenhill.ie)

Café

Grangecon Café

Richard and Jenny Street produce the most delicious food. What is so interesting about Grangecon, the simplest little café you could imagine, is that they lavish their dogma of deliciousness on the simplest foods – sausage rolls; shepherd's pie; red pepper and goat's cheese tart; rhubarb tart; brown bread. No bourgeois ingredients. No snobbery. Just an elemental, direct, disarming deliciousness that is nothing less than inspiring. They work with a crew of locals who have worked with them for years, and together they accomplish something magical: simple deliciousness. (Tullow Road, Blessington ☎ 045-857892 grangeconcafe@eircom.net – Open 9am-5.30pm Tue-Sat, 'till 4pm Mon)

Health Food Store

Harvest Fare Health Food Shop

Mary Davis has been doing the good thing in HF for eight years now, sourcing local foods for the blossoming population of Blessington. Vitally, Mary talks about being "committed to providing excellent food in our community", which makes Harvest Fare the definition of a vital community shop. (Main Street, Blessington ☎ 045-891636 harvestfare@eircom.net – Open 10am-6pm Mon-Sat, 'till 5pm Sat)

Bray

Farmers' Market

Bray Farmers' Market

A Coco market organised by the dynamic Jackie Spillane, the Heritage Centre is the place to be on Saturday morning to get the good stuff from great producers. (Bray Heritage Centre, Main Street, Bray, Sat, 10am-2pm)

Coffee and Tea Merchant

Clive McCabe & Co

You find them in good stores and delis here, there and everywhere, the golden bags of Clive McCabe's coffees, the green bags of his speciality blend teas. At a time when we have gone coffee roasting and tea sourcing crazy, we should remember the steadfast work of this pioneer, who was creating bespoke blends when today's coffee kids were in short trousers. Lovely work, always understated, truly classy. (Unit 56, Newtownmountkennedy Business Enterprise Centre ☎ 01-287-5835)

Yogurts and Soft Cheeses

Old MacDonnell's Farm

The McDonnell family's very fine yogurts and fresh cheeses are excellent dairy products, reflecting the high-quality milk that comes from their farm. (Glen of the Downs, Bray ☎ 01-282 8992
oldmacdonnellsfarm@eircom.net)

Brittas

Cookery and Gardening Courses

Hunting Brook Gardens

Jimi Blake was the man who transformed the Airfield gardens in Dublin over a ten-year period, and he has now moved south to Hunting Brook to establish another destination for garden lovers. And for food lovers, for he has been running one-off courses with luminary chefs such as Denis Cotter, Troy Maguire and Ben Gorman. Sumptuous gardens, good grub: sounds cool to us. (Hunting Brook, Lamb Hill, Blessington ☎ 01-458 3972 jimi@huntingbrook.com www.huntingbrook.com)

Delgany

Butcher

Farrelly's Butchers

The Farrelly brothers archetypal butcher's shop in little Delgany is a food lover's jewel. Their knowledge of meat and their respect for preparing it to exacting standards means that whatever you buy in here is top-class. They don't use mechanisation, preferring instead to prepare meat with exemplary knife skills, and this craftsman's utility blesses everything they sell. Fantastic. (Main Street, Delgany ☎ 01-287 4211 – Open 9am-6pm Mon-Sat. Closed for lunch 1pm-2pm Mon-Fri)

Donard

Organic Vegetables and Herbs

Castleruddery Organic Farm

Dominic and Hilda have been farming organically at Castleruddery, ever since we wrote our first book back in 1989, taking good advantage of the richness of Wicklow soils to produce exemplary foods. You can buy them from the farm shop on Thursdays and Fridays, and at the busy Naas farmers' market on Saturday. (Donard ☎ 045-404925 casorg@eircom.net – Farmshop open Thur & Fri)

"The aromas from the kitchens of our childhood remain when many other things are forgotten."

THEODORA FITZGIBBON

Wicklow

Enniskerry

Café

Avoca Powerscourt Terrace Café

The mighty Avoca has one of its best locations in the grand, dreamy Powerscourt. Lunch on the terrace here is some sort of wonderful, one of the great Irish pastoral pleasures. We hear that Gordon Ramsay is going to be taking up the kitchen reins in the Ritz-Carlton Powerscourt hotel. Hope he's checked out the competition. (Powerscourt House, Enniskerry ☎ 01-204 6070 ✉ info@avoca.ie 🖱 www.avoca.ie – Open 9.30am-5.30pm Mon-Sun)

Glenealy

Organic Lamb, Poultry & Eggs

Crocker's Organic Farm

"We moved to Wicklow in 1994 to seek a quiet life", says Gary Crocker. More than a decade of organic farming later and, well how are things going, Gary? "Life is hectic", says Mr Crocker. Oh well. The Crockers produce lamb, chickens, eggs, turkeys, beef and potatoes, and produce superb examples of all those foods, so life was never going to be terribly sedate, not with all those food lovers clamouring for produce of this stellar standard. When they aren't producing lovely food, Gary and Martha are selling from the farm or from local farmers' markets, to the delight of happy customers who have no intention of letting them get close to that quiet life any time soon. Oh well. (Ballydowling Farm, Glenealy ☎ 0404-44854 ✉ crockerorganics@eircom.net)

Greystones

Restaurant

Chakra by Jaipur

Sunil Ghai's cooking in Chakra, a spin-off from the popular Jaipur chain of Indian restaurants in Dublin, has been winning much critical and popular acclaim, with its modernist take on classical Indian culinary conventions. (1st Floor, Meridian Point, Church Road, Greystones ☎ 01-201 7222 ✉ info@chakra.ie 🖱 www.jaipur.ie – Open 5.30pm-11pm Mon-Sun)

Farmers' Market

Greystones Farmers' Market

One of Sean McArdle's farmers' markets, in blossoming Greystones. (Meridian Point Shopping Centre www.irishfarmersmarkets.ie – Open Sat, 10am-4pm)

Cafe & Deli

The Happy Pear

Steve and Dave Flynn are the happy pair of twin brothers behind The Happy Pear, and since their beginning as a fruit and vegetable shop into their development as a self-service restaurant, this duo has had a steady focus: vegetarian foods, great juice combos, local foods, celebrating seasonal ingredients, having fun. The HP is a key community café in its Slow Food ethos, its green politics, and its mischievously good foods. More, please. (Westview House, Main Street, Greystones ☎ 01-287 3655 www.thehappypear.ie)

Restaurant and Wine Bar Bistro

The Hungry Monk

Pat and Sylvia Keown will rack up twenty years of service to the food lovers of Greystones in 2008, and what changes they have seen since then, both in terms of their home town, and in terms of how Irish people use restaurants. They have navigated their way through two decades with good humour, good food and, in particular, good wines, for the wine list is outstanding, and is rare in having many older vintages. The food in the wine bar is simple – smokies; Thai beef salad, hamburger with gherkins – and more formal upstairs – trout terrine; Wicklow lamb with minted gravy; roast duck with star anise; pork with calvados sauce. (Church Road, Greystones ☎ 01-287 5759 hungrymonk@eircom.net www.thehungrymonk.ie – Restaurant open 6.30pm-11pm Wed-Sat, 12.30pm-8pm Sun. Wine Bar Bistro open 5pm-11pm Mon-Sat, 4pm-9pm Sun)

Food To Go

Indian Spice Co.

Ronan Fleming's wonderful take-away produces some of the most echt Indian cooking you can find, quite a surprise coming from a white guy, but no real surprise when you speak to this most auto-didactic of cooks. So much Indian restaurant food aspires to be posh, but Mr Fleming loves the street food style of Asian cooking, he loves the simplicity of good vegetarian cooking, he love dishes like railway lamb and chicken tikka and punjabi curries. Delightful, and terrific value. (Church Road, Glendalough ☎ 01-201 0868 – Open 5pm-10pm Mon-Thur, 5pm-10.45pm Fri & Sat, 4pm-10.15pm Sun)

Fishmonger

● Moran's Fish Shop

Wicklow's champion fish shop is a vital address in the county for good wet fish and shellfish. Suzanne O'Keefe also stocks very fine wild Wicklow game, when in season. (Latouche Place, Greystones ☎ 01-287 6327 – Open 8.30am-5.30pm Tue-Sat)

Wholefood Shop

● Nature's Gold

Nature's Gold goes all the way back to the 1970's, when wholefood stores were rare as could be. Today, Brod Kearon's shop continues to provide a vital service, with a great range of organics and essential wholefoods. (Killincarrig Road, Greystones ☎ 01-287 6301 natgold@iol.ie – Open 9am-6pm Mon-Sat)

Café

● The Three Q's

There aren't too many trios of brothers working together in kitchens – though the three McCoy brothers, Tom, Peter and Eugene, were well-known in England back in the late 1970's, and there are three Doyle brothers working in different functions in the Brook Lodge Inn at Macreddin – but in The Three Q's we have Brian, Paul and Colin Quinn firing out the good stuff. The menus range all over the world for influences, and one senses a kitchen that gets a big kick out of finding and fiddling with new ideas. Good value, and there is a triple-layer of ambition at work here. (Gweedore Church Road, Greystones ☎ 01-287 5477 – Open noon-4pm Tue-Fri, 6pm-10pm Tue-Sat, Brunch 9am-3pm Sat & Sun)

Local Specialities

ORGANIC VEGETABLES
ORGANIC HERBS AND SALADS
WILD GAME

"Food is about flavour."

DERRY CLARKE

Kilmacanogue

Café

Avoca

With new Avocas in Rathcoole and at Ashford, the Pratt family's dynamic business seems to have entered a new phase of rapid growth. In other companies, such a phase would entail dilution of the central core and principles of their work. But Simon Pratt and his team have always shown that they can grow without compromise. They established this concept early on: if you cook for large numbers of people, you could still cook, you didn't have to bow down and compromise with 'catering'. Quality and volume are not enemies: they are simply a challenge. And so, Avoca cook beautiful food, and serve it in beautiful stores. They are a global luxury brand to rank alongside Valrhona chocolate, Illy coffee, Krug champagne. They have a unique aesthetic, and we are all enriched by it. (Kilmacanogue ☎ 01-286 7466 info@avoca.ie www.avoca.ie – Open 9.30am-5.30pm Mon-Sun)

Chutneys & Relishes

Janet's Country Fayre

You can't stop Janet Drew. A new kitchen in Kilcoole is now the centre for her state-of-the-art creations in chutney-land. She has teamed up with Odaios foods to assist distribution. With James McGough of Oughterard she has created a new Fig & Apricot Chutney to pair with the legendary Connemara air-dried lamb, a perfect example of the sweet music artisan producers can make when working together. She is developing a range to be sold via the Craft Butchers shops throughout the country "and I've a few more ideas up my sleeve yet to come to fruition". Phew! Endlessly inventive and creative, Janet's Country Fayre is one of the most radical of Ireland's artisan companies, and any time a jar of those relishes, ketchups, pestos and sauces graces your table, things just got to taste a whole lot better. (Copsewood Farm, KIlmacanogue ☎ 01-204 1957 janet@janetscountryfayre.com www.janetscountryfayre.com)

Kilpedder

Organic Shop & Café

Marc Michel Organic Life Shop & Café

"With his tight haircut, sandy-brown fatigues, Yasser Arafat-style scarf, and self-aware strut, he could easily pass for a French Foreign Legionnaire who fell to earth with the wrong co-ordinates". Paul O'Doherty's memorable description of the dashing Marc Michel gets the man just right: Mr Michel dances to the beat of a different drum, and has always done so, in his work as organic farmer and restaurateur. His restaurant is an old greenhouse, with an old olive tree in the centre. "Slow Food fast" is what they do, show casing the superb local meats of Wicklow along with their own vegetables and fruit. It's like the café that fell to earth, fully-formed, and fully-different to what any-one else is doing. (Kilpedder ☎ 01-201 1882 – Shop open 10am-5pm Tue-Sat, Cafe noon-4pm Tue-Sun)

Kiltegan

Bio-Dynamic Produce

Penny & Udo Lange

Penny and Udo Lange have been selling veg-etables since 1987. Twenty years a-growing, twenty years of agricultural – and intellec-tual – pioneering, twenty years of creating goodness, sustainable, significant goodness. The Langes' work has shown how alternatives can exist, in every way: in agriculture, in distribution, in retailing, in philosophy. They have brought art to agriculture, and enriched the lives of everyone who has bought from them over the twenty years. They are the philosopher king and queen of Irish agriculture. (Ballinroan House, Kiltegan ☎ 059-647 3278)

Organic Farmer

Denis Healy's Organic Delights

Twelve hard working enthusiasts work with Denis Healy on his 20 acres, and work with him in the myriad markets he services in Dublin and Wicklow and elsewhere, bringing hamburg parsley, and yellow carrots, and scorzonera and lamb's tongue lettuce and Connolly's organic eggs to the food lovers of the east coast. Mr Healy's achievement is mighty. More than anyone else he has identified farmer's markets with organic produce, and in so doing he has created a paradigm shift in the way in which people think about organics. He has succeeded in making organics the mainstream of the market culture, an incredible achievement. And he works harder than ever, with his free-form, free-rolling bunch of helpers, woofers, family and friends. Bohemianism and business mix elegantly in these Organic Delights. (Talbotstown Lower, Kiltegan ☎ 059-647 3193 info@organicdellights.ie www.organicdelights.ie)

Macreddin

Country Hotel

● The Brook Lodge Inn & Strawberry Tree Restaurant

Eight years on since its opening in 1999, and the Brook Lodge has shifted up a gear, or maybe two. Our last couple of visits have shown that Evan Doyle's grand design has finally been sharply brought to focus, with a fabulous crew working to achieve the holistic totality that this inspired restaurateur has been aiming for. The compass of the Lodge, from its template of wild and organic food, through the spa, the restaurant, the market, the shops and most recently with their radical concept of the big table, is daunting to consider, yet this team are right on top of it, and right on top of their game. The kitchen is producing food that seems utterly of itself – home-smoked salmon; home-smoked beef; partridge; monkfish with leeks and hollandaise; roast duck with cabbage stew; slow-roasted lamb with kohl-rabi; red gurnard with fennel. Wild foods, organic foods, sublime foods, and the glam romance of the dining room, and of the new extension, makes everyone feel like they are an icon. The book needs to be written about how the Doyle brothers took a few green fields and created this oasis of hospitality, thanks to a vision of food and cooking that Evan Doyle first carved out back in 1985 when he opened his first restaurant way out west in Clifden. (Brook Lodge Inn, Macreddin ☎ 0402-36444 brooklodge@macreddin.ie www.brooklodge.com – Strawberry Tree Restaurant open 7pm-9.30pm Mon-Sat, 1pm-3.30pm Sun)

Organic Market

Macreddin Village Organic Market

You just can't beat the atmosphere at the monthly Macreddin market. With families eating, and kids playing on the lawn, music playing, shoppers strolling, a throng of sellers and exhibitors, the sun shining (of course!), it is a mighty jamboree of good times and great foods. (The Brook Lodge, Macreddin Village. 1st Sun of each month from Mar-Oct, 1.30pm-6.30pm
www.brooklodge.com)

Organic Bakery, Smoked Foods, Preserves

The Store Rooms

The Store Rooms at the Brook Lodge offer an organic bakery, a range of smoked foods from their smokehouse and lots of good pantry foods created with wild and organic ingredients. (The Brook Lodge, Macreddin Village
☎ 0402-36444 brooklodge@macreddin.ie
www.brooklodge.com)

Newcastle

Country Market

North Wicklow Country Market

The excellent North Wicklow Country Market has had a change of venue, and now takes place every Saturday morning from 11am in the Newcastle Community Centre. Lots of good local foods, and a lovely, community atmosphere. (Newcastle Community Centre, Newcastle, Saturdays 10.30am-12.30pm)

Farm Shop

Sweetbank Farm

David and Debbie Johnston are another pioneering pair of Wicklow producers. They have led the way in creating an excellent farm shop as a store front for their beautiful foods, a feature of empowered agriculture that is still all-too-rare in Ireland. And they have shown how one can attract an audience, thanks to top-class produce, in the case of Sweetbank that is their wonderful seasonal fruits and juices, and their spring lamb and Angus beef. They also support other local producers by selling their foods in order to supplement their own range. Brilliant. (Tiglin, Newcastle ☎ 01-281 9280/086-173 0497
sweetbankfarm@iolfree.ie www.sweetbankfarm.ie)

Rathdrum

Butcher

● Synnott's

Synnott's is always one of our stops when we find ourselves touring through Wicklow. John and Richard do the good thing, the old way, so don't be worried by the simple style of the shop, just pay attention to that superb beef, which is as good as it gets. (Rathdrum ☎ 0404-46132 – Open 8.30am-6pm Mon-Sat)

Game Producer

● Wild Irish Game Ltd

Ross Lewis of Chapter One restaurant cooked a soup of pheasant and chestnut, for a Bridgestone dinner, using Michael Healy's superb game, and the dish was a pure sensation. Aside from pheasant, Mr Healy sources rabbit, grouse, partridge, woodcock, wild duck, pigeon and venison, and it is no exaggeration to say that encountering these primal tastes and textures can have a dramatic impact on how you view food ingredients, for the savour of wild game is narcotic in its taste encompass. (Glenmalure, Rathdrum ☎ 0404-46773 wigltd@eircom.net)

Rathnew

Bakery

● Country Lane Bakery

A distinctive brown soda bread is their signature of Adrian Murray's bakery, but there are lots of other nice breads, scones, tarts and sweet cakes in the range. Look out for them in good shops and at local farmers' markets. (6 Charvey Lane, Rathnew ☎ 0404-20707 countrylanebakery@eircom.net)

Roundwood

Country Inn

● The Roundwood Inn

Paul Taube's cooking in Jurgen and Aine Schwalm's ever-popular inn is good and gutsy, everything from Irish stew to goulash, just the thing after a big hike in the Wicklow hills, when the hunger and the thirst are on you, and you need a big fire to sit in front of, and a big pint to nurse. (Roundwood ☎ 01-281 8107 – Open noon-9.30pm Mon-Sun)

Wine Shop

The Organic Herb Company

Paul Pritchard and Michael Martin's company produces the most beautifully presented organic herbs, spices, snacks and herb blends. Get a taste of their savoiury mixed seed selection and you will never have another salad without it. Really good stuff that makes every kitchen better. (Wicklow Enterprise Park, The Murrough, Wicklow ☎ 0404 66433 organicherbco@eircom.net)

Organic Vegetables and Meat

An Tairseach

The farm shop at the Dominican Convent enjoys the produce of 70 acres of organic farmland, producing beef, pork, lamb, eggs and vegetables. Aside from the shop itself, you will find their brilliant produce at farmers' markets in Dalkey and Wicklow. Their ecology centre runs courses on organic growing, cooking, nutrition and much else. Only terrific, and another example of the garden of Ireland at its most deliciously productive and sustainable best. (Dominican Farm & Ecology Centre, Wicklow ☎ 0404-61833 ecenw@eircom.net www.ecocentrewicklow.ie)

Wine Shop

Wicklow Wine Co

Ben Mason and Michael Anderson run one of the best bespoke wine operations in the country, and together with Inis Wines of Donegal and Simon Tyrrell they team up to exhibit new arrivals and new vintages to the media, under the monicker The Wine Bunch. This pair have real nerve: they go off hunting in deeply unfashionable places like Germany and Portugal and Bergerac and where have you, and come back with good Rieslings and lovely Daos and Douros, and then they quietly convince you that they have found something wonderful, secure in the knowledge that they have done just that. The list is a treasure, the shop is jam-packed, the enthusiasm and love for the whole world of wine is infectious, and the WWC makes your life better, simple as that. (Main Street, Wicklow ☎ 0404-66767 info@wicklowwineco.ie www.wicklowwineco.ie)

Northern Ireland

Northern Ireland

Belfast

Restaurant

Alden's

Jonathan Davis will celebrate ten years in Alden's in 2008. In all that time, since our first lunch here shortly after they opened, we have never, ever had a single dish that was less than superb, and every great dish has been complemented by some of the best service to be found in the city. Mr Davis deserves to be acclaimed for this, to be recognised as one of Ireland's greatest restaurateurs, but he's a quiet, hard-working guy, and he just gets on with fronting up a great team in a great restaurant. In a perfect world, all restaurants would be like Alden's. (229 Upper Newtownards Road ☎ 028-9065 0079 info@aldensrestaurant.com www.aldensrestaurant.com – Open noon-2.30pm, 6pm-10.30pm Mon-Sat, 'till 11pm Fri & Sat)

Delicatessen

The Arcadia

The archetypal Belfast deli, right down to the luridly-coloured salads and the pile-it-high jumble of the shop, a tiny arcade with the foods of arcadia. Delightful. (378 Lisburn Road ☎ 028-9038 1779 – Open 8am-6pm Mon-Sat)

Asian Supermarket

Asia Supermarket

This is the best ethnic store in the entire country, and one of the best shops in the entire country. If they don't have it, then it can't be eaten, but if it can be eaten, then they have it. Fantastic fun, especially on a Saturday morning when it is absolutely manic. (189 Ormeau Road ☎ 028-9032 6396 – Open 9.30am-6.30pm Mon-Sun)

Bagel Bar

Bagel Bagel

The Bill Clinton. The Hugo. The Spaniard. The Simply Salmon. The Fandango. The Cranmore. Where do Joan and Paul Barr get the names for their bagel creations? Godness knows, but they have the right sort of chutzpah it takes to man a New York-style bagel bar, so expect plenty of big bagely flavours and lots of cool attitude. (60 Donegall Street ☎ 028-9024 2545 www.bagel-bagel.co.uk – Open 8am-3.30pm Mon-Fri 10am-3pm Sat)

Asian Supermarket

● The Balgla Supermarket

African and Asian specialities are the Balgla's signature, arrayed in charmingly souk-like style, with the requisite dim lighting. (175-177 Ormeau Road ☎ 028-9033 1110 – Open 10am-7pm Mon-Sun)

Homeware

● Batik at the Gasworks

We love June Elliott's fantastic furniture and design emporium, even if we can't afford the sort of cutting-edge, Milan furniture expo gear she sells. But, we can all dream, so you will find us wandering around admiring the design classics, working out just where to put that Corbusier chair, that Eileen Gray table. An utterly brilliant store, made all the better by the presence of delightful staff. (Metter-Hoose Raa, The Gasworks ☎ 028-9024 9311 www.BATIKonline.co.uk – Open 10am-6pm Mon-Fri, 10am-1pm Sat)

Local Speciality

BELFAST HAM

BELFAST BAPS

Bistro

● Beatrice Kennedy

Housed in what was Beatrice Kennedy's house, Beatrice Kennedy today is home to owner-chef Jim McCarthy's measured, polite cooking, which is served in a charming room with linen tablecloths. Both the style and the cooking are a gracious alternative to the design-fever hype of so many city addresses. so settle in for haunch of venison with spring cabbage or roast cod with caponata or an excellent sticky toffee pudding. (44 University Road ☎ 028-9020 2290 reception@beatricekennedy.co.uk www.beatricekennedy.co.uk – Open 5pm-10.15pm Tue-Sat, 12.30pm-2.30p, 5pm-8.15pm Sun)

Tea Room & Coffee & Tea Merchant

SD Bells

Robert Bell's company doesn't get half the kudos it deserves as Belfast's true tea and coffee specialists. Their tea sourcing is meticulous, their coffee roasting is brilliantly achieved, and their shop is simply a pure delight. Food lovers shouldn't take this company for granted, for there is true artisan skill here, and a great history of blending and roasting which is deserving of proper recognition and respect for the service S.D. Bell's have provided over many years. (516 Newtownards Road ☎ 028-9047 1774 sales@sdbellsteacoffee.com www.sdbellsteacoffee.com)

Belfast
Northern Ireland

Diner

Bennett's on Belmont

Colleen Bennett's casual diner contrast nicely with her slightly more formal Fontana, just a few miles away in Holywood, but the same precise and apt intuition for good cooking graces both rooms, and this is a darling space in which to enjoy ham hock linguini, or king prawns baked with lemon, chilli and garlic butter, or a classic Angus burger with Monterey jack and fries. Cool room, cool sounds, cool staff. (4-6 Belmont Road ☎ 028-9065 6590 – Open 8am-10pm Mon-Sun)

Café & Pizzeria

Cafe Renoir

One of the stars of Botanic Avenue, Café Renoir is the bistro and pizza offspring of the original CR, which opened in Castle Street as long ago as 1991. Their wood-burning pizza oven is a major feature of a café that changes from day-time self-service to evening-time waiter service, and which does so seamlessly and gracefully. What is also characteristic of CR is the fact that they source produce from their own farm, and have a laudable policy of using organically produced foods. This farm to fork ethos, coupled with a sharp sense of style, gives them a deserved edge and a vivid signature, and this is true tasting. invogorating cooking. (95 Botanic Avenue ☎ 028-9031 1300. Also at 5-7 Queen Street ☎ 028- 9032 5592 info@cafe-renoir.com www.cafe-renoir.com – Open 9am-5pm Mon-Sat, 9am-7pm Thu. Also 5-7 Queen's Street, ☎ 028-9032 5592 – Open 9am-5pm Mon-Sat, 'till 7pm Thu)

Café & Delicatessen

Cargoes

Rhada Patterson and her son Neil cook and serve in the indispensible Cargoes, one of the most important – and one of the first – great food destinations on the Lisburn Road. Ms Patterson is a most gifted cook – and a most gifted cookery teacher – and the verve and finish of everything that comes out of this kitchen is heart-warming. Cargoes is also a great store for essential fine foods. (613 Lisburn Road ☎ 028-9066 5451 www.cargoescafe.com – Open 9am-5pm Mon-Sat, 10am-4pm Sun)

Belfast Northern Ireland

Restaurant

Cayenne

Paul Rankin's fusion restaurant is one of the few places in Ireland that can make fusion cooking both logical and delicious. The dishes veer between his much-loved Mediterranean signatures – gnocchi; duck confit; orzo risotto; pork with portobellos and soft polenta – and the Asiatic notes he juxtaposes these Med notes with – chicken and mangetout laksa; shiitake and aubergine in rice paper; peanut-crusted ribs; miso-glazed salmon. Rankin's intelligence shows in the fact that he doesn't jumble dishes – the fusion here lies in the menu choice, not in the fusion of flavours in a single dish. So, it works best when you follow a theme straight through, sticking to the Med, or heading further East. (7 Ascot House, Shaftesbury Square ☎ 028-9033 1532 www.rankingroup.co.uk – Open noon-2pm Mon-Fri, 6pm-10pm Mon-Thu, 6pm-11pm Fri & Sat, 5pm-9pm Sun)

Kitchenware

Chef's Shop

Nowadays the home to handsome, pricey, pastel-painted Aga ovens destined for the homes of Lisburn Road mavens, as well as all the kit a serious cook needs, the Chef's shop has just whatever it is you need, and Niall McKenna runs a great shop. (Bruce House, 29 Bruce Street ☎ 028-9032 9200 www.thechefshop.net – Open 9am-5.30pm Mon-Thu, 9am-5pm Fri & Sat)

Coffee Shop

Clements Coffee Shop

Excellent in-store design and good Fair Trade coffees are the spiritually uplifting signature of the Clements chain. There is a hipness about this whole operation that is disarmingly attractive, and the cool sounds, good eats and nice drinks are a well-polished totality. (4 Donegall Square Wst ☎ 028-9024 9988; 66 Botanic Av ☎ 028-9033 1827; 37-39 Castle Street ☎ 028-90434781; 342 Lisburn Rd ☎ 028-9068172; 131 Royal Avenue ☎ 028-9024 6016; Rosemary Street ☎ 028-9032 2293;139 Stranmillis Rd ☎ 028-9020 1201 – Open 7am-5pm, Botanic, Stranmillis & Lisburn Road open to 11pm)

Butcher

Coffey's

Coffey's is one of the great Lisburn Road food lover's destinations, offering superbly presented meats, an excellent assortment of game, and doing so with gret service in a pristine shop. (380 Lisburn Road ☎ 028-9066 6292 meat@coffeysbutchers.co.uk www.coffeysbutchers.co.uk – Open 8am-5.45pm Mon-Fri, 8am-6pm Sat)

Café/bar

Conor Cafe Bar

The old William Conor art studio has a delicious array of foods on offer, from sweet things to take with tea or their excellent coffees, to nice salads and comfort-cooking daily specials, to good wheat beers and a small, sharp selection of wines. Very dignified and very nice. (11a Stranmillis Road ☎ 028-9066 3266 www.cafeconor.com – Open 9am-11pm Mon-Sun)

Deli & Restaurant

Deane's Deli

So, Sally McKenna and her mum go to DD for lunch, and how was it? "It was great". What was great? A real foodie audience. Food that has a flourish, like the flourish of a well-made cocktail, classy stuff with an elegant pzazz. The chefs are having fun here, sending out burgers on a board with chips in a little galvanised bucket, with blue cheese and watercress giving everything a little twist. Walnut-crusted goat's cheese with carrot jam and leaves is ace; seafod risotto with loads of tarragon and peas is class; prawn cocktail in a big tall glass is a blast, whilst salad of smoked chicken with pancetta, egg, baby gem and aioli is right on. Simple, pure food that takes things in Belfast to a new level of sharpness. (44 Bedford Street ☎ 028-9024 8800 www.michaeldeane.co.uk – Open 11.30am-3pm, 5.30pm-9pm Mon-Fri,'till 10pm Thu, 11.30am-10pm Sat)

Restaurant

Restaurant Michael Deane

Michael Deane has always been the most gifted of chefs, and the signature of his three Belfast destinations today is one of impeccable attention to detail, every detail. Yes, the belly pork with creamed Savoy is perfect, and so is the seatrout with crayfish and braised little gem and peas, and so is the Serrano with celeri remoulade, gorgeous plates of gorgeous food. But it is the fact that the chips are so flawlessly executed that shows a kitchen that has its eye on the ball, every ball. Value is exceptional, service just needs to relax. (36-40 Howard Street ☎ 028-9033 1134 info@michaeldeane.co.uk www.michaeldeane.co.uk – Open noon-3pm, 5.30pm-10pm Mon-Sat)

Brasserie

Deane's at Queens

So, lunch with three kids at Deane's at Queens, and what is it to be? Kettyle burger on red onion focaccia with skinny fries. Walter's smoked salmon fish cake with ketchup tartare. Tomato linguine with basil. Fish yorkshires with tartare sauce. Jumbo fries with roasted garlic mayo. The room is gun-metal grey and beech-wood blonde, with a single painting brilliantly bullet-pointing the eye, with light flooding in from the plate-glass facade. Are we in Sydney? San Francisco? The children behave like angels, and eat everything. The room fills up with couples and groups. You promise to come back to try the venison mince with celeriac mash, or the beef sausage with mustard pommes purée and red wine and onion gravy. The food is a little slow in getting out to the tables, but otherwise everything is, well, perfect. (1 College Garden, Belfast ☎ 028-9038 2111 info@michaeldeane.co.uk www.michaeldeane.co.uk– Open 11.30am-9pm Mon-Tue, 11.30am-10pm Wed-Sat)

Wine Merchant

Direct Wine Shipments

The first 2003 vintage of Creu Celta from Vinedos McAlindon was released at the end of 2006, and what an amazing venture for a Northern Irish wine merchant family to be making wines in Priorat, in Spain. Sylvia Puig is the winemaker, and Oz Clarke has been fulsome in his praise for the first bottles to be released. Production is very small – 330 cases – but what an extrordinary trophy wine this promises to be. Apart from showing Europeans how to make wine, the McAlindon family have been very good at showing everyone how to sell wine for many years, and their list is only excellent, and backed up by great service. (5-7 Corporation Square ☎ 028-9050 8000 ✉ shop@directwine.co.uk 🖱 www.directwineshipments.com – Open 9.30am-6.30pm Mon-Fri, 'till 8pm Thu, 9.30am-5.30pm Sat)

Kitchenshop & Café

Equinox

Northern Ireland does great design shops, and Equinox is one of the best. Kay Gilbert's store has fastidiously delightful homewares and must-have! design objects. After an hour or two spent punishing the plastic, it is time to repair to their chic little café at the rere of the store to complete the aesthetic of this swish enterprise with some good coffee and cakes. (32 Howard Street ☎ 028-9023 0089 ✉ contact@equinoxshop.com 🖱 www.equinoxshop.com – Shop open 9.30am-5.30pm Mon-Sat, 8.30am-9pm Thur, Cafe open 9.30am-4pm Mon-Fri, 9.30am-4.30pm Sat)

Coffee and Sandwich Bar

Espresso Soul

David Semple is doing some tasty things here in Gasworks central, not least a perfect carrot cake that will draw you back again to have with an excellent latte. Soups are good, sandwiches fresh, staff are attentive, and Mr Semple has a promisingly soulful thing going on here. (Unit 4B Cromac Quay, The Gasworks ☎ 028-9032 7474 – Open day-time)

Fishmonger

Walter Ewing

If you eat a particularly fine fillet of fish in a restaurant in the greater Belfast area, the chances are that Walter Ewing is responsible for your enjoyment. If you visit his shop at the bottom of the Shankill Road, you might find this hard to believe, for it is a modest place, but Mr Ewing is fishmonger to all the serious culinary players and, as such, he is a pivotal figure in the raising of culinary standards in Northern Ireland. He is also a very fine fish smoker, and his smoked salmon is a delight. (124 Shankill Road ☎ 028-9032 5534 ✉ ewings.seafoods@btconnect.com – Open 9am-5pm Tue-Sat)

Market

George's Street City Food & Garden Market

The Saturday market is creating media heroes. Open your *Irish Times* and there is Ann Stone, hero organic grower. Switch on your telly and there are the visionary Mullan family of Derry. Trevor Barclay is a media stalwart, Jilly Dougan is the most important woman in Northern Irish food, Pheasant's Hill Farm is in *The Irish Times* with Ann Stone, thanks to their exemplary rare breeds meats. These brilliant artisans have created two audiences; the regulars who get here early on Saturday for the craic and the culinary must-haves, and a secondary audience from further afield who see them as representing the future, the promise, the potential of Northern Irish food. Sure, we knew them when no one knew them! (4-10 Linenhall Street, Belfast ☎ 028-9032 0202 – Open Saturday, 10am-4pm)

Market

George's Street Friday Market

The proof of just how echt the Friday market is lies in the fact that at the crack of dawn the local ethnic restaurateurs are in here to get their fish and shellfish. But there is much more to the market than just fresh fish, for stalwarts such as Cheese Etc also sell on Friday, and the meat, bread and deli offerings are also good these days – the market is fast improving. There is also, should you seek it, the greatest collection of the most splendiferous collection of tat ever offered for sale. Surreal. (Linenhall Street, Belfast ☎ 028-9032 0202 – Open 8am-1pm Fri)

Restaurant

Ginger Bistro

Simon McCance has streamlined his café and restaurant into one fine room, and it's the perfect spot for some of the best bistro cooking you can find anywhere in Ireland. This man has a subtle, generous touch that makes food a sensual treat, but he also never simply cooks bistro clichés, preferring to work out new ideas all the time: water melon and carrot salad with squid; seared sirloin with wasabi and mango purée; hake with crayfish and parsley salad; tuna with ginger and green bean curry. Lovely, lovely food, food that makes you feel youthful. (68-72 Great Victoria Street ☎ 028-9024 4421 www.gingerbistro.com – Open noon-3pm, 5pm-10pm Tue-Sat)

Restaurant

The Ginger Tree

Happily installed in the centre of town after its move in from Ballyclare, which wasn't the most obvious location for a good Japanese restaurant, The Ginger Tree is formal, calm and in dishes such as kabayaki of eel – which uses Lough Neagh eel – they show echt authenticity. Bento boxes make excellent funky lunches, and we like the Zen-ness of it all. (23 Donegall Pass ☎ 028-9032 7151 – Open noon-2.30pm Mon-Sat, 5pm-9.30pm Sun-Thur, 5pm-10.30pm Fri & Sat)

Belfast
Northern Ireland

Café

Graffiti

Graffiti gets the essential things right. They make an excellent burger; they do fine chicken wings with chilli; the rib-eye steak with garlic butter is just spot on. They do good brunch, they run the room well and they don't take themsleves too seriously, they just get on with doing a good job, day in, day out. So, all told, Graffiti is a classic neighbourhood restaurant. (258 Ormeau Road ☎ 028-9069 3300 – Open 9am-5pm Sun-Tue, 9am-9.30pm Wed-Sat)

Restaurant

Hillmount Nursery Centre

Hillmount isn't so much a garden centre as an alternative world unto itself. It's a massive complex and along with everything you might need for the garden, it has a craft shop, a kid's play area, and a café, where they offer hot homemade pies, lasagnes, bangers and mash and lots of sandwiches and salads, along with nice sweet things. (56-58 Upper Braniel Road, Gilnahirk ☎ 028-9044 8822 info@hillmount.co.uk www.hillmount.co.uk – Open 9am-8pm Mon-Fri, 9am-6pm Sat, 1pm-5pm Sun. From Sept-Mar open to 6pm Mon-Fri)

Restaurant

James Street South

Niall McKenna's restaurant is always a pleasure, always a treat, always a statement of the joys of dining. He is a great chef, and has proven himself to be a great restaurateur. There are such lovely twists with his food – celeriac and turnip gratin with lamb; pork crackling with chicory; quail with asparagus; chicken with trompettes and tarragon; beef with bone marrow gratin. Great modern cooking in a great room. (21 James Street South ☎ 028-9043 4310 ✉ info@jamesstreetsouth.co.uk 🖱 www.jamesstreetsouth.co.uk – Open noon-2.45pm, 5.45pm-10.45pm Mon-Sat, 5.30pm-9pm Sun)

Gastropub

● The John Hewitt

A weekly menu with snappy cooking – herb crumbed whiting with champ and lemon butter sauce; broccoli and blue cheese tart with sauté potatoes; loin of pork with buttery mash and green peppercorn sauce – is the USP of this altruistic gastropub from the Unemployment Resource Centre. The JH also serves great craft brews from the north, has an art gallery, excellent trad gigs of all hues, and will, no doubt, secure the dictatorship of the proletariat sometime soon. Any Clause 4 socialists left out there, or are we all down in West Cork nowadays? (51 Donegall Street ☎ 028-9023 3768 🖱 www.thejohnhewitt.com – Food served noon-2pm Mon-Sat)

Home Bakery

● June's Cake Shop

June has been making nice cakes, breads and sandwiches for so long that there is a danger she might be taken for granted. Don't make that mistake: little bakeries such as June's are precious beyod belief. (376 Lisburn Road ☎ 028-9066 8886 – Open 7.30am-5.30pm Mon-Sat)

Restaurant

● Macau

Everyone's favourite BYO Chinese restaurant has the friendliest staff, the liveliest buzz, and some wizard cooking:bah won chicken; West Lake beef soup; Peking spare ribs; kai lan with prawn paste. The fascinating thing about Macau is that it feels like a Chinese restaurant run by Italians, two cultures fused into one brilliant culinary experience. Now, that is multi-culturalism. (271 Ormeau Road ☎ 028-9069 1800 – Open 5.30pm-10pm Tue-Sun)

Hotel

● Malmaison

We like Malmaison, but we would like it even more if there was a strong hospitality presence here, a good glad-handler to welcome you and see you off, rather than just efficient staff doing their job. As Malmaison grows, of course, the chances of their branches getting more individualistic decreases, but head office needs to be told that this beautiful boutique hotel needs a big, bold Belfast presence at the desk. Whilst young people love the moodiness of the bar and the restaurant, we find them simply underlit, but then this may be just a generational thing. (34-38 Victoria Street, Belfast ☎ 028-902 20200 belfast@malmaison.com www.malmaison.com)

Greengrocer

McCormick's Fresh Foods

Ricky Barrett's fruit and veg shop is one of those priceless local stores that Belfast is priviliged to have, and a place where it always feels a privilege to shop. (357-359 Ormeau Road ☎ 028-9049 1140 – Open 8am-5.30pm Mon-Sat)

Butcher

Thomas McCreery's Butchers

A busy butcher's shop, as much for their hot take-away food as for the fine meat selection, prepared and presented astutely and attractively. (439 Ormeau Road ☎ 028-9064 4911 – Open 7.45am-5.45pm Mon-Fri, 6.45am-5.45pm Sat)

Butcher

McGee's Butchers

Joe McGee is a fearless man, happy to take on the challenge of competing with the excellence of the Northern Irish butchers as his chain of stores extends from Monaghan and Donegal into Forestside and, most recently, to Quarry Lane, in Dungannon. His USP is beef from his farm at Gortnagarn, where they breed Angus-Hereford cross, and the beef is then hip-hung and dry-aged. This process makes for mighty eating, and we feel Mr McGee has maybe a few more outlets in mind before he slows down. (Forestside Shopping Centre ☎ 028-9064 8885 mail@mcgeesfood.com www.mcgeesfood.com – Open 9am-6pm Mon-Wed, 9am-8pm Thu & Fri, 8am-7pm Sat, noon-6pm Sun)

Butcher

Owen McMahon Butchers

McMahons are famed for producing especially fine sausages, amongst the best you can buy in Belfast, which is

really saying something. The rest of their meat is equally excellent, and they also stock lots of exotic meats. (3-5 Atlantic Avenue ☎ 028-9074 3535
✉ owen@owenmcmahon.com
🖰 www.owenmcmahon.com – Open 8.30am-6pm Mon-Sat)

Restaurant

● Metro

Metro is both townhouse, in which guise it offers accommodation in an excellent city location, and busy brasserie-style restaurant, in which guise the kitchen can offer some of the best eating on Botanic Avenue. (Crescent Townhouse, 13 Lower Crescent ☎ 028 9032 3349
🖰 www.crescenttownhouse.com – Open 5.45pm-9.30pm Mon-Thu, 5.45pm-10pm Fri, 5.30pm-10pm Sat, 5pm-9pm Sun)

Greengrocer

● Michael's Fruit & Veg

Just beside The Errigle, Michael's is a really excellent local fruit and veg shop. (435 Ormeau Road ☎ 028-9064 2804 – Open 8am-6pm Mon-Sat)

Home Bakery

● Millers Bakery

Marty Miller's bakery produces all the Belfast classics such as Belfast baps, Paris buns, iced fingers, a mighty nutty wheaten bread and there are excellent fresh sandwiches and good teas to enjoy also. Splendid. (18a Chapel Lane ☎ 028-9024 9166 – Open 8am-5pm Mon-Fri, 8am-5pm Sat)

Restaurant

● Molly's Yard

The micro-brewers are coming! Molly's Yard offers the brews of the Hilden Brewery, the oldest craft brewer in the country, so order up a Headless Dog – lovely elderflower notes – or sit down with a Belfast Blonde before ordering. The beers will also take your mind off the terminally bland design. If the style is cream and beige, the food is technicolour: asparagus soup is spot on; Portavogie fish chowder topped with puff pastry is excellent, and chef Mathias Llorente riffs creatively with Cooneen goat's cheese with Armagh apple chutney, or scallops with barley risotto, or sirloin with mini cottage pie. The College

Green Brewery will soon bring their drinks ever closer to home, and there is huge potential for Molly's Yard to become a major player in the city, once they make-over the design palette. (1 College Green Mews, Botanic Avenue, Belfast ☎ 028-9032 2600 – Open noon-9pm Mon-Thu, noon-9.30pm Fri & Sat)

Seafood Bar & Fish Shop

Mourne Seafood Bar

The room may feel that it doesn't quite know if it's a bistro or a bar, but there is no ambiguity about Andy Rea's cooking in The MSB: it is drop-dead delicious. Seared scallops with saffron linguini, fresh tomatoes and gremolata is masterly; hake with spinach, new potatoes and a curried mussel cream is fantastic, and with a bottle of St Patrick's Best from the Strangford Lough Brewing Co, you will be hard pressed to recall when you last had something so fine. The fish shop at the front has great fish, but again appearances aren't as optimum as they should be, but that is a small quibble: the Mourne is brilliant. (34-36 Bank Street, Belfast ☎ 028-9024 8544 – Open noon-9.30pm Mon-Sat, 1pm-6pm Sun)

Café/Bar

Nicholl's

A café bar on Church Lane, Nicholl's has added to their food offer by introducing tapas plates in the evening, a good complement to the day-time bar food offer which is extremely popular. (12-14 Church Lane, Belfast ☎ 028-9024 7824 – Bar open 11.30am-8pm Mon-Wed, 11.30am-1am Thur-Sat, food served noon-5pm Mon-Sat, Tapas 5pm-midnight Fri & Sat,)

Restaurant

Nick's Warehouse

Nick Price is the greatest cook in the history of Northern Ireland. Never mind who is allegedly the current hot-shot chef: what counts is the fact that this chef is as individual, intellectual and accomplished as ever, and his long career is a story of dedication to his craft, his ingredients and his crew. At a recent dinner, he served Kettyle beef short ribs braised in Clotworthy Dobbin beer, and it brought a collective gasp of delight from 30 diners, artisan foods from Fermanagh and County Down unified in the kitchen of a master cook. Mr Price needs to produce a book of his recipes, for he defines in his work what Northern Irish food is, and what it can be. (35-39 Hill Street ☎ 028-9043 9690 info@nickswarehouse.co.uk www.nickswarehouse.co.uk – Open noon-3pm Annix lunch, noon-2.30pm restaurant lunch, 6pm-9.30pm Annix dinner. Restaurant dinner only available to private bookings up to 50 people)

Wine Merchant

Nick's Wines

Nick Price always wrote the wittiest, best-fun wine lists, and it's no surprise now that he has his own wine company to discover that he has packed it with witty, fun wines. He likes sports of nature, such as the Finca Los Prados Chenin-Semillon, a real gender bender that has French grapes, a Spanish name and an Argentinian vineyard. The result is a fun wine that drinks superbly, and is great value for money. He has a Marlborough sauvignon from Allan Scott, a Blanc de mer from the Western Cape from Bouchad Finlayson, a cracking Rioja from Navajas that is terrific value for money, and everything is characterised by a lack of pretentiousness and a sharp focus on fun. Working with wine authority Neil Groom. Mr Price has delivered another winner. (35-39 Hill Street ☎ 028-9043 9690 info@nickswarehouse.co.uk www.nickswarehouse.co.uk

Delitcatessan & Café

Olive Tree Company

It's a friendly place, The Olive Tree. Leave your newspaper on the table when you go to the bathroom, and when you come back, the person at the next table will be reading it. Sharing and caring, then, and nice food upstairs – carrot and sweet potato soup; smoked chicken and brie sandwich with frisée, good wholesome, frill-free eating – and nice foods to buy and to take away in the shop downstairs. (353 Ormeau Road ☎ 028-9064 8898 – Open 8.30am-5pm Mon-Thur, 8.30am-5.30pm Fri & Sat)

Wholefood Shop

Open Sesame

This is a really good little wholefood-shop-health-store, not least thanks to long opening hours that means you can get your hands on those bio-yoguurts and manuka honeys, or maybe just a healthy sandwich. (32 Botanic Avenue ☎ 028-9032 4343 – Open 9am-7pm Mon-Fri, 9am-6pm Sat)

Belfast
Northern Ireland

Diner

Rain City

The mid-market bistro element of Paul Rankin's portfolio of eating houses, Rain City sends out lots of tasty burgers and T-bones, but there is a more delicate side to this kitchen and lighter, seasonal dishes often present true epicurean pleasure thanks to excellent ingredients and sympathic cookery. (33-35 Malone Road ☎ 028-9068 2929 – Open noon-9.30pm Mon-Fri, 10am-4pm Sat & Sun brunch, 5pm-9.30pm Sat & Sun)

Restaurant

Roscoff Brasserie

With Conor McCann hard at work in the kitchen, Paul Rankin's flagship brasserie is firing on all cylinders, producing pitch-perfect food: roast monkfish with oxtail jus; scallops with cauliflower purée; confit duck with colcannon; ravioli of langoustine with lemon vinaigrette. It's a great room, value is exceptional and this is one hot ticket. (7-11 Linenhall Street ☎ 028-9031 1150 www.rankingroup.co.uk – Open noon-2.15pm Mon-Fri, 6pm-10pm Mon-Thu, 6pm-11pm Fri & Sat)

Sushi Bar

Sakura Sushi

Belfast's first conveyor-belt sushi bar has the belt running down the middle of the room, with tables arranged all around it, and in addition to the belt plates there are various menus. The noodles are good, the banana crab roll is fab, the pumpkin cake is a delicious tempura-style cake that pairs beautifully with wasabi, soy and pickled ginger, and already the hip crowd that used to come here when it was the Dim Sum restaurant are back. Where do those Asian dudes source those amazingly cool spectacles? (82 Botanic Avenue, Belfast ☎ 028-9043 9590 – Open noon-11pm Sun-Thu, noon-11.30pm Fri & Sat)

Delicatessen

Sawyer's Deli

The great city centre deli soldiers on, packed to the roof with good specialist foods, staffed by delightful, white-coat-wearing staff who know where everything is, and every time you step into this tiny tabernacle of good things is a treat. We first used to shop in Sawyer's more than forty years ago, believe it or not, and it gives us enormous pleasure that has survived, and thrived for so long. (Fountain Centre ☎ 028-9032 2021 – Open 9am-5.30pm Mon-Sat)

Restaurant

Shu

Brian McCann has brought Shu to the top of the culinary tree in Belfast, and the only argument you will get in town is about who is at the pinnacle with him. In parallel with this intense cooking, the entire operation in Shu has shifted up a gear, and it is a joy to behold this sleek machine. Yes, it is cheffy cooking, with foams and ballotines and whatnots, but how nice to see a cook who works with gizzards and rillette of rabbit, and how nice to see contemporary classics given such a personal shine. We might attribute this élan to Mr McCann's time spent in one of our fave London restaurants, The Square, but the truth is that he has now synthesised all his influences into a very particular personal style, and it eats just so beautifully. (253 Lisburn Road ☎ 028-9038 1655 eat@shu-restaurant.com www.shu-restaurant.com – Open noon-2.30pm, 6pm-9.30pm. Two sittings on Fri & Sat, 7pm & 9.30pm)

Shop & Café

Smyth & Gibson

Packed with lawyers during the morning, S&G then offers smart, simple lunches based on excellent ingredients for the afternoon, before the lawyers come back in for hits of espresso to get them through to G 'n' T time. The shirt shop on the ground floor has wickedly desirable garments. (Bedford House, Bedford Street ☎ 028-9023 0388 – Open 7.30am-6pm Mon-Fri, 10am-6pm Sat, 7.30am-7pm Thu)

Café

Soul Food Company

A family-run café that specialises in using organically produced foods, SFC offers ace breakfasts that manage to satisfy whilst also making one feel virtuous, thanks to superb ingredients. Lunchtime sees great imagination at work in excellent pasta dishes, and some of the most soulful and unclichéd sandwiches being crafted in the city. (390 Ormeau Road ☎ 028-9064 6464 Open 9am-4pm Mon-Sat www.soulfoodcompany.com)

Kitchenware & Homeware

Still

A typically excellent homeware store, this is one of our favourite places for browsing, checking out the funky Italian tableware and lots of other well-chosen goods that seem to exercise magnetic power over your imagination. (Royston House 34 Upper Queen Street, ☎ 028-9023 0494 info@stillforlife.com www.stillforlife.com – Open 9am-5pm Mon-Sat, 9am-8pm Thur)

Restaurant

Sun Kee

Old timers like us regret that the Sun Kee moved from its shebeen-like room across the street to this smart big building. In the process it became more mainstream but, purist quibbles aside, it is still a very good Chinese restaurant, and if you assure the staff that you want the real thing, then you can get it. (42-47 Donegall Pass ☎ 028-9031 2016 – Open noon-11.30pm Mon-Sun)

Café

Swanton's Gourmet Foods

Gloria and Stewart Swanton's super deli and bakery is testament and tribute to people who really enjoy and respect food, and it means that everything coming out of this kitchen for daytime eating, through to their catering and hamper services, is blessed with goodness and care. Soups, salads, sandwiches are all hand-crafted and pristine, and there is both ambition and understanding evident here in the work of this dedicated crew. (639 Lisburn Road ☎ 028- 9068 3388 swantons@aol.com www.swantons.com – Open 9am-5pm Mon-Sat)

Sandwich Bar

Tang Sandwich Excellence

Tang have won almost as many awards for their sandwiches as they offer varieties of ingredients wrapped up in bread, baps, rolls and ciabattas. They love to mix up the classics – brie with avocado, bacon and garlic mayo; Peking duck with hoi sin and gingered cucumber; goat's cheese with caramelised onion – but they have the respect to offer egg and spring onion, classic BLT and Belfast ham with tomato. (246 Ormeau Road ☎ 028-9066 4451 tang.com@amserve.net – Open 8am-3pm Mon-Fri 9.30am-4pm Sat)

Restaurant

Taps

High-quality, authentically tasting tapas have made the reputation of Taps. You can stick with the obvious stuff – potato tortilla; patatas bravas, gambas, crema Catalan – but the funkier stuff is more rewarding, so push that Balearic boat out a bit. (42 Waring Street, Belfast ☎ 028-9031 1414 www.tapswinebar.co.uk – Open 12.30pm-6pm Mon, 12.30pm-10pm Tue-Thu, 12.30pm-11pm Fri & Sat, 1pm-7pm Sun)

Restaurant

Tedfords

Alan Foster's restaurant is home to some very well-judged fish cookery, especially when the dishes riff on classic themes such as salmon with fennel purée, or scallops with orzo and broad beans, or a beautifuly realised fish chowder. Both the rooms, upstairs and down, and the service are understated, which perhaps explains why this key address is not as well known as it deserves to be. (5 Donegall Quay ☎ 028-9043 4000 www.tedfordsrestaurant.com – Open noon-2.30pm Tue-Fri, 5pm-9.30pm Tue-Sat)

Brasserie & Bar

Ten Square Grill Bar

The Grill Room in the modern Ten Square hotel is a useful city location for meeting up, as it offers relatively simple food all day long, specialising in grills. So whether it's a breakfast meeting or a late-night rendezvous, this is a handy spot to know. (10 Donegall Square South ☎ 028-9024 1001 reservations@tensquare.co.uk www.tensquare.co.uk – Open 7am-10pm Mon-Sun)

Noodle Bar

Thai-tanic Noodle Bar

Thanidtha and Joseph Allen's noodle bar has brought some real authenticity to Thai cooking in Belfast. Classics such as Pad Thai or Thai beef salad which have become tired clichés elsewhere are concocted here into zappy, invigorating, perky masterpieces, and their curries and satay dishes are terrific. Great food, and great fun, and a truly ace take-away, with a few seats inside and outside. More, please. (2 Eglantine Avenue ☎ 028-9066 8811 – Open 5pm-11pm Tue-Sun)

Wine Shop

The Vineyard

With half a century of service under its belt, Tony McCurran's wine shop and off licence sails on, distinguished in particular by an astonishing range of spirits. If it isn't in here, it hasn't been distilled. (375-377 Ormeau Road ☎ 028-9064 5774 info@vineyardbelfast.co.uk www.vineyardbelfast.co.uk – Open 9.30am-10pm Mon-Thu, 9.30am-11pm Fri & Sat, 11.30am-9pm Sun)

Delicatessen

The Yellow Door

Simon Dougan is one of the key food people in Northern Ireland, thanks to the consistency, imginativeness and sheer deliciousness of the food he produces for his Yellow Door delis and bakeries. Happy staff sell happy food to happy customers, a squared circle of goodness and integrity that we acclaim, and applaud. (427 Lisburn Road ☎ 028-9038 1961 info@yellowdoordeli.co.uk www.yellowdoordeli.co.uk – Open 8am-5pm Mon-Sat)

Restaurant

Zen Japanese Restaurant

A really glam design style houses the Zen offer, which works best when you choose the most echt Japanese sashimi, though for those nervous of raw fish there are also European and fusion dishes. The same owners have recently developed the Fat Buddha restaurant on the Lisburn Road, which features a Robata grill. (55-59 Adelaide Street ☎ 028-9023 2244 – Open noon-3.30pm Mon-Sat, 5pm-10.30pm Mon-Fri, 5.30pm-11.30pm Sat, 1.30pm-10pm Sun)

County Antrim

Ballycastle

Fishmonger

Morton's

Morton's is a popular local store with good wet fish. (30 North Street, Ballycastle ☎ 028-2076 2348 – Open 10am-5pm Thu & Fri. Closed 1pm-2pm. Open other days during July & Aug)

Butcher

Wysner Meats

Roland Wysner opened his store back in 1962. 45 years later, and everything is still made by hand – the celebrated black puddings with their marbling of back fat; the milk-based white puddings; the sausages in their splendid myriad of flavours; the carefully prepared beef, lamb and pork. It's a splendid shop, true to the values of great charcuterie. Next door, the family also run a café with good, homely cooking. (18 Ann Street, Ballycastle ☎ 028-2076 2372 – Open 8am-5pm, Mon-Sat. Closed Wed. Cafe opens 9am-3pm Mon-Sat, 7pm-8.30pm Fri & Sat)

Ballyclare

Organic Farm Shop

Ballylagan Organic Farm

"This is not a forum for the exchange of views. It is merely an opportunity for me to give vent to my feelings. If you have any comments, contributions or amusing things to say, please contact us. At my whim, I may mention them on the site. The power has corrupted me." Tom Gilbert is the philosopher genius of Northern Irish organics – a field of endeavour in which he has much competition, let us add. Farmer, shopkeeper, thinker and doer, his Irregular Rant and his Newsletter on his website are the voice of sanity, wit, irreverence and intelligence. There is so little culture left in the world of agri-business farming that to read this man's thoughts, and to hear of his actions and endeavours, is to be brought back to the real world, the world of agriCULTURE. So, you simply must visit the shop to buy his superb produce and his superb meats, and to see a farming enterprise that will surely set the template for the enlightened actions of the new Government. Mr Gilbert is the Wendell Berry of the North East. (10 Ballylagan Road, Straid, Ballyclare ☎ 028-9332 2867 ✉ ballylagan@aol.com 🖱 www.ballylagan.com – Open 2pm-6.30pm Thu, 9.30am-6.30pm Fri, 9.30am-5pm Sat)

Butcher

● Errol Jenkins Butchers

Errol Jenkins is one of the pioneering butchers who created the Elite Guild in Nothern Ireland. Like every member of the Guild, his charcuterie standards are stratospheric, right the way through to all the cooked foods they sell, and even those fine stuffed sausages. (41 Main Street, Ballyclare ☎ 028-9334 1822 – Open 8am-6pm Mon-Sat)

Ballymena

Artisan Cheese

● Causeway Cheese Company

Damian and Susan McCloskey make the Cheshire-style Drumkeel, a mild-tasting and enjoyable cheese, which you will recognise by its very unusual hexagonal shape, crafted of course after the famous Causeway stones. (Loughgiel Millennium Centre, Lough Road, Loughgiel ☎ 028-2764 1241 🖱 www.causewaycheese.co.uk)

Coffee bar

● Ground

This is the sister shop to the excellent Ground coffee shop in Coleraine. The style is good, the coffee more than good, the food is fresh and tasty, and these are hip addresses. (30-32 Ballymoney Street ☎ 028-2565 0060 🖱 www.groundcoffee.net – Open 9am-5.30pm Mon-Sat)

Guesthouse

● Marlagh Lodge

Think of the great aesthetes of Irish hospitality – Paddy Foyle; Ken Buggy; Myrtle Allen; Maura Foley, to name a handful of folk with supremely unique taste. You will have your own names to add to the list, but what you need to remember is that no such list is complete without Robert and Rachel Thompson, of the beautiful Marlagh Lodge.

Their work in renovating this old house, and their work in running this old house, places them in that elite league of folk whose design sense is second to none. And, like all those great designers, they are also great cooks: Mrs Thompson cooks some of the best food you can enjoy in Northern Ireland, and Marlagh Lodge is a treasure, a beacon for the rest of the province. (71 Moorfields Road, Ballymena ☎ 028-2563 1505 info@marlaghlodge.com www.marlaghlodge.com – Open all year)

Ballymoney

Preserves and Catering

● Causeway Chutneys & Minor Events

Virginia Maxwell is a seriously talented woman. She runs an ace catering company – Minor Events – which will take the strain out of your party or celebration, and she makes fantastic relishes, jams and chutneys – Causeway Chutneys. It is a sign of the quality levels Ms Maxwell achieves that the gifted Derek Alcorn, of Dunfanaghy's The Mill Restaurant, uses Virginia's jams for breakfast and has her spiced apple chutney on the cheeseboard. The spicy onion relish is a storecupboard necessity, the lemon-grass and chilli jam is just what your chicken wrap needs, and function, utility and hearty epicureanism distinguish the entire range. (19 Semicock Road, Ballymoney ☎ 028-2766 6394)

Ballyrobert

Restaurant

● Oregano

Dermot and Catherine Regan's restaurant has a good spirit, and interesting food which is developing very nicely and hitting high standards. If the menus read like a roll-call of contemporary classics – chicken Caesar salad; Finnebrogue venison with soft polenta; crab crème brulée; slow-cooked pork belly with mustard mash; squash risotto with crisp sage – the food nevertheless has a strong personal signature and is very well executed and served. There is keenness here and ambition, and it will be fun to see this restaurant develop and mature. (21 Ballyrobert Road, Ballyrobert ☎ 028-9084 0099 www.oreganorestaurant.co.uk – Open noon-2.30pm, 5.30pm-9.30pm Tue-Fri, 6pm-10pm Sat, noon-3pm Sun)

Ballyvoy

Herb Garden & Café

Drumnakeel Herb Garden

Drumnakeel makes for a lovely stop on a tour of the beautiful North Antrim coast. So, park the car, peruse the beautiful herbs and decide what to buy, then relax and enjoy some nice simple food. (Drumnakeel, Ballyvoy, Ballycastle ☎ 028-2076 3350 – Café open day-time, except Wed, Easter-end August; herb garden open Easter-end Sept)

Bushmills

Garden Centre Cafe

Bushmills Garden Centre

The Creative Gardens company has two excellent garden centres and cafés, the second being at Donaghadee in County Down. Great news for gardeners, of course, but what sets these places apart is a crew who are passionate about their cooking. "Old-fashioned, home-style cooking of the highest order" is their manifesto, and it is one they live up to with gas in the tank. So, bring on the New England chowder, the cream of asparagus soup, the beef pies, the banana muffins, and can we have waffles for the kids, yes, with maple syrup, please. Terrific. (Ballyclough Road, Bushmills ☎ 028-2073 0424
bmgc@creativegardens.net
www.creativegardens.net – Open 9.30am-5pm Mon-Tue, 9.30am-8pm Wed-Fri, 9.30am-5pm Sat, 12.30am-5pm Sun)

Hotel & Restaurant

The Bushmills Inn

Almost as much of an institution in the town as the Distillery, the Bushmills is a comfortable old coaching inn, and the emphasis on comfort in every aspect of the operation explains its long and enduring success. (9 Dunluce Road, Bushmills ☎ 028-2073 2339 mail@bushmillsinn.com
www.bushmillsinn.com – Open noon-5pm Mon-Sat, 12.30pm-2.30pm Sun, 6pm-9.15pm Mon-Sun)

Local Speciality
POT STILL WHISKEY

Distillery

● The Old Bushmills Distillery

The guided tours of the beautiful Distillery are very worthwhile and supremely informative, as they give a sharp insight into the magical process that is the distilling of whiskey. Our favourites? 10-year-old Single Malt, and the unique Black Bush – brilliant. (Bushmills ☎ 028-2073 1521 ⌖ www.bushmills.com)

Carnlough

Hotel & Restaurant

● Londonderry Arms Hotel

A sweet and lovely old-style coaching hotel, where things are still done as they have always been done, with chicken liver pâté, and steak with onions and grilled tomatoes, served by delightful waiters in bow ties. The O'Neill family have been in charge for almost sixty years now, and long may they continue to respect the timeless nature of this grand coaching inn. (20 Harbour Road, Carnlough ☎ 028-2888 5255 ✉ lda@glensofantrim.com ⌖ www.glensofantrim.com – Open all year)

Cushendall

Potatoes

● Glens of Antrim Potatoes

Charlie and Kathleen McKillop's company is one of the dynamic potato growing concerns that you will find in Northern Ireland. Look out for their organic potato range, and for the Glens of Antrim Finest range in supermarkets. (118 Middle Park Road, Cushendall ☎ 028-2177 1396 ⌖ www.goapotatoes.co.uk)

Glenarm

Organic Farmed Salmon

● Northern Salmon Company

Glenarm organic salmon is an excellent product, and with new owners in charge whose plans for the company aim to build on its reputation as a superior farmed fish, we can expect to see this top-quality food becoming more widely available. (Glenarm 🔔 028- 2884 1691 ✉ northern.salmon@btclick.com)

Glengormley

Butcher

Thompson's Butchers

David Thompson is a fastidious and talented butcher, and like the best practitioners, he is in no hurry to get things done, so your sirloin will have been hanging for three weeks before he will sell it to you. Slow food, slow meat. (7 Ballyclare Road, Glengormley ☎ 028-9083 2507 – Open 8am-5pm Mon, Wed & Sat, 8am-5.30pm Tue, Thu & Fri)

Lisburn

Bar, Grill & Night Club

The Cardan

The Cardan is quickly establishing itself as one of the best places to eat in Lisburn. Simple, tasty food, cooked consistently well at affordable prices is going to be a winning formula anywhere, and it is proving to be so here, across from the railway station. Fish crumble with salmon and smoked haddock is just divine, whilst linguini with smoked bacon and field mushrooms is delicious. They step things up a gear in the evenngs, when slow cooked pork belly, halibut with creamed spinach, and roast lamb take centre stage. Good room, smart food, great value. (41 Railway Street, Lisburn ☎ 028-9267 8065 info@plateglassinns.com www.thecardan.com – Open noon-8pm Mon-Wed, noon-9pm Thur-Sat, noon-8pm Sun)

Brew Pub

Hilden Brewing Company & Tap Room

Owen Scullion now manages the Hilden Brewery, the first-established craft brewer in Ireland. Owen oversees five draft brews, including the Molly Malone porter and the Hilden Halt, and two bottled brews, Hilden Original and Scullion's Irish, all characterised by skilful, artisan brewing. And isn't it marvellous to see a second generation brewer at work in Ireland, hopefully just the first of many. (Grand Street, Lisburn ☎ 028-9266 3863 www.hildenbrewery.co.uk – Tap Room Open 12.30pm-2.30pm, 5.30pm-9pm Tue-Sun)

Home Bakery

Country Kitchen Home Bakery

Chris Ferguson runs a splendid bakery, known in

particular for its shortbread and its oat flakemeal biscuits amongst a fine range of breads. There is also a tea room which is a good spot in which to take lunch. (57-59 Sloan Street, Lisburn ☎ 028-9267 1730 – Open 8am-5pm Mon-Sat)

Restaurant

● Sabai Thai

Sabai is causing a quiet little stir in Lisburn with its authentic Thai cooking. We like the drunken noodles with prawns, and the beef kratian prig Thai. The take-away menu is very extensive, and even has a few European dishes, but it's the Thai specialities you want to explore here. (71-73 Bachelors walk, Lisburn ☎ 028-9264 0202 www.sambaithai.co.uk – Open 6pm-11pm Mon-Thurs, 5pm-midnight Fri & Sat, 6pm-10pm Sun, noon-3pm Sat & Sun)

Portrush

College Canteen

● The Academy

The Academy restaurant in the Portrush College is, if you like, the original testing ground for the college students, who cook lunch as well as four evening dinners for guests, a taste of the real world before they have to venture out into the real world. (Portrush College, Portrush ☎ 028-7032 3970 www.ulster.ac.uk/portrush/academy – Telephone for details of opening times)

Pizza & Pasta Bar

● Coast Pizza Pasta Bar

George McAlpin's Italian constituent is part of the Ramore complex of addresses he runs, the food an expert and informal spin on Italian classics. (The Harbour, Portrush ☎ 028-7082 3311 www.portrushharbour.co.uk- Open high season only, seven days.

Bistro

● The Harbour Bistro

Ths bistro element of the gloriously ancient Harbour Bar, this time with French-accented cooking from George McAlpin. (The Harbour, Portrush ☎ 028-7082 2430 www.portrushharbour.co.uk– Open 5pm-10pm Mon-Fri, 4.30pm-10.30pm Sat, 5pm-9pm Sun

B&B

● Maddybenny Farmhouse

Rosemary White is one of the great figures of Northern Irish hospitality, and her B&B and equestrian centre has flown the flag for decades up in the far north. (18 Maddybenny Park, Portrush, Coleraine ☎ 028-7082 3394 ✉ accommodation@maddybenny22.freeserve.co.uk 🖱 www.maddybenny.com)

Restaurant

● The Ramore Restaurant & Wine Bar

The Ramore is on the top floor, and serves George McAlpin's contemporary take on Asian-fusion food. The busy wine bar is underneath the Ramore and has a very accessible menu designed to suit all ages. (The Harbour, Portrush ☎ 028-7082 4313 🖱 www.portrushharbour.co.uk – Open 12.15pm-2.15pm Mon-Sat, 12.30pm-3pm Sun, 5pm-10pm Mon-Thu, 5pm-10.30pm Fri, 4.45pm-10.30pm Sat, 5pm-9pm Sun)

Templepatrick

Farmers' Market

● Colemans Garden Centre Sunday Market

Colemans Garden Centre plays host to a colourful farmers' market, which is held on the last Sunday of the month, and draws stall holders from far and wide. There's a great mix of traders selling breads, organic veg, cheese, soups, cookies, cordials, honey, and sausages are sizzling on the pan. There is often music and dancing and everything sells out very quickly. Join the early queue. (6 Old Ballyclare Road, Templepatrick ☎ 028-9443 2513 – Last Sun of the month, 1pm-5pm)

County Armagh

Armagh

Home Bakery

● The Cake Shop

Pamela Johnston's cake shop has lots of sweet treats – whiskey cakes; jam turnovers; treacle tarts, potato cakes stuffed with stewed apples – along with nice lunch-time savouries. The shop also offers baking and sugarcraft necessities, either to buy or to rent. (20 English Street ☎ 028-3752 2883 – Open 8am-5.30pm Mon-Sat)

Butcher

● A Flanagan & Son

David Flanagan's shop has been a top-class butcher's shop for more than 75 years. During that time, they have sold the meat reared on their own farm, and hung the steaks for a whopping three weeks to maximise the flavour. They have developed their deli operation, which is in a separate section of the shop, so the cooked food range is as impressive as the fresh meat section. Every bit as elite an operation as one would expect from a member of the Elite Guild. (1 Scotch Street, Armagh ☎ 028-3752 2805 – Open 9am-5.30pm Mon-Thur, 8.30am-6pm Fri & Sat)

Craigavon

Tea Room & Pottery

● Ballydougan Pottery

A popular pottery with a handy tea rooms. (Bloomvale House, 171 Plantation Road ☎ 028-3834 2201 ✉ info@ballydouganpottery.co.uk 🖱 www.ballydouganpottery.co.uk – Open 9am-5pm Mon-Sat)

Artisan Charcuterie

● Moyallon Foods Ltd

Jilly Dougan's rare breeds meat business has been a pioneer on so many different fronts – agricultural, commercial, retail – that it marks this singular woman out as the most singular mix of artisan creativity allied to commercial savvy. She saw a niche market in rare breeds when no one else did. She pioneered farm shops when no one else did, and followed this up by selling in farmer's markets at a time when everyone predicted they would fail. She took her produce into the food service area when no one else did and, at all time, Moyallon has been an exemplar not simply about how to develop rare breed meats, but also in how to market and sell them. A new Government should recognise this achievement, for it has not been matched by anyone else in Ireland, and Ms Dougan is the person to show the farmers and breeders how to get out of the spiral of deflationary prices and zero job satisfaction. The first step to doing that, of course, is to make a world-class product, and everything Ms Dougan produces is world-class. She thinks differently, and we eat better. (The Farm, Crowhill Road, Craigavon ☎ 028-3834 9100 mail@moyallonfoods.com www.moyallonfoods.com)

Lurgan

Butcher

John R Dowey & Son

John Dowey's shop is both excellent butcher's shop and excellent delicatessen, a haven for cooks and a haven for those who don't feel like cooking but who want some good food ready to go. (20 High Street, Lurgan ☎ 028-3832 2547 jrdowey@aol.com – Open 8.30am-5.30pm Mon-Sat)

Portadown

Artisan Cider

Armagh Cider Company

Kelly Troughton's cider company makes Carson's Cider, with their own apples processed in the UK to make a clean, clear, refreshing farm cider. (Ballinteggart House, 73 Drumnasoo Road, Portadown ☎ 028-3833 4268 info@armaghcider.com www.armaghcider.com)

Apple Juice

Barnhill Apple Juice

Ken Redmond has over thirty varieties of eating apple growing in his orchards, a valuable example of intelligent bio-diversity at work from an intelligent farmer. Ken then selects different varieties of apple to create different blends of apple juice, bracingly refreshing drinks with sweet blush colours, depending on whether the apple juice has been mixed with soft fruits, or even scented with cinnamon. Fascinatingly, Mr Redmond always varies his mixes, so every batch of Barnhill, every bottle of Barnhill, is unique. (Barnhill, Portadown ☎ 028-3885 1190)

Butcher

Knox's Food Court

Barry Knox is one of the great progressive and pioneering butchers in Northern Ireland, and his food court is a pristine example of superb butcher's store with fresh meat, and superb delicatessen with great prepared foods. (388 West Street, Portadown ☎ 028-3835 3713 – Open 8.30am-5.15pm Mon-Sat)

Charcuterie

William Sprott Ltd

Sprotts are one of the few remaining examples of traditional bacon curers, producing both green and smoked bacons, and supplying them in muslin-wrapped sides to butchers shops – wrapping in muslin was always the old way in the trade, another proud tradition sundered by greedy pig manufacturers. Their curers trust to instinct rather than banal machinery, they use immersion in brine rather than injection methods, and they continue to make great specialities such as Belfast hams, a dry-cured leg of pork. An iconic enterprise. (Edward Street, Portadown ☎ 028-3833 2157)

Local Specialities
ARMAGH APPLES
ARMAGH HONEY
ARMAGH POTATOES

Potatoes

Wilson's Country Potatoes

Angus Wilson's company has conquered the potato market, and has done so by clever packaging and rigorous quality control – you will never get a bag of Wilson's where the spuds are blotchy and of poor quality. And yet. A few years ago, Mr Wilson told *The Belfast Telegraph*: "A rough skin is the sign of a better eating quality of potato. Every farmer knows that. Yet the consumer doesn't seem to know it," he said, and he regretted that consumers are fixated on the appearance of potatoes. So, here is an idea for the brilliant Mr Wilson: for the epicureans who read this book, please produce some ugly, rough-skinned, dirt-crusted spuds. We will buy them. The uglier the better. We don't want the Kate Moss catwalk spuds. Give us some Serge Gainsborough spuds, in brown paper bags. (33 Mahon Road ☎ 028- 9042 1883 sales@wilsonscountry.com www.wilsonscountry.com)

Delicatessen

● The Yellow Door Deli & Patisserie

Simon Dougan has an instinct for food and cooking that is positively Dionysian. His grub is packed with relish, so much so that it doesn't need relish. Whatever he bakes, whatever he makes, whatever he cooks, is a thing of goodness, and a joy to eat, and it makes TYD a one-stop shop for food lovers. Brilliant. (74 Woodhouse Street, Portadown ☎ 028-3835 3528 info@yellowdoordeli.co.uk www.yellowdoordeli.co.uk – Open 9am-5pm Mon-Sat)

County Down

Annahilt

Gastropub

The Pheasant

Part of the same family-run group that includes The Plough and Barretro in Hillsborough, William Patterson's The Pheasant specialises in steaks, which are served with a variety of sauces such as Bourbon whiskey, Roquefort blue cheese, and even with prawns and hollandaise. (410 Ballynahinch Road, Annahilt ☎ 028-9263 8056 www.barretro.com – Bar open 11.30am-11pm, food served noon-2.30pm, 5pm-9pm Mon-Sun)

Annalong

Fish and Chip Shop

Galley Fish and Chip Shop

Superlative fish 'n' chips is what The Galley do, fried in dripping, cooked and served in a sparkling shop, with smart tables outside for those who want their chips al fresco. Locals, of course, eat 'em sitting in their cars. (43 Kilkeel Rd, Annalong ☎ 028-4376 7253 – Open noon-8pm Mon & Tue, noon-10pm Wed & Thu, noon-10.30pm Fri & Sat)

Down Northern Ireland

Local Speciality

ARDGLASS POTTED HERRING

Ardglass

Restaurant & Bar

Curran's Seafood & Steak Restaurant

A cosy mix of bars with contenting fires, and a restaurant, the best bet in Curran's is to follow the title: steaks and fresh seafood are their signatures and offer the best choices on an expansive menu. (83 Strangford Road, Chapeltown, Ardglass ☎ 028-4484 1332 info@curransbar.net www.curransbar.net – Bar open 11.30am-11.30pm. Restaurant open 12.30pm-9pm Mon-Sun, last orders 8.50pm. Sunday carvery 12.30pm-4pm)

Fish Van

S&P Milligan

A movable feast of a fish van which attracts big queues as it moves all around the province, from Belfast Market on Friday to Cookstown and points in between during the rest of the week. (☎ 028-4484 1595)

Ballynahinch

Fish and Chip Café

Ginesi's

Ginesi's is a famous chipper, with devotees attracted as much by the charm of Gillian and Romano as they are by the cracking fish and chips they cook. (34 Main Street, Ballynahinch ☎ 028-9756 2653 – Open 9am-8pm Mon-Tue, 9am-8.30pm Wed, 9am-9pm Thu-Sat, 2.30pm-9pm Sun)

Ballyward

Smokehouse

Drumgooland Smokehouse

Suzanne Smyth is one of the most important artisans in Northern Ireland, and her incredibly inventive ways with marinades and with the smoker create what may well be the most original foods the North has seen. She has an alchemist's way with the use of herbs and smoke and her salmon, trout, mackerel, smoked chicken and duck are masterly statements of a great food artisan's craft. (4 Gargarry Road, Ballyward, nr Banbridge ☎ 028-4065 0720 www.drumgoolandsmokehouse.co.uk)

Bangor

Bistro

Back Street Bistro

The BSB is a pleasant little room at the top of High Street, on Holborn Avenue, and there is some nice cooking going on from an enthusiastic team. Battered cod is beautifully done; squash risotto is spot on; pork burger is more than good, and the staff generate a lot of energy. There is promise and potential here. (7 Holborn Avenue ☎ 028-9145 4741 – Open 11am-4pm Mon-Sat, 5pm-9.30pm Mon-Thurs, 'till 10pm Fri & Sat)

Butcher

David Burns Butchers

Brian and George Burns' thunderously busy butcher's shop is a statement of how to run a specialist business. They have great meats, from their classic pork sausage – one of the very best – through to superb turkeys for your Xmas feast. They look after their customers in a way that inspires great affection, and many of these customers would be positively lost if they didn't have Burns as their first port of call. They work hard, extra hard, and they have a dedicated team working alongside them. They innovate and experiment, always trying new variations with their products. Put those elements together and you have a pristine machine, a model business that thrives on stellar service and stellar quality. (112 Abbey Street, Bangor ☎ 028-9127 0073 – Open 7.30am-5.30pm Tue-Thur, 6am-7pm Fri, 6am-5pm Sat)

Delicatessen and Café

Café Spice

Bangor's best deli has a good cheese counter, shelves lined with interesting foods, and a neat little café where Kerry O'Brien and her crew serve some good daytime eating. (7-9 Market Street ☎ 028-9147 7666 – Open 9am-5pm Mon-Thu, 9am-5.30pm Fri & Sat)

Gastropub

Coyle's

Mark Coyle's gastropub serves good quality bar food downstairs during the day, before the evening menu upstairs in the restaurant lets them get a whole lot more funky. There is a good crew at work here who enjoy their food, and it shows. (44 High Street, Bangor ☎ 028-9127 0362 – Open 11.30am-midnight Mon-Thur, 11.30am-1am Fri & Sat, 12.30pm-11pm Sun)

Home Bakery

Heatherlea

Bangor's champion bakery is where you go for great wheaten bread, wickedly fine scones, Belfast baps and their interesting sides, two farls joined together. Excellent baking of a consistent and superior standard. (4 Main Street, Bangor ☎ 028-9145 3157 – Open 8.30am-5.15pm Mon-Sat)

Restaurant

Jeffers by the Marina/The Boat House

Stephen Jeffers has always offered good food at the various addresses in Co Down where he has worked and on Grays Hill he continues the tradition of conservative but clever food – Toner's Cumberland sausage with crushed potatoes and onion rings; duck confit with choucroute; smoked haddock fishcake; risotto of prawns with coconut and ginger. The room is informal and well-kept, and service is sharp. The success of Jeffers has led Mr Jeffers to take over The Boat House, on Seacliff Road, directly across the bay, where one can expect more of the same smartly delivered, contemporary cooking. (The Boat House, Seacliff Road, Bangor ☎ 028-9146 9253; Jeffers by the Marina, 7 Grays Hill, Bangor ☎ 028-9185 9555 info@stephenjeffers.com www.stephenjeffers.com)

Fishmonger

McKeown's Fish Shop

An excellent wet fish shop just at the seaside end of High Street, McKeown's is a vital resource for good fish and shellfish, and they smoke some very good fish themselves. (14 High Street, Bangor ☎ 028-9127 1141 – Open 8.30am-5.30pm Tue-Sat, 'till 5pm Sat)

Preserves

The Offbeat Bottling Company

The OBC produce wonderful preserves, and the testament to their success is just how many of the leading delis in Ireland, even shops as far away as West Cork, will stock their pretty jars. You will also find them at the St. George's Market, and look out in particular for the legendary Extremely Orange marmalade. (Unit 73 Enterprise House, 2/4 Balloo Avenue, Bangor ☎ 028-9127 1525)

Butcher and delicatessen

The Primacy

The Primacy has the most out-of-the-way location, but its rock-solid reputation means that food lovers are more than happy to drive off the Bangor ring road to track down this smart little food village. The butcher's shop has many fans, but it is only one element of a smart food complex that deserves to be better known, but which its devotees are quite happy to keep as a valuable secret that improves the quality of their culinary lives. (26A Primacy Road, Bangor ☎ 028-9127 0083)

Butcher

MA Quail

Joseph Quail is the fourth generation butcher to work in Quail's, another of those masterly butchers and delis and cafés that are such a distinctive feature of Northern Ireland's food culture, Indeed, it is no exaggeration to say that shops such as Quail's are the backbone of the food culture: their application, their standards, their knowledge and experience, their levels of service and their superb design, are the definition of a food culture. Jim Quail sources his beef from his own farm, and backs up the outstanding meat offer with a great deli and a smashing, stylish café. They also have a small art gallery, but the art in Quail's lies as much in what they do and the way they do it, as in anything hanging on the walls. (13-15 Newry Street, Banbridge ☎ 028-4066 2604 www.quailsfinefoods.co.uk – Open 8.30am-5.30pm Mon-Sat)

"Ireland is discovering, or re-discovering its culinary resources; in the world of food, it's the place to watch."

COLMAN ANDREWS

Home Bakery

Windsor Bakery

There are four Windsor bakeries, with a pair in Banbridge and one in Lisburn and one in Lurgan. But, you could have 44 outlets for Gordon Scott and John Edward's bakery products and it wouldn't be a shop too far, it would simply be an enrichment of the food culture. "In many ways, we are the 'old' housewife of 20/30 years ago", says Mr Scott, by which he means that their handmade, carefully prepared foods are the staple of many an Ulster dinner table, whilst their hot foods are the staple of many a lunchtime repast. Their bakery does a hugely successful range of speciality cakes, in addition to their comprehensive range of morning bakes, savouries and sweet things. It all adds up to a superlative business, which this year celebrates half a century of trading. Now, that is worth a party! (36-38 Newry Street, Banbridge ☎ 028-4062 3666 winbake@btconnect.com 7.30am-5.30pm Mon-Sat)

Comber

Restaurant & Café

The Georgian House

With a series of bistro evenings held at the weekends, the Georgian House is developing its food offer nicely, at the same times as running a very popular daytime restaurant, and a spiffing shop with crafts and homeware upstairs. It's a beautiful space and a lovely place, and a major asset to the village. (14 The Square, Comber ☎ 028-9187 1818 – Open 10am-5pm Mon-Wed, 10am-7pm Thu, 10am-5pm Fri, 7pm-9pm Sat)

Vegetable producers

Mash Direct

The Bridgestone Guides don't do prepared foods – life may be too short to peel a grape but it ain't too short to peel a spud – and yet, if time pressures are a factor in your busy life, then Mash Direct is the sort of company you need to know about. Martin and Tracy Hamilton are talented farmers – we wrote about their blue potatoes many years ago – and they make various forms of mash that do genuinely achieve what they wanted to achieve; they taste as if your mammy had made them, or they taste as good as your mammy would want them to if you had the time to make them for her. Aside from their potato dishes, the mashed carrot and parsnip is particularly good – the McKenna children wolfed it down – and Mash Direct is the very acceptable face of compromise for time-poor folk who want to eat well. (81 Ballyrainey Road, Comber ☎ 028-9187 8316 info@mashdirect.cm www.mashdirect.com)

Down Northern Ireland

Farm Shop

Pheasants Hill Farm & Butcher's Shop

Alan and Janis Bailey opened their bed and breakfast – Pheasant's Hill in Downpatrick – in 1997. A decade later, they ally that business with one of the best – and most significant – shops in the entire country, their rare-breeds butchery and organic shop, just off the main square in Comber, which opened in 2003. Pheasant's Hill is a food lovers' dream, a place where you can choose the breed of meat you want – Dexter beef; Wensleydale sheep; Berkshire pork, Oxford Down mutton. "It's the breed, the feed, the maturity", is how Alan explains the astonishing singularity of his meat selection, but part of the secret of the success of the shop is Mr Bailey's epicurean appreciation: when this guy talks about food, he can see and taste the finished dish on the plate. Superlative. (3 Bridge Street Link, Comber ☎ 028-9187 8470 – Open 9am-6pm Mon-Sat)

Crossgar

Wine Merchant

James Nicholson Wine Merchants

It is fitting that Jim Nicholson should have a gorgeous new building in which to house his wine selection, a dazzling piece of design by Peter Minnis of Todd's Architects. For just as winemakers are creating stunning new wineries and bodegas and destinations that make an architectural statement about who they are and what they do, it is right that this gifted wine importer should have a building that makes a statement about what he and his team do. So, how do we read the new building? Well, Nicholson is a modernist, a person firmly rooted in his time, and yet he is also a person somewhat out of his time, for modernism has always had a somewhat uneasy relationship with the built environment in Northern Ireland. But then, Nicholson has always been out of step with the mainstream, and it is this singularity that has allowed him to be ahead of the crowd, and to stay ahead of the crowd. He finds the best wines from the best producers, he sells them in the most radically beautiful wine shop in Ireland, and his work defines the entire spectrum of the culture of food and wine. He is not simply a modernist: he is an iconoclast, and the work of Jim Nicholson and his wife, Elspeth, is as important to the food culture as the achievement of Myrtle Allen in Ballymaloe House. (Killyleagh Street, Crossgar ☎ 028-4483 0091 shop@jnwine.com www.jnwine.com – Open 10am-7pm Mon-Sat)

Down
Northern Ireland

Donaghadee

Garden Centre Café

Donaghadee Garden Centre

Jimmy Hughes and his kitchen crew do the good thing at Donaghadee, more than living up to their mantra of "good, old-fashioned, home-style cooking of the very highest quality". Lovely food, from a team who really relish their work. (34 Stockbridge Road, Donaghadee ☎ 028-9188 3237 ✉ ddgc@creativegardens.net 🖱 www.creativegardens.net – Open 9.30am-5pm Mon-Tue, 9.30am-8pm Wed-Fri, 9.30am-5pm Sat, 12.30am-5pm Sun)

Gastropub

● Pier 36

The Waterworth family have always fizzled with energy, and since the second generation came along to assist with running the multi-award winning Pier 36, the energy levels have been extraordinary. 36 is just what you want a seaside pub to be – friendly, helpful, comfortable, with good drinks and fine food: lamb's liver on smoked bacon mash with caramelised shallots; chicken supreme with celeriac purée; Portavogie prawns with skinny chips; Pier 36 steak burger. They even serve a 32-ounce steak! (36 The Parade, Donaghadee ☎ 028-9188 4466 ✉ info@pier36.co.uk 🖱 www.pier36.co.uk – Open 11.30am-9.30pm Mon-Sun)

Downpatrick

Gastropub

● Denvirs

A famous traditional pub and coaching inn, and a useful address for something to eat after dark in Downpatrick. (English Street, Downpatrick ☎ 028-4461 2012 🖱 www.denvirshotel.co.uk – Open noon-9pm Mon-Sat, noon-8pm Sun)

Venison

● Finnebrogue Venison

You can now buy Denis Lynn's superb red deer venison on line, and any food lover who searches for an alternative to the chewy, dense wild game tastes with which we associate venison will get a nice surprise with Finnebrogue's healthful, tender, delicate game. Finnebrogue is yet another of Northern Ireland's dynamic, different food enterprises, a radical food producer whose products improve the quality of everyone's life. (Finnebrogue Estate, Downpatrick ☎ 028-4461 7525 ✉ sales@finnebrogue.com 🖱 www.finnebrogue.com)

Local Shop

Hanlon's

A lovely, old-style general store packed with lots of good things. (26 Market Street, Downpatrick ☎ 028-4461 2518 – Open 8am-5.45pm Mon-Sat)

Farm Shop & Guesthouse

Pheasant's Hill Guesthouse

Janis Bailey's pretty B&B offers the food of their rare breed farm for breakfast, the most superb pork products you could possibly eat. See also the entry for their farm and butcher's shop in Comber. (37 Killyleagh Road, Downpatrick ☎ 028-4461 7246
www.pheasantshill.com)

Dundrum

Restaurant

The Buck's Head

Pub lunches, high teas, and then dinners which exhibit finely calibrated culinary judgement at work with superb ingredients. How on earth does Alison Carruthers manage to do all she does, how does she switch so effortlessly between these three competing demands, managing to satisfy each and every one of them? "None of our food is fussy", Alison once explained to food writer Caroline Workman. "It's seasonal. It's local. We rely on what we've got and the flavours of the ingredients." Now, that's a woman chef talking, so bring on the Dundrum oysters in pin-head oatmeal with smoked bacon, the Finnebrogue venison with sweet potato rosti, the turbot with orzo cream, the sirloin with chimichurri, the hot and dark chocolate brownie. Lovely food, sweet and lovely place. (77 Main Street, Dundrum ☎ 028-4375 1868 – Open noon-2.30pm, 5pm-9.30pm Mon-Sun)

Guesthouse

The Carriage House

Three pretty bedrooms in a pretty B&B, Maureen Griffith's home is a lovely parade of subtle good taste in design, style and, in particular, in breakfast cookery. (71 Main Street, Dundrum☎ 028-4375 1635
inbox@carriagehousedundrum.com
www.carriagehousedundrum.com)

"Running a restaurant is no joke so I always try to see the lighter side of things."

PAUL FLYNN

Oyster Fishery

Dundrum Bay Oyster Fishery

Suppliers of carefully cultivated shellfish to the restaurant trade, try the DBOF shellfish products – oysters, mussels, cockles – in The Buck's Head Inn. (☎ 028-4375 1810 🖱 www.dundrumbayoysters.co.uk)

Seafood Bar

Mourne Seafood Bar

Bob McCoubrey's original MSB has been joined by a second branch in Belfast where Andy Rea is currently firing out the most masterly seafood cookery. In Dundrum, they again start with the major advantage of having their own shellfish beds, so start with Mourne oysters or Mourne mussels, then enjoy gorgeously handsome hot and cold seafood platters, or choose from the daily seafood specials on the blackboard. It's a lovely room with salvaged wooden furniture and nautical art, and a major attraction for pretty Dundrum. (10 Main Street, Dundrum ☎ 028-4375 1377 🖱 www.mourneseafood.com – Open noon-9pm Mon-Sun)

Greyabbey

Butcher

Angus Farm Shop

Noel's Angus Farm Shop is unusual in that meat is cut to order for customers, much as one would find in a French charcuterie, and the fact that Noel will not sell any meat that is not at the perfect point of maturation and ready for the oven is another signal of what a singular shop this is. The good people of Greyabbey appreciate this care, and a constant queue in the little shop is proof that locals know a good thing when they eat it. (42 Main Street, Greyabbey ☎ 028-4278 8695 – Open 8.30am-12.30pm Mon, 8.30am-5.30pm Tue-Sat)

Coffee Shop

Hoops Coffee Shop

Sandra Kelso's coffee shop is just the place for a good cup of tea, some lemon drizzle cake, and a good lunch, with nice quiches, good pies and lively fresh salads. (7 Main Street, Greyabbey ☎ 028-4278 8541 – Open 10am-5pm Tue-Sat, open 'till late Thu & Fri)

Craft Shop & Café

Pebbles

A pretty craft shop and café with some nice savoury and sweet things on the menu along with many conventional foods. (12 Main Street, Greyabbey ☎ 028-4278 8031 – Open 10am-5pm Tue-Sat, 2pm-5pm Sun)

Groomsport

Wine Merchant

Classic Wine

Robert Neill and his allies in Classic Wine are in expansion mode these days, with a new shop in Belfast at Ballyhackamore, and a new wine bar and café, Café Rouge, adjacent to the new wine shop, signalling a whole new direction for the company. But, in terms of their core business, CW simply source and sell great wines with unbridled enthusiasm, and they do so without lapsing into pretension or becoming bourgeois; these guys understand that wine is part of the good life, and that we need to enjoy every aspect of it. Excellent. (49 Main Street, Groomsport ☎ 028-9147 8982 info@classicwine.biz www.classicwine.biz – Open noon-8pm Mon-Thu, noon-9pm Fri, 10am-9pm Sat, 1pm-6pm Sun))

Helen's Bay

Organic Farm

Helen's Bay Organic Farm

Organic farmer John McCormick runs a brilliant box delivery system, bringing his organic foods to a wide audience in North Down and beyond. Mr McCormick is a pioneer organic farmer, and a great potato zealot, so sign up for the box delivery and get ready to enjoy some of the best spuds you have ever eaten. (Coastguard Avenue, Helen's Bay ☎ 028-9185 3122)

Hillsborough

Café Bar

● Barretro

Barretro is the funky younger sister of the Patterson family's trio of businesses, and its modern style is a direct contrast to the traditional style of The Plough, which is next door. The Bistro serves food for most of the day, and it's a busy, lively place. (Coastguard Avenue, Hillsborough ☎ 028-9268 2985 🖰 www.barretro.com – Open noon-2.30pm Mon-Sun, 6pm-9.30pm Tue-Sat)

Bistro

● The Plough Bistro

Derek Patterson offers both food in the bar at The Plough – Mrs Patterson's burger with tobacco onions; bookmaker's steak with blue cheese sauce; Ardglass scampi with tartare – and more formal cooking in the restaurant at the rear of the building, which has a charming, old-style feel and design. (The Square, Hillsborough ☎ 028-9268 2985 🖰 www.barretro.com – Open noon-2.30pm Mon-Sun, 6pm-9.30pm Tue-Sat)

Down

Hilltown

Chipper

● The Hilltown Chippy

Paul Smith's chipper is a legend. Mr Smith has spent more than a quarter of a century perfecting his frying, and the only question devotees of The Hilltown ask is: are these the best chips fried on Planet Earth? (Main Street, Hilltown ☎ 028-4063 8130 – Open from noon-late)

Holywood

Café

● The Bay Tree

Sue Farmer is one of the best cooks in Northern Ireland. The purity of the food she cooks is barely hinted at by the Friday night menus from TBT: lemon chicken with Puy lentils and salsa verde; escalope of salmon with sorrel sauce and champ; spiced confit of pork belly with roasted sliced potatoes; deep Mediterranean pie with tomato sauce and green salad. It reads simple, but it eats as if the entire culture of cooking has been wrapped up in every flavour, every bite, every taste. This is Ms Farmer's gift: she makes the commonplace special, she understands the art of the commonplace, and she is thereby able to transform it into something that just knocks your socks off. She is a wizard. (118 High Street, Holywood ☎ 028- 9042 1419 info@baytreeholywood.com www.baytreeholywood.com – Open 8am-4.30pm Mon-Fri, from 7pm-late Friday, 9.30am-4.30pm Sat, 10am-2.45pm Sun)

Café

Café Kina

Karen and Niko do a mighty job here in Café Kina. There are great sandwiches, savouries, pastries and cakes, and fulsomely flavoured specials of the day that draw in the crowds – coq au vin, Turkish lamb and apricot tagine; wild mushroom and pancetta tart. They have theme evenings upstairs on Friday nights when they explore different cuisines, they do outside catering, and Niko makes wickedly good personalised cakes to order. Add all this together, with seven-day opening, and you have a key Holywood address. (81 High Street, Holywood ☎ 028-9042 5216 niko@cafekina.co.uk www.cafekina.co.uk – Open 8.30am-5pm Mon-Fri, 9am-5pm Sat, 9.30am-5pm Sun)

Down
Northern Ireland

Organic Shop & Bakery

Camphill Organic Farm Shop & Bakery

Rob van Duin's fantastic shop and bakery is one of the most original stores in the country. It's a brilliant bakery, but it also sells fantastic organic produce. It's a wholefood store, but it also has really great deli foods. It is, in short, a wonderful sport of nature, both distinct and different, and a key element of Holywood's splendid culinary culture, (Shore Road, Holywood ☎ 028-9042 3203 camphillholywood@btconnect.com
www.camphillholywood.co.uk – Shop open 9am-5.30pm Tue-Sat. Cafe open 9am-4.30pm Tue-Sat)

Kitchenshop

La Cucina

A good kitchen shop which has everything from classy knives to stylish tableware to electrical kitchen equipment. (63 High Street, Holywood ☎ 028-9042 2118 lacucina.ni@yahoo.co.uk - Open 9am-5.30pm Mon-Sat)

Restaurant

Fontana

Colleen Bennett's upstairs bistro is one of the major players in Holywood's good food culture, and has been a beacon of consistency for many years. Ms Bennett now balances this busy bistro with its simpler sister diner, Bennett's on Belmont, a few miles away close to the top of the old Holywood Road. The food in both is assured, modern and invariably well-delivered, intelligent cooking that thrives on the use of excellent ingredients. (61a High Street, Holywood ☎ 028-9080 9908 www.fontanarestaurant.com – Open noon-2.30pm, 5pm-9.30pm Tue-Fri, 6.30pm-10pm Sat, 11am-3pm Sun)

Wholefood Shop & Bistro

The Iona

A wholefood shop with an upstairs bistro, The Iona is one of the enduring staples of good eating and shopping in Holywood. (27 Church Road, Holywood ☎ 028-9042 8597. Bistro Iona ☎ 028-9042 5655 – Shop open 9am-5.30pm Mon-Sat, Bistro open 6pm-10.30pm Tue-Sat)

Butcher & Deli

Orr's

A butcher's shop that also sells fresh fish and has a good deli counter, Orr's is invaluable, especially in an area where supermarket culture is not just ubiquitous but practically triumphalist. Look out for Sprott's bacon, good potted herrings, SD Bell teas and coffees and other good local foods. A really fine shop that defines what good sourcing and good shoppng means, and a key element of Holywood's culture. (56 High Street, Holywood ☎ 028-9042 2288 – Open 8am-5.30pm Mon-Sat)

Restaurant

Sullivan's

Simon Shaw's rock-steady bistro is Holywood's favourite local, attracting casual eaters and serious diners of all ages. The kitchen here has always had a sure touch, and so even though the menus read straight-ahead modern, the cooking owes more to the care of the domestic kitchen than to the slickness of a commercial operation. (2 Sullivan Place, Holywood ☎ 028-9042 1000 www.sullivansrestaurant.co.uk – Open noon-2.30pm Mon-Sun, 6pm-9.30pm Tue-Thu, 5pm-10pm Fri & Sat, 5pm-9pm Sun)

Kilkeel

Organic Farm and Accommodation

Lurganconary Organic Farm

Gerard O'Hare is creating something radical at Lurganconary, a 100 acre organic farm which offers cottage accommodation, and where the country house is being restored to its former glory. The produce from their farm has been sold at farmers markets in Newry and Dundalk and you can find it a couple of mornings each week for sale at the Quays shopping centre in Newry. People renting the cottages can also purchase the produce. Best of all, there is a genuinely holistic vision for this special place, and its development will be fascinating to behold. When they first set about clearing some woodland, they brought in two shire horses, in order not to disturb the eco-system. The horse is coming back to agriculture! Lurganconary is one to watch. (25 Lurganconary Rd, Kilkeel www.lurganconaryfarms.com)

Brewery

The Whitewater Brewing Company

The Whitewater run the White Horse Inn in Saintfield when they take a pause from brewing their beers. Most recently, the company has started to sell its Belfast Ale and Clotworthy Dobbin ale through multiples in Northern Ireland, which is great news for beer lovers as these are excellent brews. The Clotworthy Dobbin has already achieved a measure of fame, having been used by Nick Price to braise Kettyle short ribs in a dish that was outrageously wonderful. So, they cook well, but drinking them cool is really the point, and they are distinguished and expert brews with great character, and they can stand alongside the best craft brews in Ireland. (40 Tullyframe Road, Kilkeel ☎ 028-4176 9449 info@whitewater-brewing.co.uk www.whitewaterbrewing.co.uk)

Killinchy

Restaurant

Balloo House

A 19th-century coaching Inn at the cross-roads on the main Comber-Killyleagh Road, Ronan and Jennie Sweeney's Balloo House has a small upstairs restaurant and a busy bistro and bar downstairs. The bistro food is classic, punchy fare: haddock and scallion chowder; Kilkeel scampi with tartare; Strangford mussels with smoked bacon, garlic and white wine; venison shepherd's pie, aromatic, spot-on food that pushes the button. Upstairs, chef Danny Millar brings experience and intuition to bear with precision and craft on a series of lovely dishes – sautéed foie gras with duck confit spring roll, rhubarb, soy and ginger is perfect cooking, Strangford langoustines with garlic, lemon and parsley are melt-in-the-mouth delicious. Mains of john dory with lobster and prawn sauce, and Strangford scallops with leeks, ham hock, sauté potatoes and roast hazelnut oil, show wonderfully complementary and contrasting flavours and textures. Good service, and very good value, means Balloo adds up to a major new destination. (1 Comber Road, Killinchy ☎ 028-9754 1210 www.balloohouse.com – Bistro food served noon-9pm Mon-Sun, 'till 8pm Sun. Restaurant open 6pm-9pm Tue-Thu, 6pm-9.30pm Fri & Sat)

Killyleagh

Gastropub

Dufferin Arms

The music sessions are a major attraction of the Dufferin Arms, a venerable pub which has been serving ale and porter for more than two centuries. But you can also eat well here, for they make a good chowder and put local foods to good use in the basement restaurant.
(35 High Street, Killyleagh ☎ 028-4482 1182, – Open noon-2.30pm 5.30pm-8.30pm Mon-Fri, noon-9.30pm Sat, 12.30pm-7pm Sun)

Delicatessen

Picnic

John Dougherty's deli-café does the good stuff, with nice baking to lure you in, nice lunches with good salads, and good coffees and cakes. It's tiny, yes, but it's tiny perfect. (49 High Street, Killyleagh ☎ 028-4482 8525 – Open 7am-6pm Mon-Fri, 10am-4pm Sat, and Sunday during summer)

Craft Brewer

Strangford Lough Brewing Company

The SLBC has three brews under its St Patrick's brand – St Patrick's Gold is a wheat beer, St Patrick's Best is the bitter, and St Patrick's Ale is the ale. There are also

Legbiter, a golden ale, and Barelegs, a bottle-conditioned ale. We first tried the St Patrick's Best in the Mourne Seafood Bar in Belfast, when the bitter showed itself as a perfect foil for both seared scallops and roast hake, thanks to a well-judged balance between its sweetness and its hoppiness. These are well-made brews, and beautifully packaged, and you will find them in pubs, restaurants, wine shops and also some multiple retailers. (Braidleigh Lodge, 22 Shore Road, Killyleagh ☎ 028-4482 1461 office@slbc.ie www.slbc.ie)

Kircubbin

Restaurant with Rooms

Paul Arthurs

Paul Arthurs is one of the leading chefs of the younger generation, and he does a mighty job here in his restaurant with rooms, and his chipper. His touch with fish and shellfish is flawless – not ordering the fish of the day here is well-nigh impossible – but his touch with meat and game dishes may be even better, as his flavour-saturated cooking seems to pull out all the possible tastes from great beef and duck. It makes for a great, colourful brasserie with brasserie brashness and energy, and the way to get the best of it is to book a room and let the devil take care of tomorrow: tonight, we party. (66 Main Street, Kircubbin ☎ 028-4273 8192 www.paul/arthurs.com – Open 5pm-9pm Tue-Sat, noon-2.30pm Sun)

Lisbane

B&B

Anna's House

"I always try my best, and continue to enjoy what I do" That was how Anna Johnson signed off a little note to Bridgestone central a while back, and it explains why her amazing house is such a cult success. Everyone – but everyone – loves Anna's house, the smells of baking, the beautiful dinners, Ken's work on the interiors and exteriors, the garden in which you can simply lose yourself. A special place, close to everywhere, and a million miles from the normal. (Tullynagee, 35 Lisbarnett Road, Lisbane, Comber ☎ 028-9754 1566 www.annashouse.com)

Café & Craft Shop

● The Old Post Office Café

A lovely warren of pretty rooms in a gorgeous thatched cottage, with crafts for sale and peat burning fires, the Old Post Office is cosy in winter, and opens out in summertime with benches and a cottage garden. They serve breakfast, lunch and afternoon teas, and Trevor and Alison bake and cook with real care and application, whether you are having a slice of gateau with a cup of tea or a nice, lazy lunch. (191 Killinchy Road, Lisbane, Comber ☎ 028-9754 3335 info@oldpostofficelisbane.co.uk www.oldpostofficelisbane.co.uk – Open 9am-5pm Mon-Sat)

Millisle

Pottery

● Eden Pottery

Eden is a splendidly creative pottery, whose spongeware work is not just super-pretty, it is also extremely affordable. Heather and Phil Walton are talented people, and their idyllic representations of country life staples – nesting hens, roosters, anemones, poppies, Suffolk sheep, wheatsheafs, cows, plums, lemons, pears and other fruits – are beautifully depicted in the most glamorous tactility in all their plates, cups, serving bowls and jugs. They also run pottery courses, have a sweet tea room, and Eden is all-round idyllic. (218 Abbey Road, Ballyfrenis ☎ 028-9186 2300 eden.pottery@virgin.net – Open 9am-5pm Mon-Sat)

Moira

Restaurant

● Ivory

Housed in a supremely elegant Georgian building in Moira, there is a lot of charm to Ivory, thanks to very chatty staff who work hard and look after you well. The menus are expansive, but choose carefully and the tasty cooking will hit the spot, with lunches here being very well achieved. (Main Street, Moira ☎ 028-9261 3384 www.ivoryrestaurant.com – Open noon-2.30pm Mon-Sat, 5pm-9pm Mon, 5pm-9.30pm Tue-Thu, 5pm-10pm Fri & Sat, 5pm-8pm Sun)

Butcher

McCartney's of Moira

"There is only so such you can invent, so sometimes you have to go back in time to find new foods", said George McCartney about the new range of cuts and cures whose inspiration has been taken from an old book belonging to George's grandfather. Well, if going back in time means making real corned beef which is as glorious as McCartney's version, the sooner we all go back to go forward the better; this corned beef is a star, and we await the planned new tongue recipes and other classics. Otherwise, of course, McCartney's is simply the cutting-edge charcutier, with a level of skill across every discipline in the profession, from pie making to sausage making to black pudding making to you-name-it, accomplished at stratospheric levels. One of the great shops in these islands. (56-57 Main Street, Moira ☎ 028-9261 1422
info@mccartneysofmoira.co.uk
www.mccartneysofmoira.co.uk – Open 8.30am-5.30pm Tue-Thur, 8am-5.30pm Fri & Sat)

Down Northern Ireland

Gastropub

Pretty Mary's

A young local cook, Aaron Heasley, has been taking care of the kitchen in Pretty Mary's over the last while, and his cooking is seriously enjoyable, and extremely consistent. Add in the charm of this family pub with its architectural salvage and scrubbed pine, very good service and excellent value and you have a real winner. (86 Main Street, Moira ☎ 028-9261 1318 – Open noon-3pm, 5pm-9pm Mon-Fri, noon-9.30pm Sat, 1pm-8pm Sun)

Newcastle

Deli & Bistro

Seasalt

Caroline and Andrew Fitzpatrick have been working hard in Seasalt for 10 years now, and have created a hugely successful business in that time. During the week they produce excellent cooking for daytime eaters, and at weekends they open up in the evening and let the menu open out a bit – oriental crab cake with sesame dressing; lamb bourguignonne with champ; monkfish marinated in ginger with garlic and chilli; chicken with roasted pumpkin purée and shallots; chocolate and mascarpone cheese cake. During the summer the room gets to be positively heaving, so bring along lots of BYOB and make the most of the clamour. (51 Central Promenade, Newcastle ☎ 028-4372 5027 – Open 9am-5pm Mon-Thu, 9am-10pm Fri & Sat)

Restaurant

Zest

Zest is a café by day, and an interesting restaurant by night, when a young crew show that they can produce some interesting dishes with local foods. BYOB makes it a winningly affordable destination. (22-24 Main Street, Newcastle ☎ 028-4372 5757 – Open 10am-5pm Mon-Fri, 10am-4pm, 7pm-9pm Sat)

Newtownards

Greengrocer

Homegrown

The archetype of the local vegetable store, filled with local seasonal fruit and vegetables, Margaret White's shop is a legend in its own neck of the woods. Devoted customers turn up week in, week out, year in, year out. Excellent. (66b East Street, Newtownards ☎ 028-9181 8318 – Open 9am-5.30pm Mon-Thur, 8am-5.30pm Fri & Sat)

Home Bakery & Coffee Shop

Knott's Cake & Coffee Shop

Michael and Sharon Knott's café and bakery has all the great vernacular Northern bakery specialities, and there is also a busy self-service counter where good savoury lunches are dispensed speedily and efficiently. (45 High Street, Newtownards ☎ 028-9181 9098 – Open 7.30am-5pm Mon-Sat)

Farm Shop

McKee's Farm Shop

The view from the coffee shop in Colin McKee's farm shop business is just amazing, sweeping away over the countryside. But, to be honest, it is not as amazing as the unlikely success story Mr McKee has carved out of this farm business. The sheer number of people who come here to shop in this brilliant farm store, and the even greater numbers who now come here to have breakfast, lunch and afternoon tea, is simply unbelievable. Add in the fact that the location is – relatively – remote, or at least inconvenient, and you have a business that, like all the best food businesses, writes its own rules, and which turns received wisdom on its head. This fabulous farm industry should be a model for every farmer throughout Ireland, a lesson in how to fight off supermarket dominance by playing the game only by your own rules. McKee's is not just magnificent, it is inspirational, and we trust Colin will be given a brief advising the new Minister for Agriculture. (28 Holywood Road, Newtownards ☎ 028-9181 3202 orders@mckeesproduce.co.uk www.mckeesproduce.co.uk – Open 8.30am-5.30pm Mon-Sat)

Kitchenshop

● Presence Tableware

Presence is a very fine kitchenware and home ware store, with all the big, de luxe brands for sale and just begging for you to punish that credit card. (37 High Street, Newtownards ☎ 028-9182 0222 robinson@presence-eu.com www.presence-eu.com – Open 9am-5.30pm Mon-Sat)

Down Northern Ireland

Newry

Home Bakery & Café

● The Corn Dolly Home Bakery

Sister bakery to the Warrenpoint legend, and home to great vernacular baking, and wickedly fine lunchtime sandwiches made with their brilliant signature batch loaf. (12 Marcus Square, Newry ☎ 028-3026 0524 info@corndollyfoods.com www.corndollyfoods.co.uk – Open 8.30am-6pm Mon-Fri, 8am-6pm Sat)

Restaurant

● Newry Farmers' Market

The Newry Farmers' Market shares traders with the weekly Dundalk market, and has also been home to the produce of the Lurganconary organic farm, so look out for these and other local specialities. (John Mitchell Place, Newry info@newrydundalkmarkets.com www.newrydundalkmarkets.com, 9am-2pm Fri)

Restaurant

Graduate Restaurant

The dynamic Newry Institute is set to merge with Armagh College and the Upper Bann Insitute in a new Southern Regional College, and we hope that the Institute's wonderful Graduate Restaurant will be accorded top status for finance, R&D, and patronage. It is an inspired idea to have the culinary students cooking both lunch and dinner, giving them a taste of the heat of service before they venture out into the big kitchen outside college. (Patrick Street, Newry ☎ 028-3026 1071/028-3025 9611 www.nkifhe.ac.uk)

Café

Olive Coffee Co & Art House

The café in the warehouse gallery space is on the ground floor and has lots of good sweet things and some nice savoury cooking at lunchtime with stews, quiches and sandwiches on offer. (16/17 The Mall, Newry ☎ 028-3025 2086 – Open 10am-6.30pm Mon-Sat, 11am-7.30pm Sun)

Rostrevor

Café

Kilbroney Park Cafe

Good handmade foods single out the Kilbroney café as a destination. (Kilbroney Park, Shore Road, Rostrevor ☎ 079-2146 4589 www.sabp-web.co.uk/kilbroney-park-cafe – Open 10am-8pm Mon-Fri, 11am-8pm Sat-Sun)

Saintfield

Restaurant

Edgar's Restaurant

Good things come in small packages. Emma Noblett and Colin Edgar's restaurant may be modest, but it's a local champion for good food, and don't think it's an easy matter to get a weekend table in here when they offer an à la carte menu: either get there early or you won't have a chance. And, if you don't get the table, what you will be missing is lip smackin' starters such as confit duck with plum jam, battered squid with chillies and spring onions, and generous hearty mains like rump of Inisowen lamb with champ and grilled fish with lemongrass beurre blanc. Excellent desserts include tiramisu semifreddo and a good maple and pecan nut tart. The food during the week is equally exact, excellent cooking, with a bistro menu that runs into the evening. A local hero. (11-15 Main Street, Saintfield ☎ 028-9751 1755)

Real Ale Pub

● The White Horse Inn

The White Horse is owned by the Whitewater Brewery, of Kilkeel, so you will be able to enjoy all their brews, and it's a Clotworthy Dobbin for us, please, and whatever you're having yourself. (49 Main St, Saintfield ☎ 048-9751 1143)

Strangford

Organic Farm Shop

● Churchtown Farm Organic Farm Shop

Another pioneering agricultural concept from the Orr family, the farm shop at Churchtown is where you will see their entire range of foods, from their own beef and lamb through to organic pork, bacon, chicken and a lot of other foods. The Orrs farm 550 acres organically, and they also sell at the Saturday St. George's Market, but a visit to Churchtown is a must in order to see – and taste – the future of agriculture, in all its logical, sustainable deliciousness. (Churchtown, Co Down ☎ 028-4488 1128 – Farm shop open Thursday-Sunday 9am-6pm)

Seaforde

Local Shop

● Brennan's Garage

Famous for their ice cream, and the way to show that you are in the know is to order an oyster. (149 Newcastle Road, Seaforde ☎ 028-4481 1271)

Restaurant, Bar & Fish + Chip Shop

● The Cuan Bar & Restaurant

Peter and Caroline McErlean's small guesthouse hotel has nine comfy rooms, and a characterful restaurant with popular dishes. (The Square, Strangford ☎ 028-4488 1588 www.thecuan.com – Open noon-8.30pm Sun-Thu, noon-9.30pm Fri & Sat)

Local Specialities
SODA FARLS
FADGE

Tea Shop

● Butterfly Farm Tea Shop

If you are visiting the Seafordes gardens, make sure to take tea in the café, housed in the Tropical Butterfly Farm. (Seaforde Demesne ☎ 028-4481 1225 www.seafordegardens.com – Open 10am-5pm Mon-Sat, 1pm-6pm Sun)

Home Bakery & Café

● The Corn Dolly Home Bakery

Small in scale but big in accomplishment, The Corn Dolly bakes terrific breads, and makes those breads into rather delectable sandwiches. Just try that caramelised crusty batch bread. (28 Church Street, Warrenpoint ☎ 028-4175 3596 – Open 8.30am-6pm Mon-Sat)

Restaurant & Bar

● The Duke

Ciaran Gallagher's ground-breaking restaurant is a place where stonkingly fine modern seafood cookery is served alongside traditional seafood and meat cookery, without any seeming tension. It's an amazing balancing act, which the boss pulls off with gas in that tank, managing the seemingly impossible task of pleasing all sections of the community. (7 Duke Street, Warrenpoint ☎ 028-4175 2084 www.thedukerestaurant.com – Open 6.30pm-10pm Tue-Sat, 6pm-9pm Sun)

Restaurant

● Fresh Fields at Warrenpoint

With beef from their own farm at Narrow Water, this radical new enterprise – a 4,000 sq ft, old warehouse converted by HBK architects – also brings in specialist meats from other local producers, has an in-store bakery, a great deli counter, fresh vegetables and fruits, and a clear focus on providing local foods for local people. Freshfields is a happening space. (55 Newry Road, Warrenpoint ☎ 028-4175 2520 www.freshfieldsfarmshop.eu)

Restaurant 23

Chef Trevor Cunningham has been making mighty waves ever since Ray and Andrea McArdle opened 23. Mr Cunningham's cooking is precise, focused and – most importantly – absolutely delicious. He works superbly within that modern classical style of a main ingredient with a partner and a couple of pairings – trout with prawn tortellini, with fennel and bacon and tomato confit; old spot pork with five-spice belly, with creamed cabbage and apple chutney; Angus beef with steak and stout pie, with roast baby onions and mushroom duxelle. The pairings are rigorously thought-through, and superbly and confidently delivered on the plate, right from palate tingling starters to thunderously fine desserts. Value for such accomplished cooking is exceptional.
(23 Church Street, Warrenpoint ☎ 028-475 3222
www.restaurant-23.co.uk – Open 12.15pm-2.30pm Tue-Fri, 6pm-9.30pm Tue-Thu, 6pm-10pm Fri, 12.15pm-10pm Sat, 12.15pm-8pm Sun)

"Think flavour as you choose your ingredients."

DARINA ALLEN

County Fermanagh

Enniskillen

Home Bakeryr

Leslie's Bakery

Leslie's is your destination for wonderful farls and fadge and millionaire's shortbread and all the great, unique bakes and cakes of the north. (10 Church Street, Enniskillen ☎ 028-6632 4902 – Open 8am-6pm Mon-Sat)

Butcherr

O'Doherty's

Pat O'Doherty is light years ahead of everyone when it comes to thinking about meat. He has created one of the most singular Irish foods, Fermanagh Black Bacon, a product he endlessly refines and develops. Most recently, he has brought an island on Lough Erne where he is rearing his black pigs. "The idea was to create a paradise for the pigs", he told Catherine Cleary in *The Irish Times*. "These are all hairy pigs. They find their own nests, and it's amazing to see them tune into the natural physiology of pig society". It comes as little surprise to hear that Mr O'Doherty is an environmental science graduate, though clearly one who concentrates more on the environment than the science. But the science bit is there are well in his work. We have described him as an alchemist, but of course if you are turning base material into precious products, you need to know what is going on. It means that O'Doherty's smoked meats, for example, are superb, as if he knows what every wisp is contributing to his smoked beef and bacon. Even his burgers, for goodness sake, are a benchmark product. That Fermanagh should have O'Doherty's bacon and Kettyle's beef seems a blessing beyond compare. (Belmore Street, Enniskillen ☎ 028-6632 2152 sales@blackbacon.com www.blackbacon.com – Open 8am-6pm Mon-Sat)

Restaurantr

Café Merlot & No 6 Restaurant

Café Merlot is the laid-back basement operation of Gerry Russell and John Donnelly's pair of destinations in the famous Blakes of the Hollow pub. Upstairs, in No.6

Restaurant, Mr Russell has more space to show the sort of culinary form that first brought him to food lover's notice – this is a gifted chef with a distinct style, and he is one of few contemporary Irish cooks who can seamlessly make sense of fusion cooking. He likes the charge of hot and sour, for instance, and he also likes soy, and Thai ingredients, but he puts these elements to work with Mediterranean ingredients, and the result can be a pure blast. If the wild side is a bit too wild for you, Mr Russell also does a very good steak and excellent grilled rare breed pork. Excellent wines, exciting food. (Blakes of the Hollow, 6 Church Street, Enniskillen ☎ 028-6632 0918 rune.home@btopenworld.com – Cafe Merlot opens noon-3pm, 5.30pm-9pm Mon-Sun, 'till 9.30pm Sat. Restaurant Number Six opens 5.30pm-9.30pm Fri & Sat and for special bookings during the week)

Lisbellaw

Cookery Schoolr

● Belle Isle Cookery School

Liz Moore is an energetic, fun teacher and she is lucky to have the sublime beauty of the Duke of Abercorn's gaffe in which to stage her series of cookery classes. A state-of-the-art kitchen in a converted estate cottage is the lovely location for the instruction, and with a maximum of ten pupils per class, learning is direct, and relaxed. Guests can stay in beautiful rental cottages, and there is also accommodation and dinner offered in the main house. (Lisbellaw ☎ 028-6638 7231 www.irishcookeryschool.com)

Local Specialities

PANCAKE BOXTY

CAKE BOXTY

FERMANAGH BLACK BACON

Lisnaskea

Specialist Beef

● Kettyle Irish Foods

Maurice Kettyle is a quietly-spoken revolutionary. Quietly, quietly, he is showing food lovers that the beef industry has no concern for quality. Having spent 15 years working in that industry, Mr Kettyle realised that the problem was that "people neglect the end user. So, I got talking to chefs, and I realised that there is a market for the 'best of the best'". He also realised that "another problem is the space between the farm and the factory", that critical area when stress on the animal destroys the eating quality of the meat. When Mr Kettyle is selecting his beef, he wants to see the animal walk 50 metres, slowly. Today, Kettyle beef is exactly that: the Best of the Best, driven as far as Athens to the best of the best chefs. It is truly outstanding beef, and we recount elsewhere in this book how a dish of Kettyle short ribs braised in Clotworthy Dobbin ale bought a gasp of delight when diners tried it in Nick's Warehouse. Mr Kettyle, and Mr O'Doherty, both of them finishing their animals on the Lough Erne islands, are Fermanagh's greatest artisans, and they are amongst the world's greatest artisans. (Manderwood Business Park, Drumhaw, Lisnaskea ☎ 028-6772 3777
maurice@kettyleirishfoods.com
www.kettyleirishfoods.com)

County Londonderry

Aghadowey

Organic Farm

Culdrum Organic Farm

Brian Wallace produces superlative foods on his farm, and completes the charmed circle of control over his destiny that organic farmers enjoy by selling his produce both through a box scheme, and via an excellent stall at the Saturday St. George's Market in Belfast. The stall is virtually a one-stop shop for good things, from organic chickens to dry-cure bacon to smashing aubergines. (31 Ballintagh Road, Aghadowey ☎ 07764-638356)

Ballykelly

Bakery and Café

Hunter's at the Oven Door

Sean Hunter runs three excellent bakeries-with-cafés in Derry, here in Ballykelly, and also in Coleraine and Limavady. The tea loaves are a legend, and should be enjoyed – slowly – with a cup of tea. Ah, bliss. (34 Main Street, Ballykelly ☎ 028-7776 6228 huntersbakery@aol.com www.huntersbakery.com – Open 8.30am-5.30pm Mon-Sat)

Castledawson

Home Bakery & Café

Ditty's Home Bakery

Robert Ditty talks about things like credibility, and passion, and simplicity. He is not just the most credible, and passionate, and simple, baker in Northern Ireland, he is one of those mighty figures – like Myrtle Allen, or Peter Ward, or Giana Ferguson – who can galvanise a group of people into a food community, for he can see synergies, he knows what culture is – simplicity! – he knows what opponents he faces: the bland, the industrialised, the barbarians at the gate. His bakeries are testament to a man who envisions food as a primal act of culture, the culture that is the glue of local communities. "It is part of our heritage, the breads and the soda farls", Ditty told Betsy Klein in the book *Cottage Industry*. "This is something we should be so proud of". Well, food lovers should be proud of Robert Ditty, for his work is peerless and powerful. His latest creation has been a collaboration with Gubbeen farm to make cheese oatcakes: they are, of course, as deliciously singular as everything this quiet, intellectually assured baker has ever produced. (44 Main Street, Castledawson ☎ 028-7946 8243 dittysbakery@tiscali.co.uk – Open 6.30am-5.30pm Mon-Sat)

Restaurant & Guesthouse

● The Inn at Castledawson

Simon and Kathy's lovely Inn is the sort of place you might stumble across in Spain or Italy: a small, privately owned hotel, with great cooking from the chef-patron, and great hospitality from the lady at front-of-house, a place where the culture of food and the culture of hospitality are handled deftly and expertly by professional people who enjoy their work. It is thoroughly charming, and all the more valuable in a world of chain hotels with industrial cooking. (47 Main Street, Castledawson ☎ 028-7946 9777
info@theinnatcastledawson.co.uk
www.theinnatcastledawson.com – Open noon-2.30pm Mon-Fri, 5pm-9pm Mon-Thu, 5pm-10pm Fri-Sat, noon-2.30pm, 5pm-8pm Sun)

Claudy

Butcher

● O'Kane Meats

In a country where butchery businesses frequently run through the generations of a family, the O'Kane brothers are unusual in being first generation charcutiers. What isn't unusual about Michael and Kieran, however, is their utter competence and creativity in their work, and their ferocious sense of competition when it comes to meat cookery competitions. When these guys go in for a competition, they expect to win, and frequently they do just that. Their fresh meats are brilliant, their own culinary creations – they seem to feed at least half of Claudy – are just as inspired as one would hope. Excellent. (Main Street, Claudy ☎ 028-7133 8944
mail@okanemeats.com www.okanemeats.com
– Open 7.45am-5.45pm Mon-Sat)

Coleraine

Delicatessen and Cafe

Belfry Deli

Good breads are the main attraction in the Belfry, but whilst you are queuing for a loaf, do take a gander at the good cheese counter and the shelves with their interesting jars and ethnic foods. (Church Lane, Coleraine ☎ 028-7034 2906 – Open 9am-5.15pm Mon-Sat)

Coffee Shop

Ground

The original Ground now has a sister-destination in Ballymena. It's a lovely space – stylish, hip, modern, confident – and it offers stylish, hip, modern, confident food. (25 Kingsgate Street, Coleraine ☎ 028-7032 8664 www.groundcoffee.net – Open 9am-5.30pm Mon-Sat)

Home Bakery & Café

Hunter's at Kitty's of Coleraine

Part of Sean Hunter's chain of three bakery cafés, and invaluable as a source of great handmade breads, wee buns, and lovely pancakes made with good buttermilk. (3 Church Lane, Coleraine ☎ 028-7034 2347 – Open 9am-5.30pm Mon-Sat)

Restaurant

The Watermargin

The big eating-out destination in Coleraine for many years now, The Watermargin has a great location upstairs beside the river, and is a winningly efficient, reliable source of popular and delicious Chinese cooking. Those who fancy something more than their somewhat westernised cooking should ask for the wilder stuff, for the crew enjoy a challenge and are well up for it. (The Boathouse, Hanover Place, Coleraine ☎ 028-7034 2222 – Open 5pm-10.30pm Mon-Sun)

Local Specialities

WEE BUNS
OATCAKES
YELLOWMAN

Desertmartin

Farm Shop & Charcuterie

Moss Brook Farm Shoppe

With a new range of cooked meats and pies added to their portfolio of wonderful pork products, Trevor and Irene Barclay are showing that after eight years of being brilliant, they intend to get even more brilliant. This pair are dream artisans, taking the situation of collapsing pork prices, back in 1999, to create a silk purse of a business out a situation that was, well, a sow's ear, you might say. In the last years they have developed as epicureans – their products seem to be on a continual graph of improvement – and as business people, and their Saturday stall in St. George's Market is a world unto itself. Every sow's ear in Moss Brook turns into a silk purse. (6 Durnascallon, Desertmartin ☎ 028-7963 3454 – Open by arrangement)

Garvagh

Farm Shop

Arkhill Farm Shop

Paul Craig's sweet cottage-style farm shop sells the organic produce of the farm – vegetables, fruits, pork, beef; lamb, chicken and turkeys – abetted by a range of foods from other local food producers. They deliver their produce within the area and have added an on-line shopping facility for those who want good organics but can't make it up the A29. This is another optimistic and successful endeavour by enterprising farmers who wanted to produce the finest quality food they possibly could, whilst also protecting the environment and creating sustainable food systems for the next generation. (25 Drumcroone Road, Garvagh ☎ 028-2955 7920 info@arkhillfarm.co.uk www.arkhillfarm.co.uk – Open 9am-5pm Mon-Fri)

Limavady

Home Bakery & Café

Hunter's at the Oven Door

Sean Hunter's reputation for great breads is based on the bakery's more than forty years of proving and baking. Recently, their tea loaves have become the most celebrated product of the bakery, their toasted-hazelnut and cherry succour nothing more than a sheer delight. As well as the bakes and cakes, there is a café with good cooking and nice coffees (5-9 Market Street, Limavady ☎ 028-7772 2411 🖱 www.huntersbakery.com – Open 8.30am-5.30pm Mon-Sat)

Butcher

Norman Hunter & Son

Hunters could simply have coasted by on their reputation for producing and selling superb meat, and for quoting John Ruskin in their shop, not the sort of thing you expect to find in a butcher's shop. But, Norman and his team are typically restless, and they are now producing a range of ready-made meals. "Starting with a good product and enhancing it", is what they call it, so head in to find lasagne; classic shepherd's pie; fine roast beef in red wine gravy; or tuna and pasta bake. A great shop just got better. (53-55 Main Street ☎ 028-7776 2665 📫 normanhunterandson@yahoo.co.uk – Open 9am-5.30pm Mon-Sat)

Farm Shop

Keady Mountain Farm

Michael Mullan and his family run an exemplary organic food producing farm, Their latest innovation is a brand-new packaging and labelling system which will allow them to sell meat through the North West Co-op Box Delivery system. As if that wasn't enough, in addition to their weekly stall at the St. George's Market, they are also beginning pork production to complement their outstanding beef, lamb and chicken. The Mullans are typical of the cutting-edge of farmers and producers in Northern Ireland – Moyallon, Moss Brook, Arkhill, Culdrum, Ballylagan, McKee's, Churchtown – in that they have established answers to the problems of distribution which seem insurmountable to so many farmers, which allows them to get their produce to as many people as possible. (Limavady ☎ 028-7776 4157 📫 info@mullansorganicfarm.com 🖱 www.mullansorganicfarm.com)

Fish & Chips

McNulty's Fish & Chips

Brian McNulty's chipper is a legend. It's as pristine as any 5-star palace, and their food is so rigorously sourced and cooked that the only conclusion one can draw is that McNulty's is the ultimate 5-star chipper. This is fish and chips as an art form, with care taken over every detail, right down to Brian himself taking a bag of fries from the new season's potato crop off for a drive in his car so he can check they are perfect. Perfect. (84 Main Street, Limavady ☎ 028-7776 2148 www.mcnultysfishandchips.com – Open 9am-11pm Mon-Sat, 4.30pm-11pm Sun)

Londonderry

Hotel

Beech Hill Country House Hotel

Patsey O'Kane has put her heart and soul into the beautiful Beech House Hotel, and it shows. She leads from the front, orchestrating a dedicated staff who clearly adore their boss, and everyone here works extra hard to look after their guests. The result is a hotel which is hugely popular with locals, a wonderful space where everything gleams, and where the bedrooms and suites in the old house are of the highest standard. The restaurant is popular, but the young crew at the stoves need to relax a little more, and simplifying their dishes would give them more impact. (Londonderry ☎ 028-7134 9279 info@beech-hill.com www.beech-hill.com)

Brasserie

Brown's

Ivan Taylor has done a good job over the years in Brown's maintaining a creative restaurant and offering a personal vision of modern cooking. His work contrasts with other establishments in the city who attempt to be all things to all men and who wind up creating a dyspeptic mish-mash, making for the city with the least good food in all of Ireland. Thankfully, Brown's gives a real alternative to the blandness. (1 Bonds Hill ☎ 028-7134 5180 eat@brownsrestaurant.com www.brownsrestaurant.com – Open noon-2.15pm Tue-Fri, 5.30pm-late Tue-Sat)

Café

Café Artisan

Part of the Bookworm bookstore, this bright, inviting café has a good array of sandwiches, nice salads, and good puds, plus an engaging left-field ambience which is rather treasurable. (18-20 Bishop Street, Derry ☎ 028-7128 2727 – Open daily)

Café

● Fiorentini's

Perennially packed, Fiorentini's has good chips, ice cream for the bairns, and sticky buns and cups of tea to fortify you mid-morning and mid-afternoon. (Clooney Terrace, Derry ☎ 028-7126 0653 – Open 9am-5pm Mon-Sat, 11am-5pm Sun)

Two Town Houses

● The Merchant's House, The Saddler's House

Joan Pyne runs both the keenly-priced Saddler's House, a fine Georgian three-storey B&B, and the more formal The Merchant's House, on Queen Street, a handsome comfortable destination whose central location gives a great alternative to bland hotels. (Saddler's House, 36 Gt James Street, Derry, Merchant House, 16 Queen Street, Derry ☎ 028-7126 9691 ✉ saddlershouse@btinternet.com 🖱 www.thesaddlershouse.com)

Maghera

Butcher

● McKee's Butchers

George McKee rears his own cattle, so you can expect the stellar-standard beef that the best Ulster butchers produce in his Maghera shops. McKees have latterly become well known for a range of pies sold both in their two shops and further afield, and these are excellent, convenient and good value. (26 & 78 Main Street, Maghera ☎ 028-7964 2559 – Open 9am-6pm Mon-Sat)

Magherafelt

Home Bakery & Café

● Ditty's Home Bakery

See the entry for Ditty's under Castledawson. (33 Rainey Street, Magherafelt ☎ 028-7963 3944 – Open 8am-5.30pm Mon-Sat)

Brasserie

● Gardiner's

Sean Owens is the best-known chef in mid-Ulster, and his restaurant, in a much-made-over former rugby club, is home to generous modern cooking, and lots of lively, big-night-out weekend fun. The menu is generous in terms of choice and in terms of portions, for Mr Owens knows his customers and likes to cook for them, but it's the special dishes they cook on Friday and Saturday nights that demand special attention: chicken with black-eyed beans; Swedish meatballs with mustard; duckling with Agen prunes. (7 Garden Street, Magherafelt ☎ 028-7930 0333 gardiners2000@hotmail.com www.gardiners.net – Open 5.30pm-10pm Tue-Sat, noon-3pm, 5pm-9.30pm Sun)

Coffee Bar

Relish

Aisling Duffy and Tania McGeehan's fine coffee bar and restaurant has a great location right in the centre of town, and the room itself is hip and metropolitan. The menu is the modern, eclectic composition of drinks and eats, such as wraps and hot melts, but everything is carefully put together by very competent, helpful staff. (1 Broad Street, Magherafelt ☎ 028-7930 1501 www.relishmagherafelt.com – Open 8am-5.30pm Mon-Sat)

Supermarket

JC Stewarts

JC Stewarts is one of our favourite shops. We love the design – brilliant! – we love the selection of local foods – fantastic! – and we love the calm, informed, genteel service from staff who enjoy their work and enjoy helping their customers. Every supermarket should be like JC Stewarts. (1 Union Road, Magherafelt ☎ 028-7930 2930 – Open 8am-7pm Mon-Wed, 8am-9pm Thur & Fri, 8am-6pm Sat)

Portstewart

Butcher

JE Toms & Sons

Alan Tom's shop on the seafront at windswept Portstewart feeds the hungry caravanning hordes who take over the town in summertime with brilliantly conceived barbecue foods, and for the rest of the year the shop produces exceptional meats, and some of the very best pies we have tasted from a butcher's shop. (46 The Promenade ☎ 028-7083 2869 – Open 8am-5.30pm Mon-Sat, from 7.30am Sat)

County Tyrone

Castlederg

Dairy

● Erganagh Dairy

The Erganagh Dairy processes Ayrshire, goats' milk and sheep milk for retail sale by multiple retailers in the North. We like the clean lacticity of the Ayrshire milk, which is very well worth hunting down, and the butter is also very good, and an alternative to the standard butters in Northern Ireland which are frequently too pale and salty. (29 Erganagh Road, Castlederg ☎ 028-8167 0626)

Organic Delivery

● Organic Doorstep

This brilliant company developed out of a family dairy farm, who decided to bring their milk direct to the people. It all grew from there, they converted to organics, and they now bring more than 50 organic products to more than 1,000 customers twice a week. Their smashing buttermilk has been getting a lot of attention from leading chefs, and look out for their Oakdene brand organic milk if you are crazy enough not to sign up to their delivery system. Brilliant foods, revolutionary logistics, life-improving, and right to your doorstep. (125 Strabane Road, Castlederg ☎ 028-8167 9989 ☎ Freephone 0800-783 5656 info@organicdoorstep.co.uk www.organicdoorstep.net)

Sheep's Cheese

● Springwell Speciality Sheep's Cheese

Linda Gourley milks 150 ewes on her 70 acre farm, and creates her Springwell sheep's milk cheeses at the Erganagh dairy where the milk is processed. Although the cheeses are somewhat like feta cheese in style, they are not brined, and as well as the plain cheese, there are two flavoured varieties, one with red pepper and another with chives. You will find Linda selling her cheeses in country markets in Coleraine and Londonderry and also at the busy Strabane market on the last Saturday of each month. (c/o 29 Erganagh Road, Castlederg ☎ 028-8167 0626)

Cookstown

Seed Sprouters

● Good4U

"The real stars of good4U's range are their sprouting seeds, particularly a combination of broccoli, clover, alfalfa and radish called brocco shoots ... brocco shoots boast a delicate spicy taste of their own and are as deliciously pretty as a tangle of fine hair". Well, if it is good enough for the terrific Philippa Davenport of *The Financial Times*, it's sure good enough for us. The Butler family are leading the way with their good4U foods – smart shoots, ready-to-eat seeds, grow your own kits and juicers. This is health food for epicureans, and getting into the world of sprouting is a joyous discovery: did you know that if the early seafarers had sprouting seeds and some fresh water on board, then they would never have suffered from scurvy, and advocates of sprouted seeds argue that their nutritional profile is so complete that man could live on sprouted seeds alone. Mind you, we're sure the advocates would want us to have a little white Burgundy with that. (45 Tullywiggan Road, Loughry College, Cookstown ☎ 028-8676 1914 ✉ info@good4u.co.uk

Butcher

● J Hutton & Sons

A pretty, striped awning that extends out over the street and a gently curving front window will alert you to Hutton and Son's, and inside you will find an excellent selection of fresh and prepared meats, and an equally fine selection of good, handmade, cooked foods-to-go, all beautifully presented and served with a smile by excellent staff. (33 James Street ☎ 028-8676 1390 – Open 7am-6pm Mon-Sat)

Wine Bar

● Otter Lodge

A blackboard announces the menu of the day in the flower-bedecked Otter Lodge, Harold and Heather Moffett's wine bar and restaurant. The choice is wide, from prawn cocktail to lasagne to a huge array on international-style chicken dishes, value is amazingly keen, and the views over the river are just darling. (26 Dungannon Road ☎ 028-8676 5427 ✉ www.otterlodge.co.uk – Open noon-2pm Mon-Sat, noon-2.30pm Sun, 5.30pm-9.30pm Mon-Thu, 5.30pm-10pm Fri & Sat, 5pm-9.30pm Sun)

Dunganannon

Farm Shop

● Cloughbane Farm Shop

The Robinson family continue the great farm shop tradition in Northern Ireland, running a store at the farm where they sell the meat of their Texel cross sheep, their Limousin-Angus cross heifers, along with locally reared and produced pork and chicken. The prime cuts of beef are hung for 28 days to maximise flavour, there are lots of interesting prepared dishes and even tarts and trifles for pudding, and with the fourth generation of the family hard at work both on the farm and in the shop, the future looks bright for this creative family enterprise. You will find their stall also at the Dungannon farmers' market. (160 Tandragee Road, Dungannon ☎ 028-8775 8246 www.cloughbanefarm.co.uk – Open 10am-6pm Tue-Sat)

Apple Juice

● Cumwins Apple Juice

Cumwin's is a fine apple juice, pressed from the fruit of their own orchards. As well as juice, bramley cooking apples and many varieties of eating apples are also grown and sold, along with blackberries. (Cornamuckla House, 60 Bush Road ☎ 028-8772 4637)

Guesthouse & Cookery School

● Grange Lodge

Norah Brown is one of the great figures of Northern Ireland's hospitality culture. For more than two decades she has welcomed visitors into her home and cooked beautiful, cordon bleu-style dinners for them – lamb fricassée; entrecote with green peppercorn sauce; fisherman's money bag; field mushroom with seafood gratin; pork fillet stuffed with herbs and apricots, classic dishes cooked and served with aplomb – not to mention some glorious breakfasts, with her trademark Black Bush porridge – one of the great breakfast dishes, believe us. Norah also takes small groups for up-close cookery classes held in the comfort and cheer of her kitchen, and these have proven to be a great success. The house is supremely comfortable, the welcome always true and hearty.
(Grange Road, Dungannon ☎ 028-8778 4212
stay@grangelodgecountryhouse.com
www.grangelodgecountryhouse.com)

Guest House

Stangmore Country House

A personable professionalism is the reason why Anne and Andy Brace's country house and restaurant finds itself such a popular destination, with both locals and visitors. The Braces are chatty and informal, yet also hard-working and focused, and they have created a signature style of cooking that uses as many County Tyrone ingredients as they can get their hands on to produce excellent dining in the restaurant. But using local foods doesn't mean Mr Brace only cooks provincial-style food: his menus have lots of international signatures as well, and show a committed and dedicated cook at work. Having taken over Stangmore House, following several years when they were leasing the house, they are setting off on an exciting new journey. (65 Moy Road, Dungannon ☎ 028-8772 5600
info@stangmorecountryhouse.com
www.stangmorecountryhouse.com)

Wine Importers

Wattle Tree Wines

Martin Forker's company imports a selection of wines from boutique Aussie wine makers. The company has become especially known for the classic Australian "stickies" – sweet dessert wines – it sells, made by RL Buller. These are mighty concoctions of the muscat and tokay grapes, and really must be tried by wine lovers. (PO Box 1475, Dungannon ☎ 028-8776 9206
info@wattletreewines.co.uk)

Fivemiletown

Creamery Cheese

Fivemiletown Creamery

Fivemiletown Creamery has built an impressive array of cheese types and brands over the years, from the fine Cooneen goat's cheese brand to the Ballyblue and Ballybrie varieties, mild-tasting and well-made cheeses. There is also the smoked Ballyoak, a mature cheddar cheese and a smoked cheddar, Oakwood. Latest plans include the production of Boilie cheese, a sign that this company has a dynamic and progressive attitude to the Irish cheese market. (14 Ballylurgan Road, Fivemiletown ☎ 028-8952 1209
clairemadine@fivemiletown.com
www.fivemiletown.com)

Moy

Butcher

● Robert Marshall Neill Family Butcher

A classic old-style butcher's shop, where beef is matured for four weeks, and where Mrs Neill uses the beef to make her pies for the village bakery. Charming. (Killyman Street, Moy ☎ 028-8778 4237 – Open 9am-5.30pm Mon-Wed & Fri-Sat, 9am-1pm Thur)

Moygashel

Café

● The Loft

The Loft is a great café. Start with some of their wickedly good scones – everything from cherry, mixed fruit and good plain scones to funky things like raspberry and white chocolate, or if lunch is looming then choose a tasty slice of quiche hot from the oven or a good savoury tart, along with carefully made salads. Desserts are as pristine as everything else coming from the kitchen, and The Loft is hard to beat as an eating destination, so you don't need the excuse of shopping to go to The Linen Green. Mind you, some nice homeware in The Gift Store, if you've a minute or two. (10A Linen Green, Moygashel ☎ 028- 8772 9929 – Open 9.15am-5pm Mon-Sat)

Omagh

Local Shop

● Mr Eatwells

Butcher, baker, chipper and hot food bar – Joe McMahon's array of shops hits all points. There are twenty varieties of sausage for sale here, lots of good barbecue specialities, and beautifully presented and prepared meats. (16 Campsie Road ☎ 028-8224 1104 – Open 8.30am-6pm Mon-Sat)

Strabane

Farmers' Market

● Strabane Farmers' Market

Look out for Springwell Sheep's Cheese and other local foods. (Last Sat of the month, Score Centre, Dock Rd)

Index

Notes

Notes

Notes

Keep in touch with what's happening in Irish food

www.bridgestoneguides.com

publishes regular updates to entries listed in the *Bridgestone Guides*, as well as links to hundreds of good web addresses in Irish Food.

There is also an on-line service for buying books.

Sign up for our website newsletter Megabytes, and we'll be sure to keep you posted.